G000145822

Easy AutoCAD® LT for Windows™

John D. Hood

McGraw-Hill, Inc.

New York San Francisco Washington, D.C. Auckland Bogotá
Caracas Lisbon London Madrid Mexico City Milan
Montreal New Delhi San Juan Singapore
Sydney Tokyo Toronto

Library of Congress Cataloging-in-Publication Data

Hood, John D.
Easy AutoCAD LT for Windows / John D. Hood.
p. cm.—(Visual technology series)
Includes index.
ISBN 0-07-029789-4—ISBN 0-07-029788-6 (pbk.)
1. Computer graphics. 2. AutoCAD LT for Windows. 3. Computer-aided design. I. Title. II. Series.
T385.H688 1994
604.2'4'02855369—dc20 94-23459
CIP

1 2 3 4 5 6 7 8 9 0 DOH/DOH 9 0 9 8 7 6 5 4
1 2 3 4 5 6 7 8 9 0 DOH/DOH 9 0 9 8 7 6 5 4

ISBN 0-07-029789-4 (hc)
ISBN 0-07-029788-6 (pbk)

The sponsoring editor for this book was Marjorie Spencer and the production supervisor was Suzanne W. Babeuf. It was set in Century Schoolbook by North Market Street Graphics.

Printed and bound by R. R. Donnelley & Sons Company.

To my mother, who taught me the value of reading
and
To my father, who taught me the value of hard work.

Contents

Acknowledgments

I wish to thank the people at Autodisk for their outstanding assistance and support provided through their Register Developer Program.

Thanks also to the team at North Market Street Graphics, especially Christine Furry, Selena R. Chronister, Anne Friedman, and Stephen B. McCreary, who adhered to a tight schedule to get this book out on time.

Introduction

Practice is the only way to learn a skill. My purpose in writing this book is to provide a set of tutorial notes that supplement the *AutoCAD LT User's Guide* which is supplied with the AutoCAD LT program. AutoCAD LT also has an excellent Help program that provides detailed information about utilizing AutoCAD LT menus, commands, and dialogue boxes. The procedure to utilize Help is discussed in App. A, Sec. A.3, *Easy AutoCAD LT.* It is recommended that you read that section and become familiar with AutoCAD LT's Help menu as you follow this text. The *AutoCAD LT User's Guide* and AutoCAD LT's Help program do little, however, to demonstrate the application of AutoCAD LT commands, menus, and dialogue boxes to the production of integrated drafting projects. It is the objective of this text to provide the reader with those skills.

In this text, emphasis is placed on the application of AutoCAD LT to efficiently complete drawings in a number of disciplines, using practical drawing projects.

Having taught CAD to a number of students, it has been my observation that the biggest problem students and experienced drafters have when starting to use CAD is a lack of confidence to sit down behind the computer keyboard and begin a drawing. It is really quite a simple thing to do—start at the beginning and work toward the end. It has been my goal to provide a set of projects demonstrating that fact.

I.1 The AutoCAD LT Program

AutoCAD LT for Windows is a computer-aided drafting program from Autodesk Inc. It is written in the C programming language, which is machine-independent, and is composed of an intricate set of drawing and editing capabilities.

The program is written to run on the 80386/486/pentium-based system microcomputers under Windows 3.1 or higher. Drawings made with AutoCAD LT and the DOS version and Windows version of AutoCAD are compatible, and drawings done in one version can be edited or completed in the other. Most of the 2D design and drafting features available in AutoCAD Windows (Release 12) are available in AutoCAD LT. AutoCAD LT also has basic 3D features such as 2D extrusions, 3D line creation, the creation and application of

User Coordinate Systems, and the ability to view and modify 3D drawings. AutoCAD LT users can also employ the features of the Windows environment such as linking AutoCAD LT drawings with other applications such as word processors and spread sheet packages. AutoCAD has become the de facto standard microcomputer CAD program in industry and educational institutes. AutoCAD LT puts the advantages of AutoCAD Windows within the reach of all CAD drafters.

The AutoCAD LT program is relatively easy to learn to use because it is entirely menu driven. This means that the user does not have to remember complex commands. All commands can be displayed and selected from screen menus. Job-specific menus (see Chap. 11) that contain macros (see Chap. 12) and call block files (see Chap. 10) can be purchased or written by experienced users to tailor AutoCAD LT to any drafting discipline.

I.2 How to Use Easy AutoCAD LT

This text is composed of a series of tutorial projects, each about 3 hours in length, which are designed to bring a novice user, with no CAD or other computer experience, to the level of a fully trained CAD operator in a short period of time.

Experienced CAD operators will find the text invaluable because it demonstrates the efficient use of many AutoCAD LT commands to complete complex drafting procedures.

The tutorials are written to complement the *AutoCAD LT User's Guide* supplied with the AutoCAD LT software. Commands are not introduced in a specific order but rather as required to complete specific drawing projects. You should refer to the *AutoCAD LT User's Guide* and/or the Help menu when using *Easy AutoCAD LT,* when more information about a command is desired.

It is recommended that a new user start at the beginning of this text and complete all projects. Although there is sufficient repetition of instructions in the projects, I have designed the projects assuming that the reader has completed prior projects and understands the application of commands used earlier.

There is one exception to the preceding paragraph. In *Easy AutoCAD LT* the process of plotting is not discussed until Chap. 7. This has generally proved to work best in the classroom; however, you may want to proceed to that chapter earlier.

The AutoCAD LT for Windows drawing screen is illustrated in Fig. I.1. The drawing name is shown in the *title bar.* (This drawing is "unnamed"—not yet named.) Drawing commands and settings can be chosen from the *menu bar, toolbox,* or *toolbar.* Commands can also be entered from the keyboard.

To pull down a menu from the menu bar, move the cursor into the menu bar at the top of the screen using the mouse (or digitizer puck). Then move the cursor along the menu bar until the desired menu title is highlighted, and quickly press the <pick> button (usually the left or 0 button) on the mouse. This is also referred to as clicking on a menu item or command. In Fig. I.2 the Draw menu

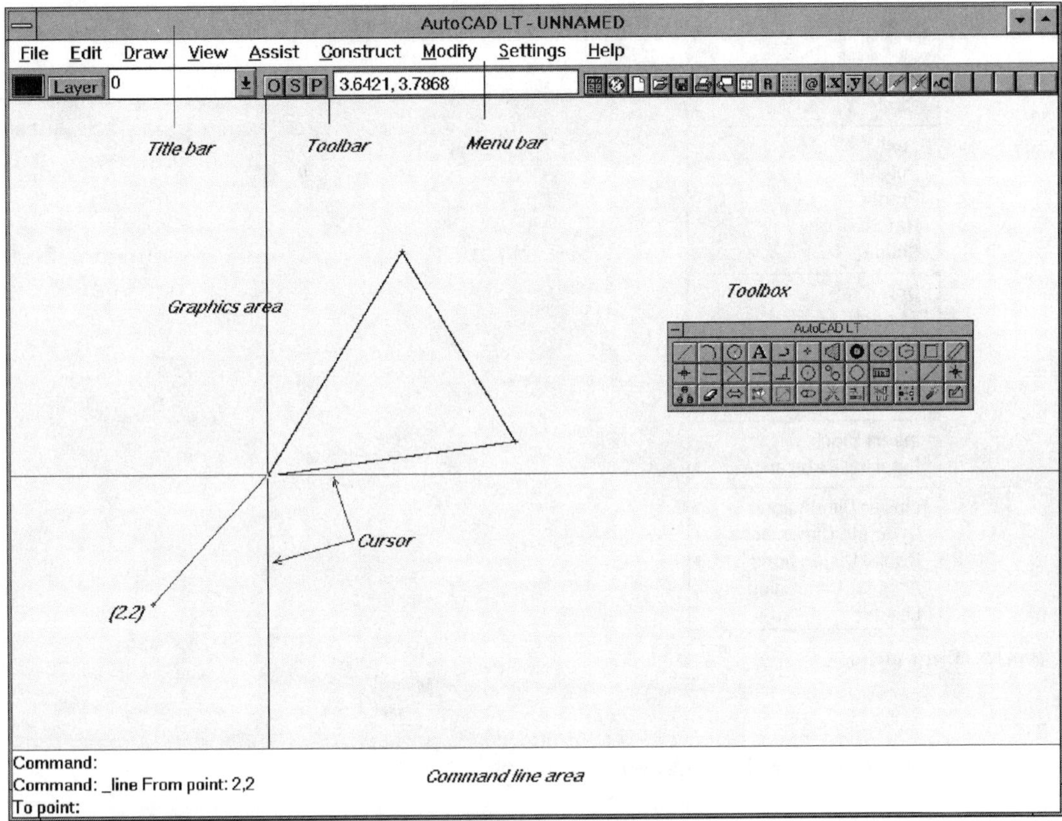

Figure I.1 Drawing screen.

is pulled down by clicking on Draw in the menu bar. Depending on default settings your Draw menu may be an icon menu.

Clicking on Line in the Draw menu invokes the Line command. In this text these commands appear as follows:

Draw <pick> **Line** <pick>

AutoCAD LT will display the commands in the Command line at the bottom of the monitor as they are entered (see Fig. I.1). When the Line command is chosen, the command line displays the following request:

```
Line From point:
```

You are to enter the start point of the line. In some cases you are to enter data by typing it on the keyboard. The AutoCAD LT request is printed in computer type in this text and the data you are to type in is in boldface type. To draw a line starting at coordinate 2,2, enter:

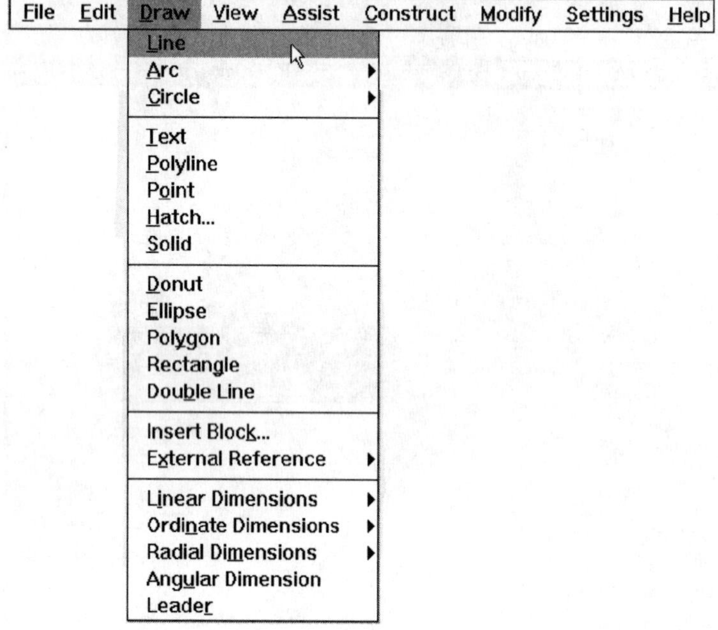

Figure I.2 Draw menu.

`Line From point:` **2,2** <return>

AutoCAD prompts you with `Line From point:` and you type in **2,2** and press the Enter <return> key on the keyboard or the Return button on the mouse (the second or 1 button).

AutoCAD will respond on the command line (see Fig. I.1) with:

`To point:`

You are to enter the next point for the line. This can be entered from the keyboard as previously illustrated, or the point can be entered by moving the cursor (cross hairs) on the screen to the point and pressing the pick button. This is referred to as *digitizing* the point. If the line from point 2,2 is to be attached to the left corner of the triangle on the screen (see Fig. I.1) by moving the cursor and digitizing the point, the information in the text would appear as follows:

`To point:` Move the cursor to the left side of the triangle and digitize the point. <pick>

AutoCAD prompts you with `To point:`, you perform the function specified, and press the pick button.

AutoCAD will draw the line and respond with:

`To point:`

If you do not want to extend the line further, you can press the mouse Return button or the Enter key without entering a value. If you do, the previous command entry would appear in these notes with a second <return> indicated:

> `To point:` Move the cursor to the left side of the triangle and digitize the point.
> <pick> `To Point:` <return>

Occasionally, for clarity of reading the text, some AutoCAD LT responses are not displayed (for instance, the last `To point:` response might be deleted, and the final entries would appear as <pick> <return>. If you want to verify what you have on the screen, refer to the *AutoCAD LT User's Guide* or help menu, which describes the command in full.

When typing in alphabetical data from the keyboard, you may use either uppercase or lowercase letters.

I.3 CAD Hardware

AutoCAD LT is written for 80386/486 and Pentium systems microcomputers. The microcomputer should have four to eight megabytes of random-access memory (RAM). You will need a floppy drive and a single hard disk drive with at least 40-megabyte capacity to run AutoCAD LT. AutoCAD LT is written to operate with MS-DOS version 3.31 or later versions, and Windows 3.1 or later versions.

A graphics monitor is required to display the drawing. The display screen can be a black and white, monochrome, or color monitor. You will need a color/graphics adapter to display the graphics.

The standard resolution for the IBM video graphics array monitor is 640 by 480 pixels, which means 600 positions across and 480 positions down the screen. A diagonal line drawn on the screen will have the "jaggies" in that it will appear as a stepped line because of the lower resolution of the screen (while all diagonal lines are composed of a number of short horizontal lines, the lower the resolution of the screen, the more jaggies). This will make it more difficult to read the drawing on the monitor but will not affect the paper plot of the drawing where the line will appear as a uniform line.

I.3.1 Pointing devices

The cursor can be moved about the screen to draw lines, select points, etc., using the cursor keypad. If you are doing a lot of drawing, you will want to have some type of pointing device. The most common pointing devices are the mouse and the digitizing tablet. AutoCAD LT uses the Windows system pointer which is usually a standard mouse.

A mouse is a locating device that uses relative motion to move the cursor on the screen as the mouse is moved about the top of a desk. A mouse might have a roller on its base that rotates as the mouse is moved along a smooth surface causing the cursor to move on the screen, or it might be an optical mouse which is moved on a small (8 by 9 in) reflecting plate set on a tabletop. The mouse usually has buttons on its surface that are used to pick (digitize) points on the monitor. A mouse usually costs around $100 and is one of the cheaper pointing devices available. The mouse is limited in that it is a relative-motion device and cannot be used to trace over paper drawings and transfer the points into the AutoCAD LT drawing.

I.3.2 Plotters

If you complete a drawing using AutoCAD LT, you will want to produce a hard copy of the drawing. AutoCAD LT supports a number of dot matrix printers to plot drawings. The standard printer will not provide the type of output you would desire for construction or production drawings but will provide quick, cheap preliminary drawings.

AutoCAD LT also supports a number of plotters. Usually the main consideration when selecting a plotter is the maximum plot size the device can draw. Most serious drafting requires an E-size (34 by 44 in) drawing, although D-size (22 by 34 in) and smaller drawings are also used. Another consideration is the number of pens the plotter can use during a plot. If drawings are to be done in a number of colors or are to have a number of different line types, the plotter should be able to access more than one pen during the plot. Different line types and colors can be used with a one-pen plotter but the process is extremely time-consuming.

Recent developments in vector-to-raster conversion and color technology have also made available to the CAD user printer/plotters that challenge pen plotters in quality and versatility.

I.4 AutoCAD LT Long versus Short Menu

All figures and commands for AutoCAD LT in this text are based on AutoCAD LT's long menu. To turn the long menu on move the cursor up into the buttons menu bar (see Fig. I.1) and click once (press the <pick> button) on Settings. If the item at the top of the menu is Long Menu, click on it. If it reads Short Menu, you are in the long menu and do not have to change the menu. The item in the menu shows you the option available. Once long menu is set on, it remains on each time AutoCAD LT is used.

I.5 Dialogue Boxes

Dialogue boxes are used throughout this text. If you do not get dialogue boxes when the text says you should, enter the following at the command line:

1. To get dialogue boxes for reading and writing files:

   COMMAND: **filedia** <return>
   New value for FILEDIA <0>: **1** <return>

2. To get dialogue boxes for plotting:

```
COMMAND: cmddia <return>
New value for CMDDIA <0>: 1 <return>
```

I.6 Utilization of Appendixes

Appendix E lists the menu bar pull-down menus for AutoCAD LT. Those tables will help you locate commands in menus when using AutoCAD LT. The equivalent menu bar pull-down menus for AutoCAD Windows (Release 12) are in App. F. If you are using AutoCAD Windows as well as AutoCAD LT you will find those tables useful for comparison when reading *Easy AutoCAD LT*.

Appendix A gives trouble-shooting hints and demonstrates how to use AutoCAD LT's Help function. You may want to look at that section as you begin Chap. 2.

Other appendix sections are referred to throughout this text, and should be reviewed at that time.

Chapter 1

First Steps

First, turn on all peripherals, i.e., plotter, printer, etc. Then turn on the computer (see your manual for the location of the power switch).

To run any programs the microcomputer must first have a copy of the operating system, referred to as DOS, loaded into it. In order to run AutoCAD LT for Windows you must also have Windows loaded on your computer. DOS is started when the computer is turned on (booted), and the DOS prompt, `C:\>_`, is displayed. Your system may be set up to start Windows automatically. If Windows is not started when the computer is turned on, enter the following command from the DOS prompt:

`C:\>`**Win** <return>

1.1 Handling Floppy Disks

If your system has two floppy drives, usually the left or upper drive is drive A and the right or lower drive is drive B. The drives may be for 3.5- or 5.25-in diskettes.

To insert a floppy diskette into the drive, open the drive latch and slowly insert the disk into the drive, with the label on the disk pointing up and under your thumb when grasping the disk. Do not under any circumstance touch the magnetic surface of the disk or you may lose data stored on the diskette. Disks should not be inserted or removed from the disk drive when the red disk operation light is on. If the disk light is on, wait until it goes off (indicating that the drive is not reading or writing) and then insert the disk. Close the drive latch.

1.2 Windows Operations

When Windows is started, Program Manager appears on the screen with various *application windows* as illustrated in Fig. 1.1. Depending on how Windows is set up your system may have more or fewer application windows displayed

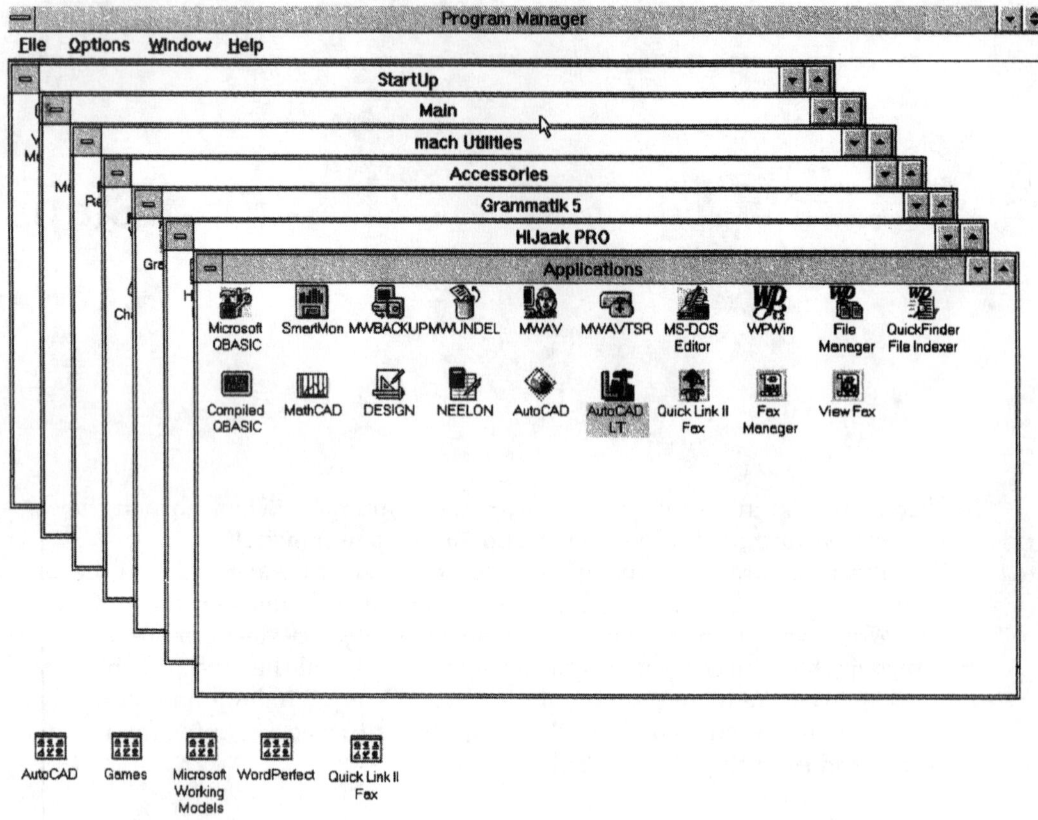

Figure 1.1 Program Manager.

on the desktop than illustrated. If you are starting Windows for the first time, refer to your *Windows User's Guide and Reference* manual for instructions on how to set up Windows.

Application windows display *program-item icons* which may be run from that window. Program-item icons are small pictures representing applications you can start from Windows. The Application window illustrated in Fig. 1.1 includes program-item icons for AutoCAD (Windows), AutoCAD LT, DESIGN, etc.

1.2.1 File manager

Windows File Manager is an application that helps you organize files. It is started as follows:

1. Boot up DOS and start Windows (see the preceding).
2. Choose the *Main* application window by placing the mouse pointer on its window title as illustrated by the arrow in Fig. 1.1, and quickly pressing and releasing the <pick> button (usually the left or 1 button) on the mouse. The

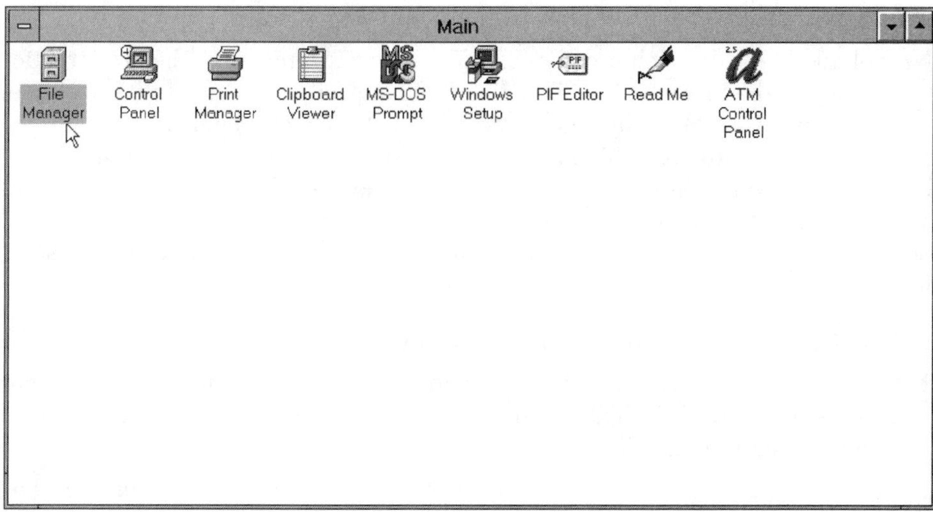

Figure 1.2 Main application window.

Main application window is displayed on the desktop (in front of the other windows) as illustrated in Fig. 1.2.

3. Choose File Manager by placing the mouse pointer on its icon as illustrated in Fig. 1.2 and quickly pressing the <pick> button twice, i.e., <pick><pick>. Alternatively you can <pick> the icon and then choose RUN from the File menu. This is discussed later.
4. The File Manager dialogue box illustrated in Fig. 1.3 is displayed.

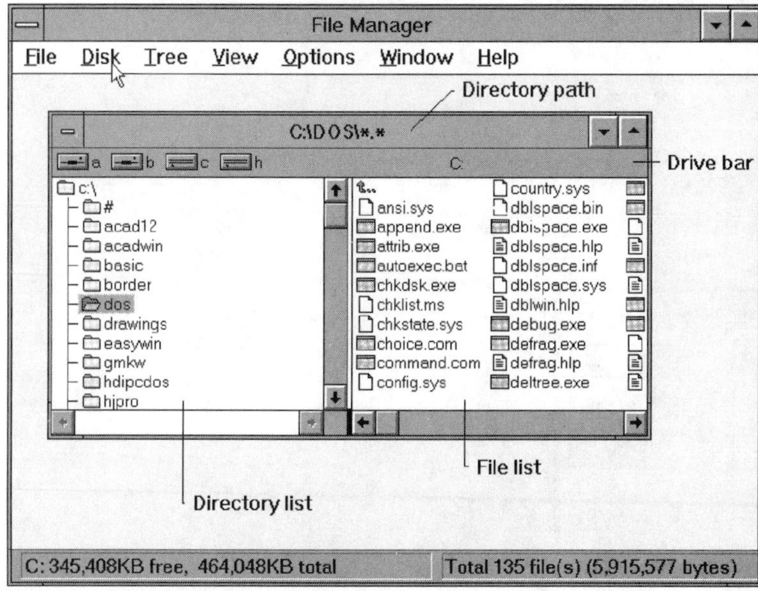

Figure 1.3 File Manager dialogue box.

1.2.2 Preparing a data disk

New blank disks (disks that do not contain any programs) must be prepared for use. This is called *formatting*. The disk is formatted only prior to its first use. If it is reformatted after data is stored on it, the data will be lost.

When using AutoCAD LT in a classroom setting, your drawings will usually be stored on a data disk in a floppy drive. In this text, drive A (usually the left or upper drive) is used. Other users with fixed drives will also want to store original or backup drawings on a data disk. A data disk is formatted for use as follows:

1. Insert a new blank diskette into a floppy drive as outlined in Sec. 1.1.
2. Choose `Disk` from the File Manager window menu bar by placing the cursor on it as illustrated in Fig. 1.4 and pressing the <pick> button on the mouse. The Disk menu is displayed.
3. From the Disk menu, choose `Format Disk...` to display the dialogue box illustrated in Fig. 1.5.
4. Place the mouse pointer on the arrow at the right of the *Disk In* selection box as illustrated in Fig. 1.5 and press the <pick> button. This displays a *drop-down list box*. Select the drive containing the disk to be formatted by choosing it in the drop-down box.
5. If necessary choose the drive capacity from the Capacity drop-down list box. Normally the capacity of a 3.5-in disk is 1.44MB and for a 5.25-in disk is 1.2MB.

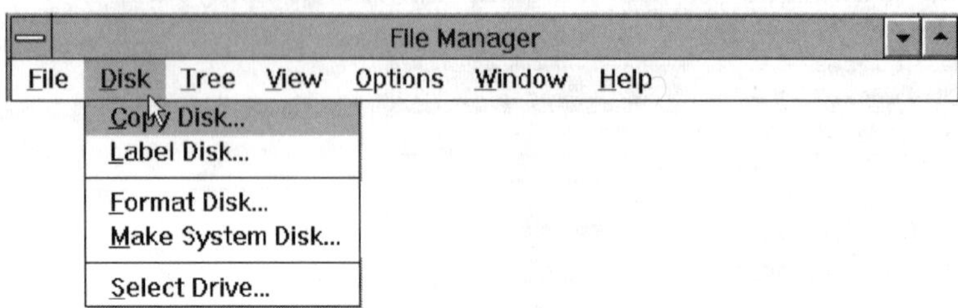

Figure 1.4 Disk menu.

Figure 1.5 Format Disk dialogue box.

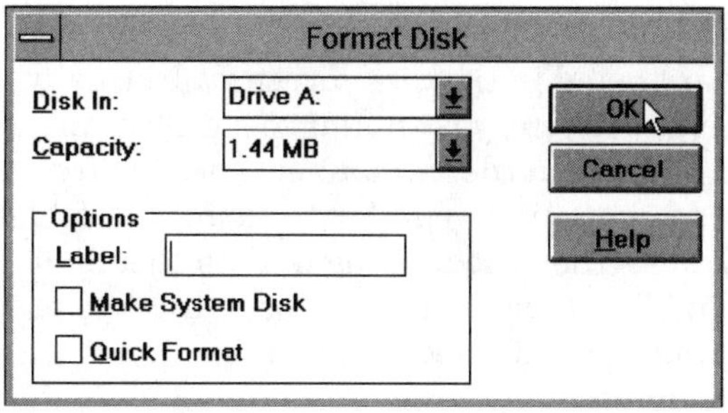

Figure 1.6 Start format.

6. Press the OK button by clicking it with the mouse as illustrated in Fig. 1.6 to start the diskette format process. Windows will display a Confirm Format Disk box, illustrated in Fig. 1.7. Select Yes.
7. When the format process is complete you will be asked if you wish to format another diskette. If you do, select Yes. If you are through, select No.
8. Close the File Manager window by clicking on the Control menu box containing the single dash, –, in the top left corner of the window, and the top left corner of Fig. 1.8. This displays the *Control menu* illustrated in Fig. 1.8. Select the Close option.

After a window is closed, if you want to place the windows in their original order (see Fig. 1.1), click on each window starting with the one to be in the back of the pack, and proceed sequentially to the front of the pack. This will bring each window to the table in order. The last one selected will remain at the top of the pack.

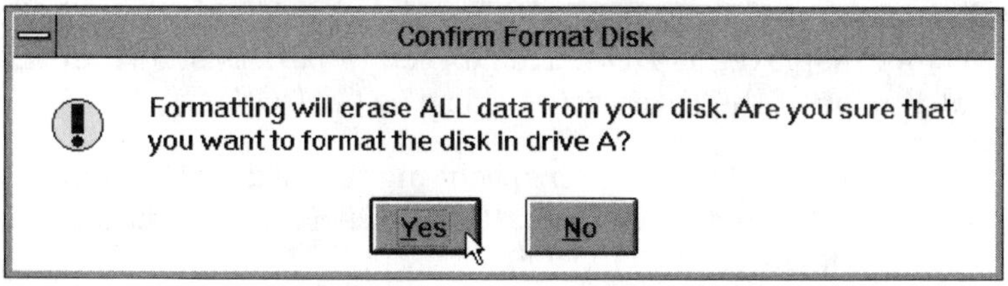

Figure 1.7 Confirm Format Disk box.

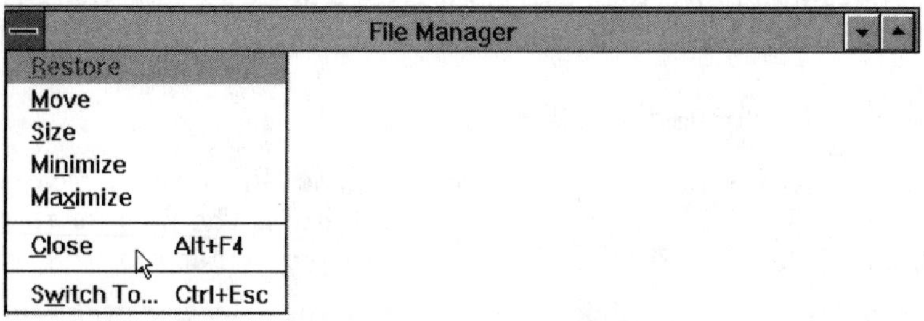

Figure 1.8 Closing a window.

1.2.3 Displaying the directory of a disk

The files stored on a disk are listed in the disk directory. Normally a drive will also have subdirectories. A subdirectory is similar to a drawer in a file cabinet. It allows you to store files in a more orderly manner. The subdirectory can also have subdirectories, and so on. This is similar to using file folders in a file drawer in a file cabinet, and further subdividing data in the file folders.

A file is the primary unit of storage. A file may be a drawing produced with AutoCAD LT, or a letter produced with a word processor. Every file must have a name. File and directory names:

- Can be up to eight characters long, and may also have an extension up to three characters long. The name is separated from the extension using a period, i.e., HOUSE.DWG.
- Can be entered as uppercase or lowercase letters.
- Can be composed of letters A through Z, numbers 0 through 9, and the following special characters: & –_^~!#%{}'@"().
- Cannot contain spaces, commas, backslashes, or periods (except the period that separates the name from the extension).
- Cannot be identical to the name of another file or subdirectory in the same directory.

The directory of a disk is displayed as follows:

1. Choose File Manager from the Main application window as illustrated in Fig. 1.2.
2. The *Directory window* is the rectangular window displayed inside the File Manager window illustrated in Fig. 1.3. In Fig. 1.3 the default drive is C: and the subdirectory displayed is DOS. This directory path is shown in the directory path at the top of the Directory window as *C:\DOS**.*.

The asterisk, *, is used as a wild card when specifying file or directory names. In the preceding file path, *.*, indicates that all files (with any first name and last name) are listed for the directory C:\DOS.

On the left side of the Directory window closed file folder icons indicate directories on the default drive. The current directory icon is displayed as an open file folder and the icon and directory name, dos, are shaded in Fig. 1.3. The right-hand side of the Directory window shows a list of the files in the current directory.

The default directory is changed as follows:

1. Move the cursor pointer onto the directory icon (i.e., acadlt) in the *directory list* of the Directory window and press the <pick> button. The files for that directory will be displayed in the *file list* of the Directory window.
2. The default drive is changed by clicking on its icon in the *drive bar* at the top of the Directory window. This is discussed further in following sections. If

you wish to close the File Manager window, select Close from the Control menu (see step 8 in Sec. 1.2.2).

1.2.4 Making a subdirectory

A new subdirectory on drive C:, named Drawings, is created as follows:

1. If the File Manager window is not open, follow the procedure to open it outlined in Sec. 1.2.1.
2. Using the mouse, choose the icon for drive C: by placing the mouse cursor on the icon, as illustrated in Fig. 1.9, and pressing the <pick> button.
3. If the path at the top of the Directory window is not C:*.*, place the mouse pointer on the file folder icon for C:\ in the directory list of the Directory window and press the <pick> button.
4. Choose `File` from the File Manager window bar to display the File pull-down menu.
5. Choose `Create Directory...` from the File menu by placing the mouse cursor on the command as illustrated in Fig. 1.10, and pressing the <pick> button.
6. Enter the directory name, **Drawings,** in the Name box in the Create Directory window as illustrated in Fig. 1.11, and then move the mouse cursor onto the OK button in the box and press the <pick> button on the mouse. This is referred to as pressing OK. The box is removed from the screen and the

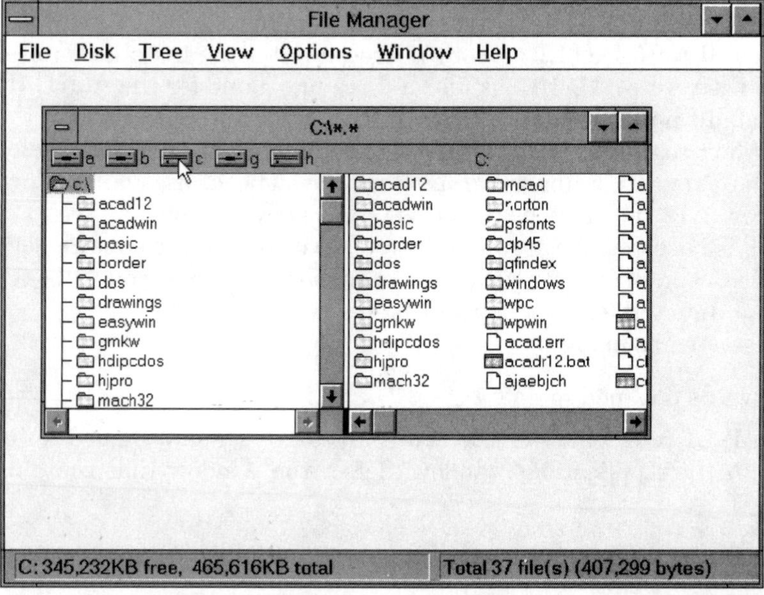

Figure 1.9 Selecting the default drive.

Figure 1.10 Create Directory option.

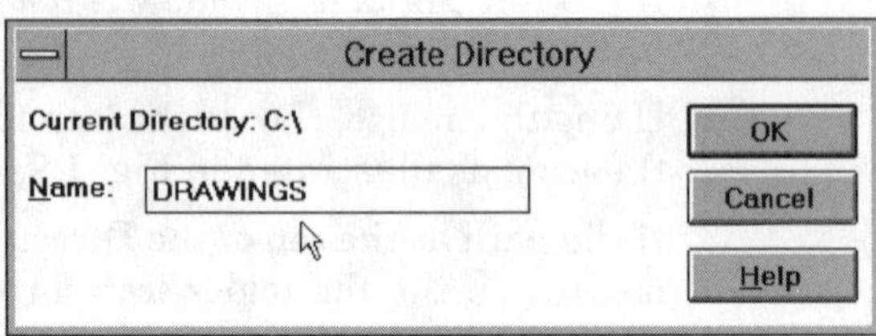

Figure 1.11 Create Directory dialogue box.

directory is created as a subdirectory on drive C:, and listed in the directory list of the Directory window (see Fig. 1.9).

7. Close the File Manager window by selecting Close in the Control menu (see step 8 of Sec. 1.2.2).

1.3 Starting AutoCAD LT

Prior to running AutoCAD LT you will have to install the software onto your fixed drive. Refer to the chapter on Software installation in your *AutoCAD LT for Windows User's Guide* for the procedure to transfer the program from the diskettes supplied by AutoCAD LT to your fixed disk.

When you install AutoCAD LT on your microcomputer the installation program provided with AutoCAD LT asks for a directory name for the AutoCAD LT files. The default name provided is Acadlt.

The installation program will also ask you to select a program item icon for AutoCAD in the Program Manager group windows. The icons available are illustrated in Fig. 1.12. The icon used in this text is shown shaded.

The following is based on the assumption you have created the subdirectory named DRAWINGS on drive C:, as outlined in section 1.2.4, and you will save drawings in that directory or on a floppy diskette in drive A:.

AutoCAD is started as follows:

1. Start Windows as outlined in Sec. 1.
2. Your AutoCAD LT program item icon is displayed in a window named AutoCAD LT or in the Applications window. Select the window that contains

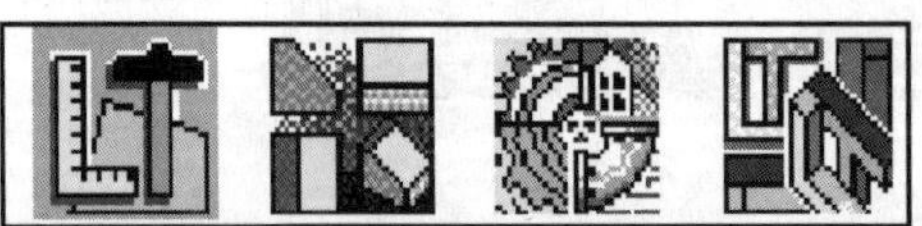

Figure 1.12 AutoCAD LT icons.

your AutoCAD LT icon by clicking on the window. [Refer to your *Windows User's Guide and Reference* if you wish to move the AutoCAD icon to the Applications window. If you do that, you can also then reduce the AutoCAD window to an application icon (relocate it to a small icon at the bottom of the screen as illustrated in Fig. 1.1). This eliminates clutter on the screen.]

3. Place the cursor on the AutoCAD LT program item icon using the mouse as illustrated in Fig. 1.13, and quickly press the <pick> button on the mouse twice.
4. AutoCAD LT boots, briefly displaying the text window with some messages, and the graphics window appears.

The AutoCAD LT graphics screen is illustrated in Fig. I.1. Your screen may appear slightly different because of screen resolution.

1.3.1 Begin a new drawing

If you are starting a new drawing you can name the drawing at the beginning of the drawing session using the New command, or at any time during the session using the SaveAs command. Normally the drawing is named prior to beginning drawing.

Move the cursor to the top of the screen into the menu bar using the mouse, and choose <pick> `File` (see Fig. I.1). This pulls down the File menu illustrated in Fig. 1.14 and App. E.1. Move the mouse into the File menu and select the `New...` command. Command names followed by an ellipse (. . .) indicates the command displays a dialogue box. The Create New Drawing dialogue box illustrated in Fig. 1.15 is displayed.

The drawing is to be stored in the **C:\Drawings** directory created in Sec. 1.2.4. (If you want to save your drawing on drive A:, read on but do not enter these commands.) Log onto C:\ by clicking on `New Drawing Name...` in the New Drawing Name dialogue box, as illustrated in Fig. 1.15. The directories list box illustrated in Fig. 1.16 is displayed. Choose drive `C:\` in the directory list box by moving the cursor onto its icon as illustrated and clicking on it twice, <pick> <pick>. Then choose the `Drawings` directory as shown in Fig. 1.17, by clicking

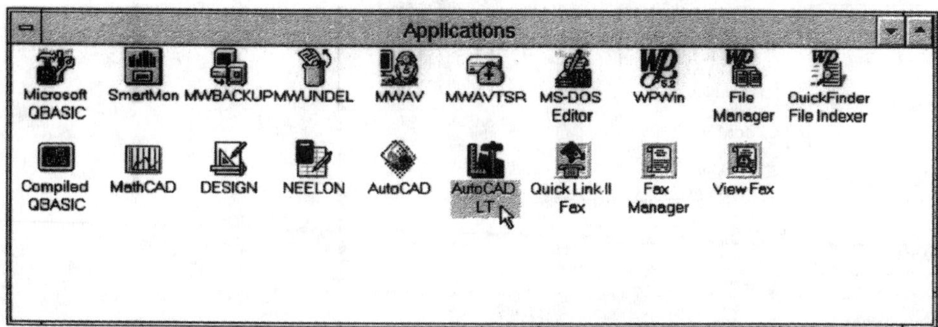

Figure 1.13 Starting AutoCAD LT.

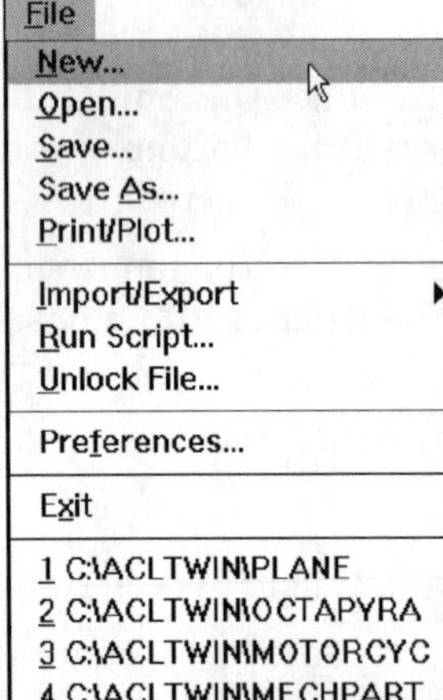

Figure 1.14 File menu.

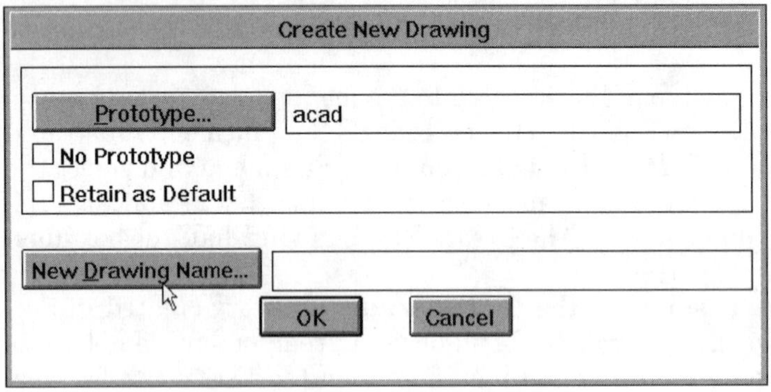

Figure 1.15 Create New Drawing dialogue box.

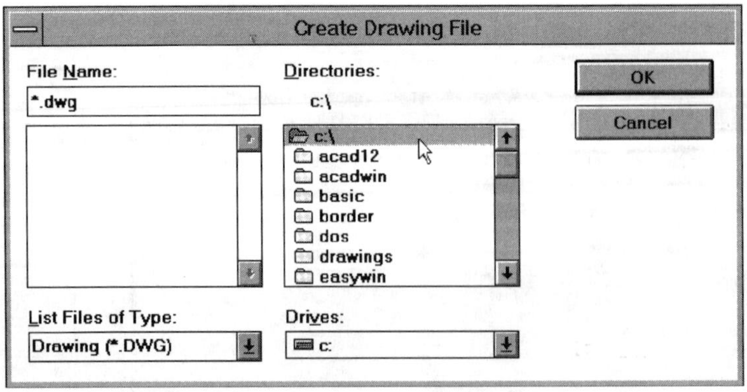

Figure 1.16 Directories list box.

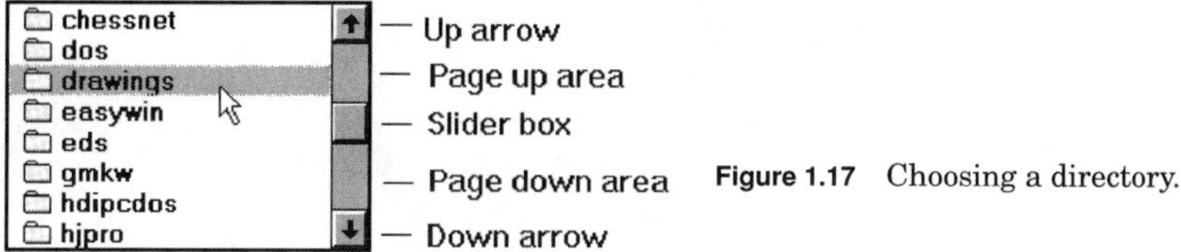

Figure 1.17 Choosing a directory.

twice on its icon. If the Drawings directory is not visible in the directory box you may have to use the slider bar located on the right side of the box to scroll the list up or down.

Using the slider bar. The slider bar in a dialogue box is used to scroll a list up or down. Clicking the Up arrow or Down arrow (see Fig. 1.17) scrolls the list down or up one item. To scroll the list one page select a point in the Page up or Page down area (above or below the slider box). To scroll through the list, move the cursor onto the slider box and hold the pick button down. The slider box is then dragged up or down scrolling the list. Release the pick button when the slider box is in the position you want.

The File Name: entry box in Fig. 1.16 shows the file name as *.dwg. AutoCAD drawings always have the extension .DWG. This drawing is to be named Proj-1.Dwg. Move the cursor into the File Name entry box and type **Proj-1** as shown in Fig. 1.18. It is not necessary to enter the extension .dwg since it is the default extension in the List Files of Type box (Press the OK button to exit the dialogue box. The Create New Drawing dialogue box is redisplayed with the drawing name entered in the New Drawing Name box as **C:\DRAWINGS\PROJ-1.DWG.** as shown in Fig. 1.19.

If the drawing is to be saved on a floppy diskette, for example on drive A: instead of C:\Drawings, select the drive from the drop-down Drives: list box located below the directories list box in Fig. 1.16. Then enter the drawing name in the File Name: box as outlined in the preceding.

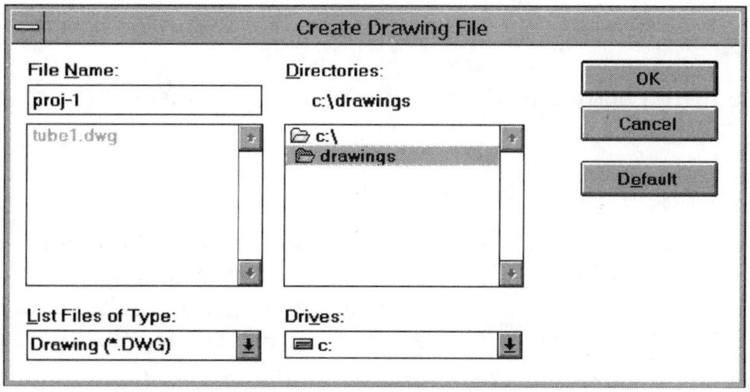

Figure 1.18 Naming a drawing.

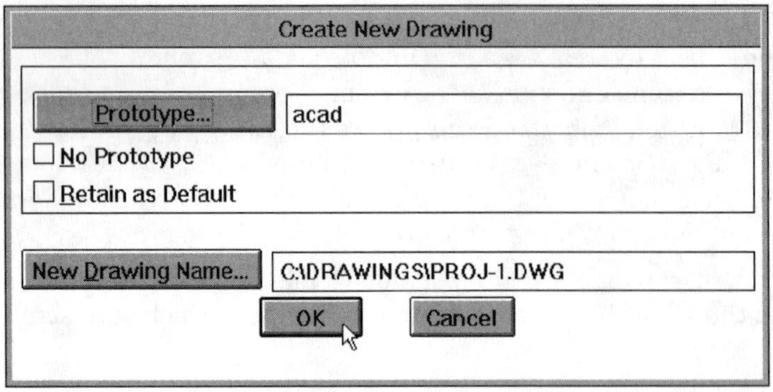

Figure 1.19 New drawing name.

1.3.2 Entering commands

AutoCAD Lt commands can be entered by typing them using the keyboard or by selecting them from the menu bar, toolbar, or tool-box.

In *Easy AutoCAD LT,* commands will normally be selected from menus pulled down from the menu bar or from the toolbox. Appendix E lists the contents of the menu bar pull-down menus, along with the action associated with each menu item.

To choose commands in the menu bar, move the cursor arrow to the top of the screen into the menu bar, using the mouse, until one of the menu titles is highlighted as illustrated in Fig. I.2. Moving the mouse to the right or left moves the cursor along the menu. When the desired menu title is highlighted, quickly press the pick button on the mouse. A pull-down menu is then displayed under the menu title selected.

Choose the Draw menu by moving the cursor arrow along the menu bar until Draw is highlighted. Then quickly press and release the pick button on the mouse <pick>. The Draw pull-down menu illustrated in Fig. I.2 is displayed. Choose the Line command by moving the cursor onto Line in the Draw menu and quickly pressing the <pick> button. The selections appear as follows in *Easy AutoCAD LT:*

`Draw` <pick> `Line` <pick>

The command line at the bottom of the monitor should now display the following:

```
Line From point:
```

(AutoCAD LT command line requests are printed in computerlike type in this text.) This means that AutoCAD LT has invoked the LINE command and is waiting for you to enter some data—the start point of the line. Move the cursor into the drawing area of the screen and *digitize* a point by pressing the <pick> button on the mouse. The command line should now say:

```
To point:
```

Move the cursor to another point and press the <pick> button on the mouse. Notice the command line. Move the cursor to another point extending a line at an angle to the previous point and <pick> that point. Now type a c in response to the command as indicated below and then press the Enter key on the keyboard, or the Enter button on the mouse (usually the second or the 1 button). AutoCAD LT commands are printed in bold computerlike type, AutoCAD requests are printed in normal computerlike type, and data you type in is bold type. The pick button is indicated as <pick> and the Enter key is indicated as <return>:

`To point:` **c** <return>

Notice how the line segments closed onto the first point and the Command line is no longer prompting for a point.

You have now completed your first drawing. Before continuing save the drawing by choosing the following from the pull-down menu bar (refer to Fig. 1.14 and App. E, Fig. E.1):

`File` <pick> `Save...` <pick>

The Save . . . option invokes the QSAVE (quick save) command which saves the current named drawing without requesting a file name. QSAVE can also be entered by typing it from the keyboard. If the current drawing has not been named (see Sec. 1.3.1), you will be asked to enter a file name for the drawing. This drawing is saved using the file name, C:\DRAWINGS\PROJ-1.DWG or A:\PROJ-1.DWG, entered with the New.. command when the drawing was started (see Fig. 1.19).

Save . . . (QSAVE) does not exit the current drawing so you can continue the drawing. It is a good habit to save your drawing whenever you have drawn enough that you would not like to redraw it if the system were to crash. Should that happen you could reboot AutoCAD and continue the drawing from what was saved the last time QSAVE was invoked. Draw another line and then quick save the drawing again. Each time the drawing is saved AutoCAD makes a backup copy of the last save by changing the file extension from .Dwg to .Bak, and saves a new copy of the drawing with a .Dwg extension. You now have two copies of this drawing saved. The initial copy saved is named Proj-1.Bak and the latest copy saved is named Proj-1.Dwg. If you save to drawing a third time, the first copy is deleted, the second is given the extension .Bak and the third is saved with the extension .Dwg.

1.3.3 Exiting AutoCAD LT

You have completed your first AutoCAD drawing. To exit the drawing editor and save your drawing, execute the following from the pull-down menu bar:

`File` <pick> `EXIT` <pick>

If you have already saved the drawing and not made any changes to the drawing since the last save, AutoCAD Lt will be exited. If you have not saved

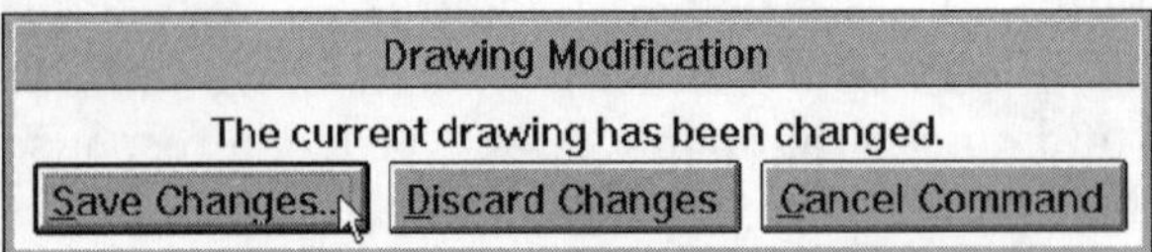

Figure 1.20 Drawing Modifications options box.

the drawing or made changes to the drawing since the last save, the Drawing Modifications options box illustrated in Fig. 1.20 is displayed. Select `Save Changes...`, to save the drawing and exit AutoCAD.

1.4 Copying a File in Windows

If you have exited AutoCAD LT you can copy a file in Windows using the File Manager window. As outlined in Sec. 1.2.1 bring the Main application window to the desktop. Then choose the File Manager icon to display the File Manager dialogue box illustrated in Fig. 1.3. Highlight the file to be copied following procedures discussed in this chapter. Then choose the File menu (see Fig. 1.10) and select `Copy...` to display the Copy dialogue box illustrated in Fig. 1.21. Note the current directory and drawing name in the From: box. Enter the location to copy the file to, i.e., A:\ in Fig. 1.21.

1.5 Renaming a File in Windows

To rename a file in Windows choose the File Manager window as outlined in Sec. 1.2.1. Highlight the file to be renamed, as outlined above. Then choose Rename . . . in the File menu. A Rename dialogue box similar to that illustrated in Fig. 1.21 is displayed. Enter the new file name in the To box.

Copy

Current Directory: C:\DRAWINGS

From: PROJ-1.DWG

To: A:\

Copy to Clipboard

OK

Cancel

Help

Figure 1.21 Copy file dialogue box.

Chapter

2

Drawing Construction

Objective. Begin a new drawing—set limits, units, and precision; use draw commands—Line, Circle, Point, and Fillet; edit a drawing—Erase, Oops, Break, and Cancel; use display controls—Zoom (all, extents, previous, and window); Exit and Save procedures.

Drawing. Start Windows as outlined in Chap. 1. The procedure to draw the trapezoid illustrated in Fig. 2.1 is outlined in the following text.

2.1 Loading AutoCAD LT

Start AutoCAD Lt by clicking its icon as outlined in Chap. 1, Sec. 1.3. AutoCAD LT's graphics window illustrated in Fig. I.1 appears.

Note: In all of the AutoCAD LT commands illustrated in this text the following format is used:

- Data you are to type is in boldface.
- The Enter key is indicated by <return>.
- AutoCAD responses or requests are printed in computer-like type.
- AutoCAD commands (which can be selected from the menu bar, see Fig. I.1, or typed in) are printed in bold computer-like type.
- Instructions you are to follow are in text type.

2.1.1 Beginning the new drawing

Although you can immediately begin drawing, and name the drawing later using the SaveAs command, it is usually best to name a new drawing at the start of the session. Select the following from the menu bar at the top of the screen:

`File` <pick> `New...` <pick>

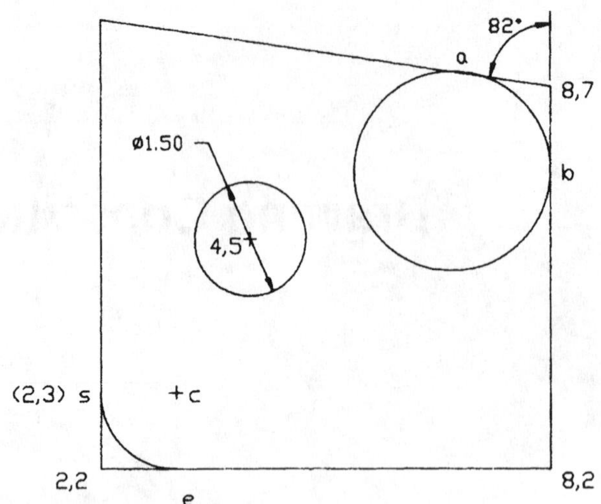

Figure 2.1 Project 2.

The Create New Drawing dialogue box illustrated in Fig. 1.15 is displayed. Click on the `New Drawing Name...` button to display the Create Drawing File dialogue box illustrated in Fig. 1.16. If the default directory is not shown as C:\, click twice on `C:\` as illustrated in Fig. 1.16. Next, select the `Drawings` subdirectory by clicking its name in the Directory box as illustrated in Fig. 1.17.

Move the cursor to the `File Name:` entry box and press the <pick> button, and then enter the file name as **Proj-2.** Close the dialogue box by clicking on `OK`. The Create New Drawing Dialogue box (see Fig. 1.19) is redisplayed showing the new drawing name as C:\DRAWINGS\PROJ-2.DWG. If the drawing name is correct, click on the `OK` button to exit the dialogue box. If the name is incorrect, click on New Drawing Name . . . and repeat the procedure outlined above.

2.2 Screen Limits

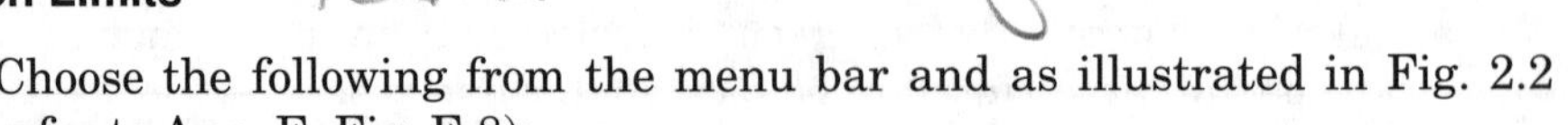

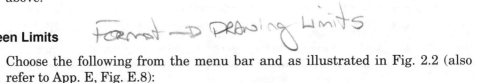

Choose the following from the menu bar and as illustrated in Fig. 2.2 (also refer to App. E, Fig. E.8):

> `Settings` `<pick>` `Drawing` `<pick>` `Limits` `<pick>` `ON/OFF` `<Lower-left corner>` `<0.0000, 0.0000>:` `<return>` This will select the default coordinates of 0,0 displayed in the wedge brackets <>. `ON/OFF` `<Upper-right corner>` `<12.0000, 9.0000>:` `<return>` This will use the default coordinates of 12 units horizontal and 9 units vertical.

The Limits command can also be invoked by typing LIMITS and pressing <return> at the AutoCAD command prompt.

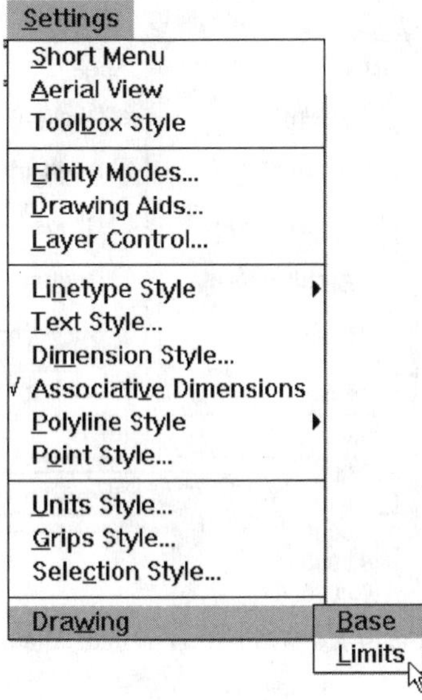

Figure 2.2 Settings menu.

2.3 Set Units and Precision

The drawing is to be in decimal units. Select the following from the menu bar (also see Fig. 2.2 and App. E, Fig. E.8):

`Settings` <pick> `Units Style...` <pick>

The Units Control dialogue box illustrated in Fig. 2.3 is displayed. The units available are:

Type	Example
1. Scientific	1.6E+01
2. Decimal	16.70
3. Engineering	1′-4.5
4. Architectual	1′-4½
5. Fractional	16½

The circles next to the options in the Units and Angles boxes are referred to as *radio buttons.* A radio button is pressed (on) when its center is filled, and only one radio button in a box can be on at a time. A radio button is pressed by clicking on it with the mouse. Pressing a new button turns the previous one off.

Select the Units `Decimal` button, and the Angles `Decimal Degrees` button as shown in Fig. 2.3.

The units are to be precise to two digits to the right of the decimal. Click on the downward pointing arrow on the right side of the Precision box at the bottom of the Units box to display the pop-up list box showing precision options,

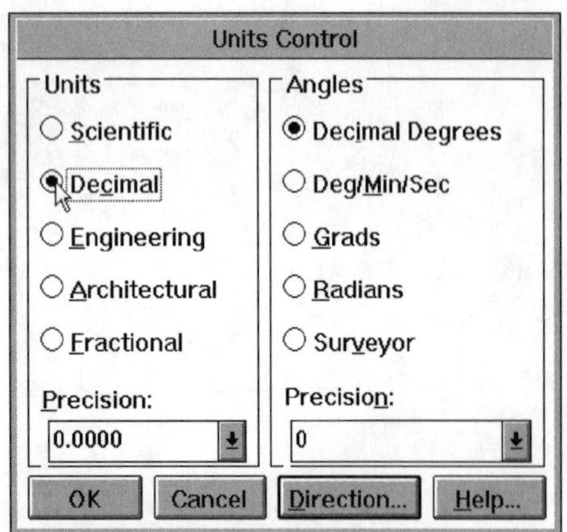

Figure 2.3 Units Control dialogue box.

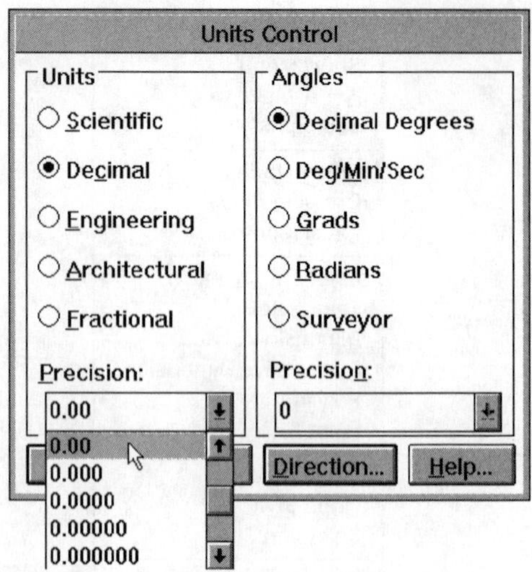

Figure 2.4 Units Precision drop-down box.

illustrated in Fig. 2.4. If the 0.00 precision is not displayed, scroll the list up or down using the slider bar as outlined in Chap. 1, Sec. 1.3.1, and select 0.00 as illustrated.

You can change the coordinate system to be used for designating angles. Generally you will use the cartesian coordinate system illustrated in Fig. 2.5. The angle 0 direction is east and positive angles are measured in a counterclockwise direction. Set the appropriate buttons as illustrated in Fig. 2.6, and press the OK button. The Units command can be invoked from the command prompt by entering UNITS.

2.4 Lines and Cartesian Coordinate System

Two-dimensional points on the AutoCAD LT drawing screen are located based on the cartesian coordinate system illustrated in Fig. 2.5.

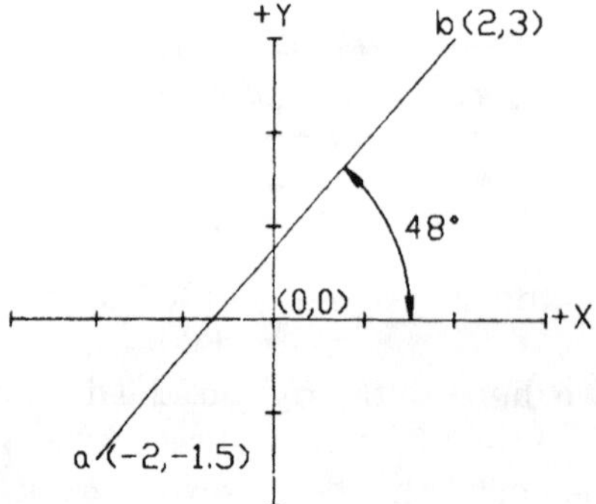

Figure 2.5 Cartesian coordinate system.

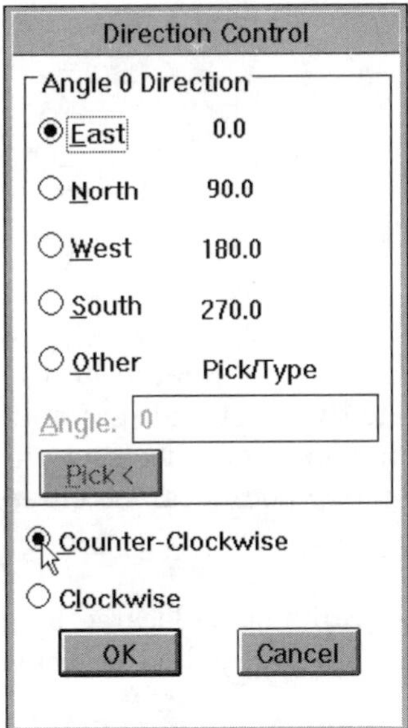

Figure 2.6 Direction Control dialogue box.

In the cartesian coordinate system, horizontal lines drawn from left to right are said to be along the x axis in a positive direction. Vertical lines drawn in an upward direction are said to be along the y axis in a positive direction. Positive angles are measured from the positive x axis in a counterclockwise direction. In Fig. 2.5, the coordinates of point b are 2,3 (2 along the positive x axis and 3 units along the positive y axis). The coordinates of point a are −2, −1.5. Line a-b is at an angle of 48 degrees. Refer to Chap. 15 for three-dimensional drawings.

Lines. To draw a line, select the following commands from the menu bar following the procedure specified in the section on AutoCAD LT commands:

`Draw` <pick> `Line` <pick>

The trapezoid illustrated in Fig. 2.1 will be drawn using the four available methods of drawing lines. Any one method is acceptable for all lines.

Lines by real coordinates. A point can be located on the drawing by entering the screen coordinates of the point:

`Line from point:` **2,2** <return>

Lines by relative xy distances. A point can be specified by entering its distances relative to the last point entered. To draw a line from coordinate 2,2 to coordinate 8,2 as illustrated in Fig. 2.7, the relative distances from point 2,2 are 6.00 units in the x direction and 0 units in the y direction. The command to draw the line using relative coordinates is:

`To point:` **@ 6,0** <return>

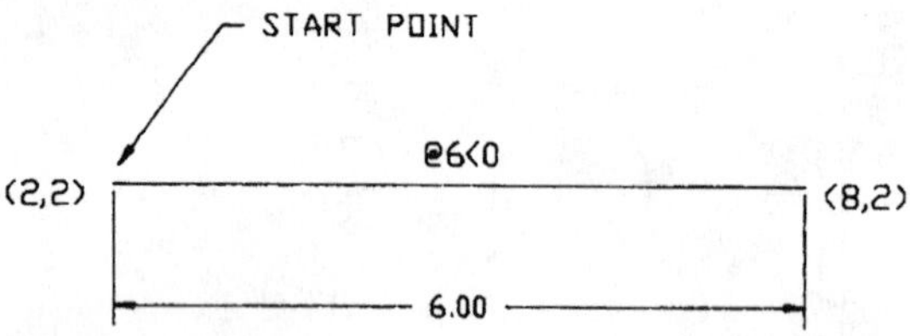

Figure 2.7 Line 1.

The @ symbol tells AutoCAD LT that the point is relative to the last point entered. In this case the point is six units to the right and zero units above the previous point. Points to the right of the previous point are positive and points above the previous point are positive. Negative points can be entered for relative points.

Lines by relative distance and angle. Points can also be located by giving their relative distance and angle with respect to the last point. To drawn Line 2 in Fig. 2.8, enter:

`To point:` **@5<90** <return>

The @ symbol tells AutoCAD LT the point is relative to the last point entered. The < indicates that the next value is the angle of the line. Angles are based on rectangular cartesian coordinates where angles are positive if rotation from the x axis is counterclockwise and negative if rotation from the x axis is clockwise. Angles are always measured from the horizontal (unless you redefine the location of 0 degrees when defining the angle units; see the previous section on set units and precision).

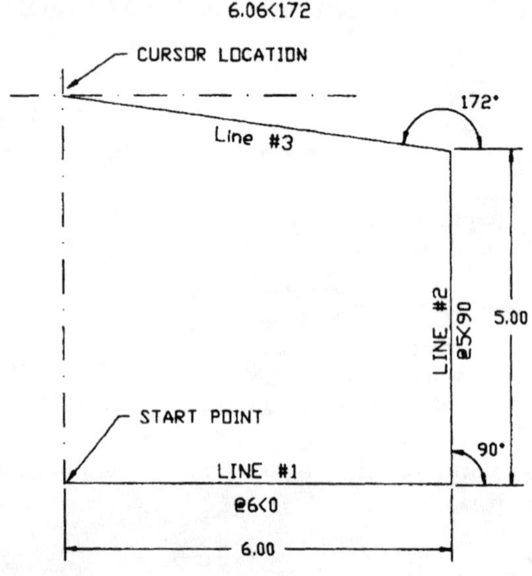

Figure 2.8 Line 4, digitizing points.

Lines by digitized points. Points can be entered by locating them on the drawing screen using the cursor control keys or a mouse. First, press Ctrl-D (hold down the Ctrl key and press the D key) to turn on the display of the current screen coordinates (also see App. E, Fig. E.10), which is located at the top of the screen.

Move the cursor around on the screen. If the coordinates displayed at the top of the screen in the coordinate display window (see App. E, Fig. E.11) do not change as the cursor is moved, press Ctrl-D again.

Coordinates can be displayed as *x,y* coordinates (i.e., 5.25,3.10) or as distance<angle (i.e., 4.10<56) by toggling the Ctrl-D key. Toggle Ctrl-D until the distance<angle is displayed and move the cursor on the screen until the distance to the next point is shown as 6.06<172. The vertical cursor should be lined up with the start point (2,2) as illustrated in Fig. 2.8. Press the pick button to digitize the point.

2.4.1 Close command

A set of lines can be closed on the first point by entering C from the keyboard or choosing the Close button (Fig. 2.9) in the buttons bar (App. E, Fig. E.11):

`To point:` **Close** (buttons bar)<pick>

If the trapezoid did not close properly, the following will help you resolve the problem.

2.5 Undo, Redo, and Cancel Commands

If the set of lines just completed was restarted from a new point (other than the original start point) the last line will close on the new start point. If the trapezoid did not close on coordinate 2,2 (the start point) choose Undo (Fig. 2.10) from the buttons bar to undo the last line. Redraw the line and close it on coordinate 2,2. If you press Undo and you want to undo the undo, press Redo (Fig. 2.11). If you do not end the line command with Close, AutoCAD LT will be requesting the next point. Choose ^C (Cancel) (Fig. 2.12) from the buttons bar to cancel the command.

Figure 2.9 Close button.

Figure 2.10 Undo button.

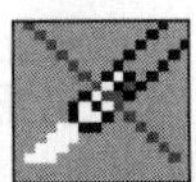

Figure 2.11 Redo button.

Figure 2.12 Cancel button.

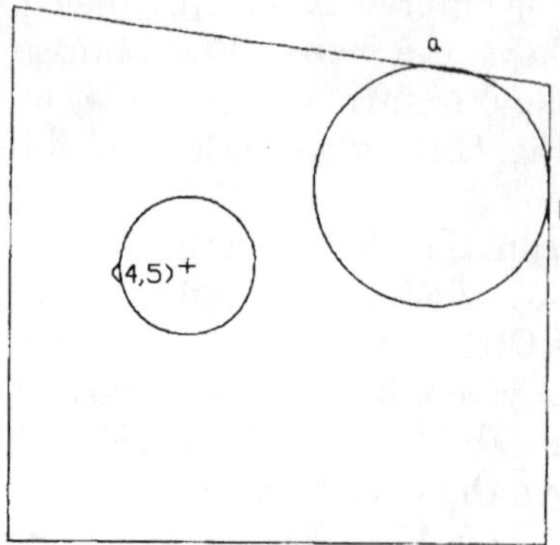

Figure 2.13 Circles.

2.6 Circle Command

A 1.5-unit diameter circle is to be drawn with its center point at coordinates 4,5. The Circle command in AutoCAD LT will not draw circles using the diameter, and the radius of 0.75 will have to be used. The commands are as follows:

`Draw` <pick> `Circle` <pick> `Center,Radius` <pick> `3P/TTR <center point>:` **4,5** <return> `Radius:` **0.75** <return>

Other circle commands are:

`3-Point` <pick> `3P First point:` Digitize point *a* on the top line of the trapezoid; see Fig. 2.13 <pick> `Second point:` Digitize point *b* on the right side of the trapezoid.<pick> `Third point:` Move the mouse and drag the circle to the upper-right corner of the trapezoid. If the keyboard is used, press the PgUp key twice and *slowly* drag the circle tangent to the upper-right corner of the trapezoid. Pressing the PgUp key sets coarse movements of the cursor. Pressing the PgDn key sets fine movements of the cursor. <pick>

2.7 Point Command

This command is used to place a single point on the drawing. The command repeats so you must enter cancel to exit:

`Draw` <pick> `Point:` <pick> `Point:` Digitize a point on the drawing <pick> `Point:` `^C` (buttons bar, Fig. 2.12) <pick>

The default point style is a dot. Other point styles can be set as follows:

`Settings` (Fig. 2.2) <pick> `Point Style...` <Pick>

The Point Style dialogue box illustrated in Fig. 2.14 is displayed. The default dot point is in the upper-left corner selection box. Select another point by clicking on its selection box and then pressing OK. Retry the point command.

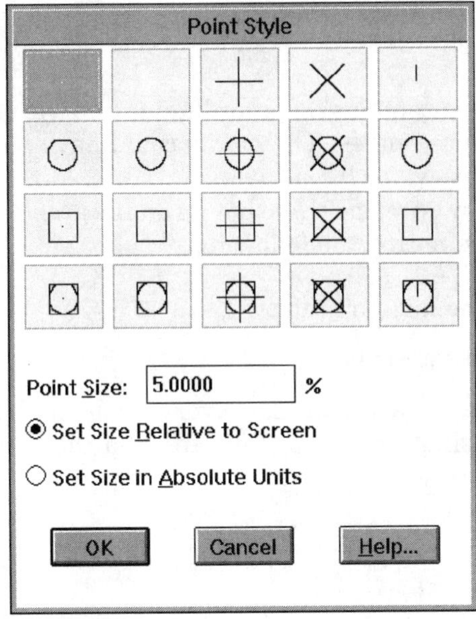

Figure 2.14 Point Style dialogue box.

2.8 ARC Command

`Draw` <pick> `Arc` <pick>

A number of Arc options are available (see App. E, Fig. E.1)

3 point
Start, Center, End
Start, Center, Angle
Start, End, Angle
Center, Start, End
Center, Start, Angle

Select `Start,Center,End`. Arcs are always drawn in a counterclockwise direction. To draw the arc illustrated in Fig. 2.15 with a radius of 1 use:

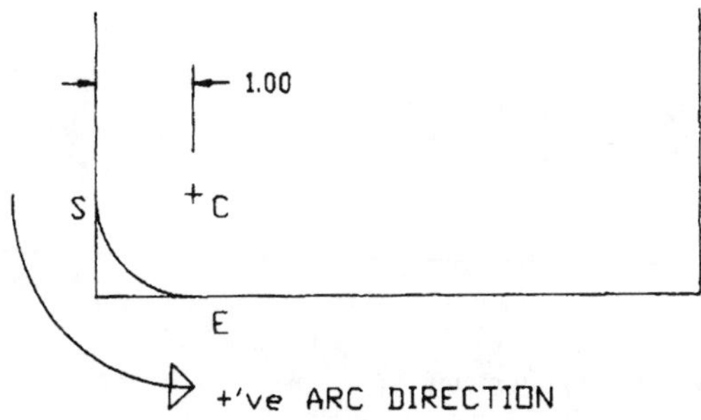

Figure 2.15 Arcs.

Arc center/<Startpoint>: **2.3**<return> Center/End/<Second point>: @1<0 <return>Angle/Length of chord <End point>: **@1<270** <return>

Notice that the start point was entered as real coordinates and the other points were entered as relative distance angles. The points could have been entered using any of the methods discussed for line drawing.

Three-point arcs are drawn by entering three points on the arc. Practice with a number of the arc commands, noting the following:

- Enter @ to start the arc on the last point drawn.
- Arcs are always drawn counterclockwise.
- AutoCAD sets the drag mode for last point; however, you do not have to drag the last point into location using the cursor. You can enter the coordinates of the last point via the keyboard.

2.9 Erase and Oops Commands

The Erase command is used only to erase whole entities, and it will not break an entity. This means that if a line is drawn, the Erase command is used to erase the entire line. If a portion of the line is to be deleted the Break command is used. In the following, the Last option of the Erase command erases the last entity drawn (also see Fig. 2.16 and App. E, Fig. E.7):

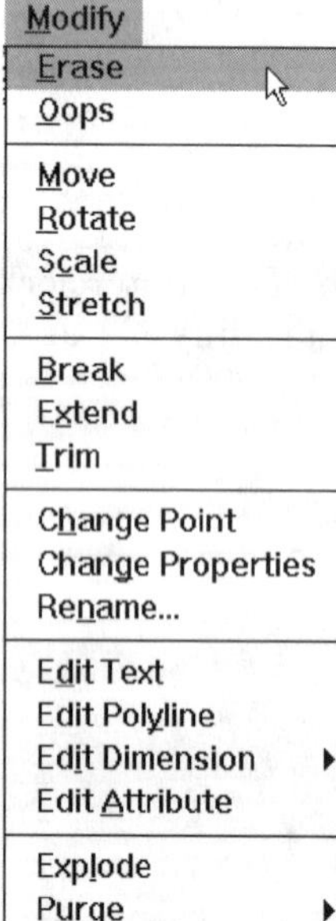

Figure 2.16 Modify menu.

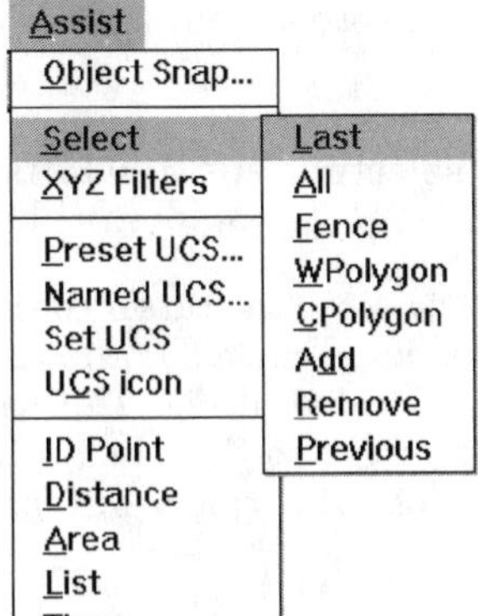

Figure 2.17 Select menu.

> `Modify` <pick> `Erase` <pick> `Select objects:` Last may be entered from the keyboard as L, or selected from the Assist menu in the menu bar (see Fig. 2.17). `Assist` <pick> `Select` <pick> `Last` <pick>

Note that the last entity drawn, the arc, is erased. Restore the arc using the Oops option:

> `Modify` <pick> `Oops` <pick>

The Oops option cancels the last erase command. It should be invoked immediately following the erase command. Choose the following:

> `Modify` <pick> `Erase` <pick> `Select objects:` Place the cursor box on the circumference of the circle as shown in Fig. 2.18. <pick> `Select objects:` Place the cursor box on the bottom line of the trapezoid as shown. <pick> `Select objects:` <return>

<Return> is entered by pressing the return button on the mouse or the enter key on the keyboard. The entities selected became dotted as they were picked, indicating they were added to the selection set, but were not erased from the

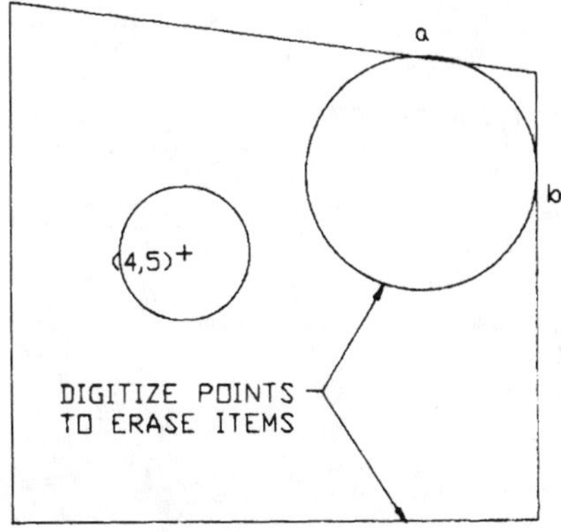

Figure 2.18 Erasing entities by digitizing.

drawing until <return> was entered. Restore the erased entities using the `Oops` command.

Window selection box. Another method of selecting entities to be erased is using a window selection box. Enter the following commands:

> `Modify` <pick> `Erase` <pick> `Select objects:` Move the cursor so the horizontal cursor line is slightly below the bottom of the large circle and the vertical cursor line is slightly to the left of the circle as illustrated in Fig. 2.19. <pick> `Other corner:` Move the cursor upward and to the right so the window created completely encloses the circle as illustrated in Fig. 2.19. <pick> `Select objects:` <return>

In a window selection box the second point selected defining the box is always to the right of the first point; i.e., in Fig. 2.19 the lower-left corner is picked first, and the upper-right corner is picked second. *Also, the first point of the window must not be on any entity.* Notice that although the top line and the right side of the trapezoid were included in the window they were not erased. Only the circle which was entirely enclosed by the window was erased. In a window selection box only whole entities are added to the selection set. When prompted by AutoCAD LT to `Select objects:` entering **w** (window) from the keyboard also puts AutoCAD LT into the window box selection mode. You will then be asked to select the first and second points defining the window box. These points can be selected from left to right or right to left, and can fall on a drawing entity. This process would be used in a cluttered drawing where the first point defining the window box could fall on an entity. Use the Oops command to restore the erased entities and enter the following:

> `Modify` <pick> `Erase` <pick> `Select objects:` **w** <return> `Window First corner:` Select a corner of the window box to enclose the entity to be erased. <pick> `Other corner:` Select the other corner of the window box <pick> `Select objects:` <return>

Crossing selection box. All entities enclosed or cutting through a crossing selection box are added to the selection set. In a crossing selection box the sec-

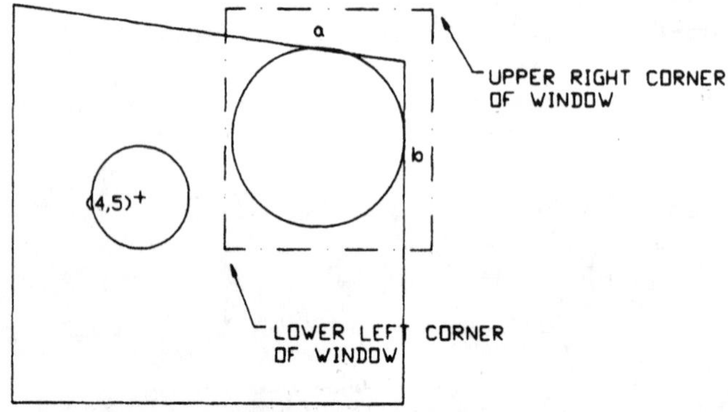

Figure 2.19 Erasing entities by window box.

ond point defining the selection box is always to the left of the first point. As with a window selection box, the first point used to start the box must not be on any entity. Use the Oops option to restore the previously erased entity and repeat the erase commands entered above for the window selection box; however, start the selection box by picking the upper-right corner of the box first (see Fig. 2.19). When the commands are completed, the circle and the top and right side lines of the trapezoid are erased.

A crossing box can also be invoked by entering **c** (crossing) in response to the `Select objects:` prompt. In this case the order of selecting the defining points for the crossing box is not critical, and the points can fall on drawing entities. Restore the erased entities using the Oops command, and use the c response to invoke a crossing box to select entities to be erased.

The Erase command can also be invoked by entering Erase at the command prompt.

2.10 Redraw Command

Phantom lines and dots often remain on the screen after entities are erased or selected with other commands. The screen may be cleaned up at any time by entering the Redraw command in the View menu. If you use Redraw and want to restore the entity erased, you will have to enter two Undo commands. One undoes Redraw and the other the command to undo.

2.11 Zoom Command

The Zoom command is used to enlarge or shrink the view of a portion of the drawing. Select the following from the menu bar (See Fig. 2.20 and App. E, Fig. E.4.1):

`View` <pick> `Zoom` <pick> `Scale` <pick>
`All/Center/Extents/Previous/Window/<Scale(X/XP)>:` **2** <return>

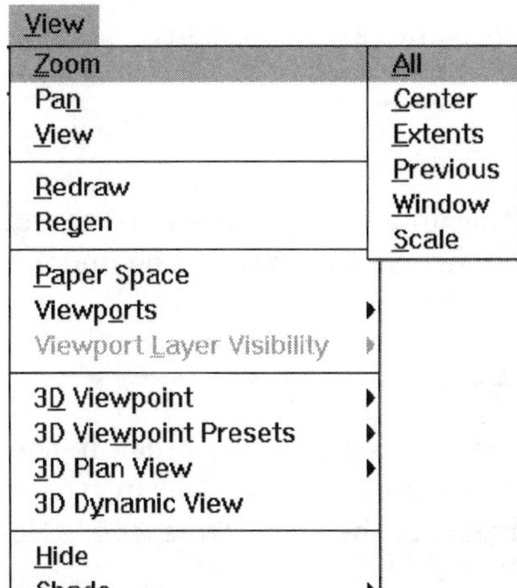

Figure 2.20 View/Zoom menu.

Entering a scale value of 2 displays the object twice as large as the full view. Press the Space bar or Enter key to recall the ZOOM command, and enter **0.5** for the zoom scale. Notice that the object is one-half as large as the *full* view. The Space bar or Enter key can be used to recall the previous command. To return the object to its original size invoke the Zoom command and enter the scale as **2X.** This zooms the screen to twice the size of the *current* screen.

Select the following from the menu bar:

> `View` <pick> `Zoom` <pick> `Window` <pick> `First corner`: Digitize a corner of a window box which is to include points a and b in Fig. 2.1. <pick> `Other corner`: Digitize the other corner of the window box <pick>

Viewing the zoomed area, how accurate were you able to place the circle along the top of the line? A more precise method of placing lines tangent to circles is discussed in later projects. This exercise should demonstrate the difficulty of placing entities on a drawing without assistance from AutoCAD LT.

Try the Previous and Extents options to the Zoom command noting the effect on the view. Restore the original view based on the drawing limits by choosing the following:

> `View` <pick> `Zoom` <pick> `All` <pick>

Other options to the Zoom command are applied in later projects.

2.12 Break Command

This command is used to delete a portion of an entity. Select the following from the menu bar (see Fig. 2.21 and App. E, Fig. E.7):

> `Modify` <pick> `Break` <pick> `Select object`: Digitize a point on the top line of the trapezoid near the left end of the line <pick> `Enter second point (of F for first point)`: Digitize a point on the same line about 0.5 inches from the previous point. <pick>

A gap is made in the line at the two points selected. Select the following from the Edit menu (see App. E, Fig. E.2):

> `Edit` <pick> `Undo` <pick>

The last command is undone and the break in the line is restored. The Undo command is used immediately following the command to be undone. Select the following:

> `Edit` <pick> `Redo` <pick>

The Redo undoes the Undo command and restores the break in the line.

The Break command will be used to form a fillet by deleting the corner of the trapezoid from a to b and the lower part of the circle from a to b. Select the following from the menu bar:

Modify
Erase
Oops
Move
Rotate
Scale
Stretch
Break
Extend
Trim
Change Point
Change Properties
Rename...
Edit Text
Edit Polyline
Edit Dimension
Edit Attribute
Explode
Purge

Figure 2.21 Modify menu.

`Modify` <pick> `Break` <pick> `Select object:` Digitize a point on the top line of the trapezoid well to the left of the circle so AutoCAD LT is clear about what item is being selected. See Fig. 2.22. <pick> `Enter second point (or F for First point):` **F** <return> `First Enter first point:` Digitize the intersection point of the circle and the top side of the trapezoid, the first point in Fig. 2.22. <pick> `Enter second point:` Digitize the end of the top line on the trapezoid at the top right corner of the trapezoid, the second point in Fig. 2.22. <pick>

In the preceding commands, the Select object entering f (first point) allows you to pick the object and then pick a first point of the break. Compare this with the precious Break command where the point used to select the object and the first point of the break were the same. If the first point of the break falls on

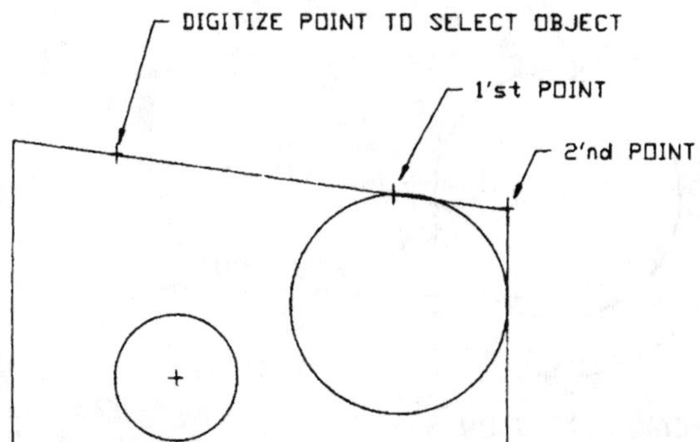

Figure 2.22 Break points on line.

two entities, such as the circle and the line, AutoCAD Lt must be told first which entity is to be used for the break.

Using the same procedure break the line on the right side of the trapezoid from point b (Fig. 2.19) to the top corner.

When breaking a circle or arc, AutoCAD LT always breaks the entity in a counterclockwise direction between the first and second point. Select the following to break the circle from a to b (Fig. 2.19):

> `Modify` <pick> `Break` <pick> `Select object:` **Digitize a point on the circumference of the circle (Fig. 2.22) <pick>** `Enter second point (of F for first point):` **f** (first) <return> `Enter first point:` **Digitize the first point in Fig. 2.23. <pick>** `Enter second point:` **Digitize second point in Fig. 2.23. <pick>**

The Break command can also be entered by typing Break at the command line.

2.13 Exit a Drawing

The following commands in the File menu (see App. E, Fig. E.1) are used to save the drawing:

Save . . . Saves the drawing using the current drawing name without exiting the drawing. This command can be entered from the keyboard as QSave.

Save as . . . Saves the drawing allowing you to enter the file name. This command can be entered from the keyboard as Save.

Exit . . . Exits AutoCAD. If the drawing file has not been saved and changes have been made to the drawing, the Drawing Modifications options box (Fig. 1.20) will be displayed. This allows you to save changes, discard changes, or cancel the command. The Quit command can be entered from the keyboard to exit a drawing without saving changes.

This drawing was named C:\Drawings\Proj-2.Dwg in Sec. 2.1.1. Choose the `Save . . .` command in the File menu to save the drawing.

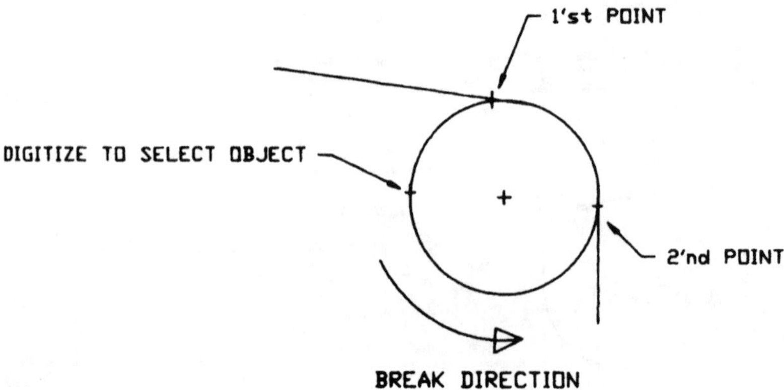

Figure 2.23 Breaking circle lines.

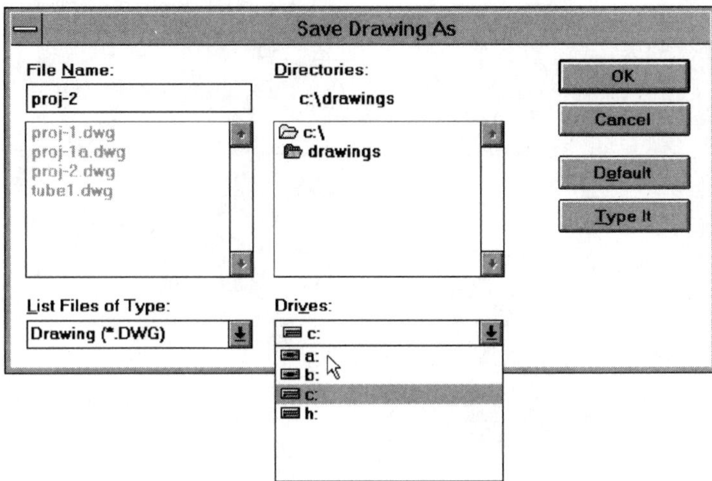

Figure 2.24 Save Drawing As dialogue box.

You should get in the habit of saving a backup copy of your drawings. To save a copy on a floppy diskette, place a formatted diskette in drive A: and select the following:

File <pick> Save as . . . <pick>

The Save Drawing As dialogue box illustrated in Fig. 2.24 is displayed. Display the drive's drop-down menu and select drive A: as illustrated. This will change the Directories to a:\. The File name is shown as Proj-2. Press OK to save the file on the floppy in drive A:.

The Type it option allows you to type the drawing directory and name from the command line.

Choose the Exit option in the File menu.

Chapter

3

Relocating Entities

Objective. Practice commands from the previous project; use Move command to relocate an entity; use the Copy command to copy entities; draw circle using Tangent, Tangent, Radius; draw center ticks and center lines for circles.

Drawing. Boot up AutoCAD LT and begin a new drawing (review Chap. 2, Sec. 2.1.1) with the name C:\DRAWINGS\PROJ-3. Draw the V block illustrated in Fig. 3.1 using the procedures outlined in this lesson.

3.1 Drawing Screen Limits

The V block will require a space of about 6 by 5 units. The default AutoCAD limits are the lower-left corner 0,0 and the upper-right corner 12,9. AutoCAD LT drawings are always drawn 1:1 scale on the monitor. If scaling is to be done, it is done when the drawing is plotted. The screen size will be reduced to 6,5. To start the lower-left corner of the V block at 0,0, the lower-left corner of the screen will be set as –1, –1, and the right corner will be 5,4. The commands are:

Settings <pick> Drawing <pick> Limits <pick>
Lower-left corner <0.0000,0.0000>: **–1,–1** <return>
Upper-right corner <0.0000,0.0000>: **5,4** <return>

A tick should appear on the screen locating the new limits. To reset the monitor to the new limits, zoom in on the limits:

View <pick> Zoom <pick> All <pick>

Note: Each time the screen limits are changed, the commands Zoom and All must be entered to reset the monitor to the new limits.

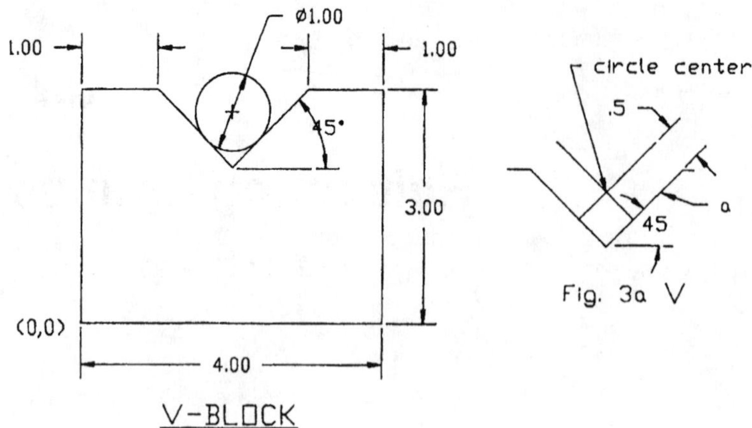

Figure 3.1 Project 3.

3.2 Set Units and Precision

Set the units to decimal with two digits to the right of the decimal point. Refer to Sec. 2.3 for the procedure. Press Ctrl-D to turn cursor position coordinate display on.

3.3 V-Block Drawing

Draw the V block (do not include the circles or arc yet). Select the Line command from the Draw menu and start the lower-left corner of the V block at coordinate 0,0. Draw the V block in a counterclockwise direction. The commands are summarized below.

Note: Try to draw the lines of the block without looking at the commands below. If you draw a line and wish to change it, use the Undo command immediately after the line is drawn. If Undo is invoked during a line sequence, only the last line is undone. If Undo is invoked after existing Line, all lines drawn in that sequence are undone. To undo Undo, invoke Redo. Refer to Chap. 2, Sec. 2.5.

`Draw` <pick> `Line` <pick> `Line from point:` **0,0** <return> `To point:` **@3<0** <return> `Undo` <pick> `To point:` **@4<0** <return> `To point:` **@3<90** <return> `To point:` **@1<180** <return> `To point:` **@–1,–1** <return> `To point:` **@–1,1** <return> `To point:` **@1<180** <return> `To point:` **c** <return>

In the preceding set of commands, the –1,–1 coordinates specify that the bottom of the V is 1 unit to the left (-ve) and 1 unit below (-ve) the top-right end of the V. The relative coordinates to draw the line from the bottom of the V to the top-left end are –1,1. Notice how the Undo command was used to correct an input error in the sequence.

3.4 Save Drawing

Prior to continuing, the work done so far should be saved:

`File` <pick> `Save...` <pick>

If you named the drawing at the start, it is saved in that file. If you have not named the drawing the Save Drawing As dialogue box (Fig. 2.24) is displayed. The drawing is to be saved as c:\drawings\proj-3.dwg.

You should also get in the habit of saving a copy of the drawing on a floppy diskette as a backup. Place a formatted floppy diskette in drive A: (or B:) and select:

`File` <pick> `Save as...` <pick>

The Save Drawing As dialogue box (Fig. 2.24) is displayed. Save the drawing as a:\proj-3.dwg.

If AutoCAD LT crashes for some reason or if the power plug accidentally comes out of the socket, etc., you will lose only the work done after the last Save command. Get into the habit of saving your drawing regularly during the operation of AutoCAD LT.

3.5 Using MOVE Command

Now the 1-unit diameter circle will be drawn in the V at the top of the V block. Three different procedures will be used. In the first, the circle will be drawn above the V and dragged into location as illustrated in Fig. 3.2. The commands are:

`Draw` <pick> `Circle` <pick> `Center, Radius` <pick> `Circle 3P/2P/TTR<center point>:` Move the cursor so that it is in the initial position shown in Fig. 3.2 <pick> `Radius` **0.5** <return>

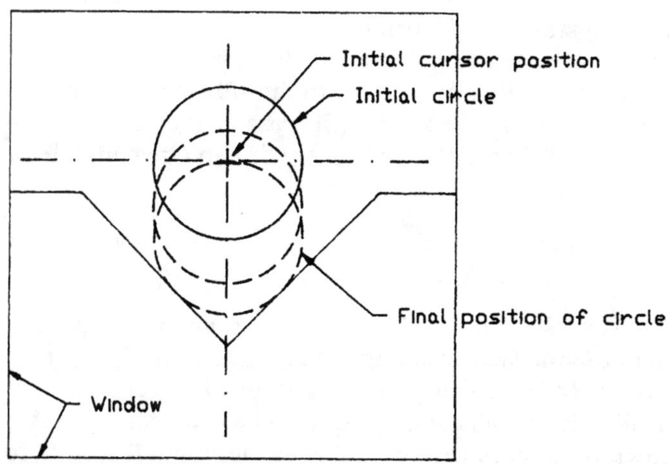

Figure 3.2 Moving entities.

Prior to moving the circle into place, use the Zoom and window commands to enlarge the view of the V:

> View <pick> Zoom <pick> Window <pick> First corner: A window is to be placed around the V and the circle, see Fig. 3.2. Digitize a point on the screen that will represent the lower-left corner of that window. <pick> Other corner: Digitize the upper-right corner of the window. <pick>

The Move command will now be used to relocate the circle so that it fits into the V and is tangent to the sides of the V. As the circle is being moved, its initial view will remain on the screen. When the final position is selected, press Enter to fix the circle in the location selected; this will delete the initial view.

The Move command is entered from the menu bar as follows:

> Modify <pick> Move <pick> Select objects:

The last item drawn, the circle, is to be moved. You could type L (Last) and press <return> in response to Select objects:, or use the Assist / Select menu (see Fig. 2.17 and App. E, Fig. E.5):

> Assist <pick> Select <pick> Last <pick> Select objects: <return> Base point or displacement: Digitize a point on the bottom of the circle directly above the V. <pick> Second point of displacement: Using the mouse, drag the circle down until its sides are tangent to the V <pick>

In the Move command, the second point can be automatically dragged into place by moving the cursor, or a numeric coordinate value can be entered. Notice that the initial circle is not erased until its copy has been moved into location and the pick button has been pressed to digitize the new location.

3.6 Using COPY Command

The next procedure used will be based on a procedure you might use if the drawing was to be done using standard drafting equipment.

The circle drawn in the V has a radius of 0.5 units. Because the circle is tangent to the sides of the V, two lines drawn parallel to the side of the V and 0.5 units from each side and on the inside of the V will cross at the center of the circle as illustrated in Fig. 3.3. To erase the previously drawn circle and draw the lines:

> Modify <pick> Erase <pick> Select object: Assist <pick> Last <pick> Select objects: <return>

Note: Notice that Enter is pressed at the end of the last command sequence. When the item is selected, its line type is changed to a dotted line. The Erase command is still in control and other items to be erased can be selected. To exit the command and erase all entities selected, the Enter key is pressed.

A line will now be drawn parallel to the right side of the V and 0.5 units to the left of it. The line will be a copy of the right side of the V, which is at a 45-

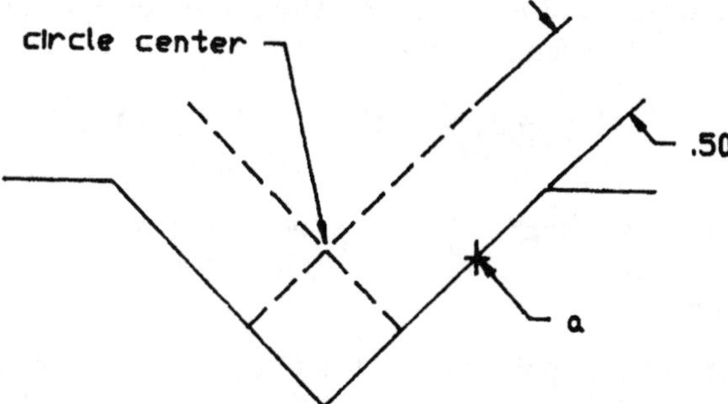

Figure 3.3 Copying entities.

degree angle (see Fig. 3.3). The direction of movement is perpendicular to the side, giving an angle of 135 (45 + 90) degrees.

The COPY command is selected from the Toolbox as illustrated in Fig. 3.4 (commands selected from the toolbox will be printed in uppercase in this text). As the cursor is moved over icons in the toolbox, the command associated with the icon is displayed at the top of the toolbox. If the toolbox is not visible on your screen, press the toolbox button in the buttons bar (see App. E, Fig. E.11). The Toolbox button toggles the toolbox to one of: a rectangular box, a column on the left side of the screen, a column on the right side of the screen, and no visible toolbox. Place the cursor on the copy icon in the toolbox and press the <pick> button. The COPY command continues as follows:

> `COPY` <pick> `Select objects:` Digitize a point on the right side of the V, point *a* in Fig. 3.3 <pick> <return> `<Base point or displacement>/multiple:` **@** (To reselect point *a*) <return> `Second point of displacement:` **@0.5<135** <return> <return>

Notice the two Enters at the end of the command string. The first is required to execute the second point of displacement entry, and the second is used to recall the Copy command. This is a handy way to recall a previous command and should be used whenever possible. The format of the Copy command follows:

- Select the object to be copied.
- Indicate the displacement by selecting a first point in response to the displacement request and then a second point with respect to the first point,

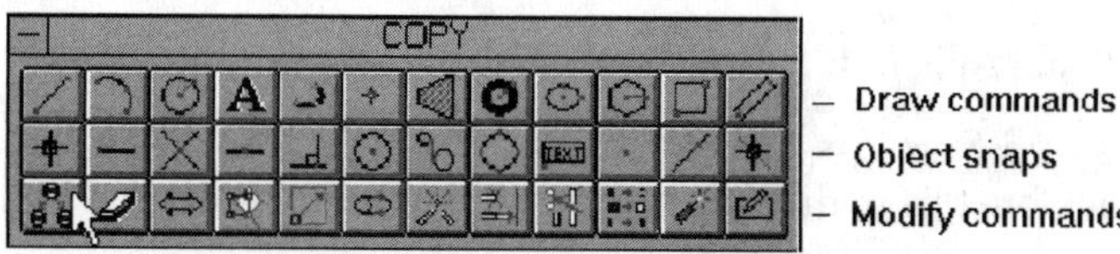

Figure 3.4 Toolbox.

which can be located by digitizing a point on the screen or via the keyboard. The displacement can be located anywhere on the monitor.

Copy the left side of the V. Try to do so without looking at the following commands:

`Select objects:` Digitize a point on the line to be moved. <pick> <return> `<Base point or displacement>/multiple:` **@** <return> `Second point of displacement:` **@0.5<45** <return>

Draw a circle with the center point where the two copied lines cross:

`Draw` <pick> `Circle` <pick> `Center,Radius` <pick> `Circle 3P/2P/TTR <center point>:` Digitize the crosspoint of the parallel lines. <pick> `Radius:` **0.5** <return>

Select ERASE from the Toolbox and erase each of the parallel lines:

`ERASE` <pick> `Select objects:` Digitize one of the parallel lines. <pick> Digitize other parallel line. <pick> `Select objects:` <return>

Notice the Enter needed to complete the Erase command. Display the entire drawing:

`View` <pick> `Zoom` <pick> `All` <pick>

3.7 Using TTR Command

A circle can be very easily placed tangent to two lines using the TTR (tangent, tangent, and radius) command as follows:

`ERASE` <pick> `Select objects:` Digitize a point on the circumference of the circle. <pick> `Select objects:` <return>

`Draw` <pick> `Circle` <pick> `Tangent,Tangent,Radius` <pick> `Enter Tangent spec:` Place the cursor target over the left side line of the V. <pick> `Enter second Tangent spec:` Place the cursor target over the right side line of the V. <pick> `Radius:` **0.5** <return>

3.8 Draw Center Marks and Lines in Circle

The style and size of circle center marks is governed by the number stored in the dimension variable Dimcen. If the number stored in Dimcen is zero, no center marks are drawn. The default value of Dimcen is 0.09. In later projects scaling of dimensions will be discussed. For this project the value of 0.09 is acceptable. Select the following from the menu bar:

`Settings` (see Fig. 2.2 and App. E, Fig. E.8) <pick> `Dimension Style...` <pick>

The Dimension Styles and Settings box illustrated in Fig. 3.5 is displayed. Press the Extension Lines button to display the Extension Lines dialogue box illustrated in Fig. 3.6.

Set the center marks to center lines by clicking the check box adjacent to

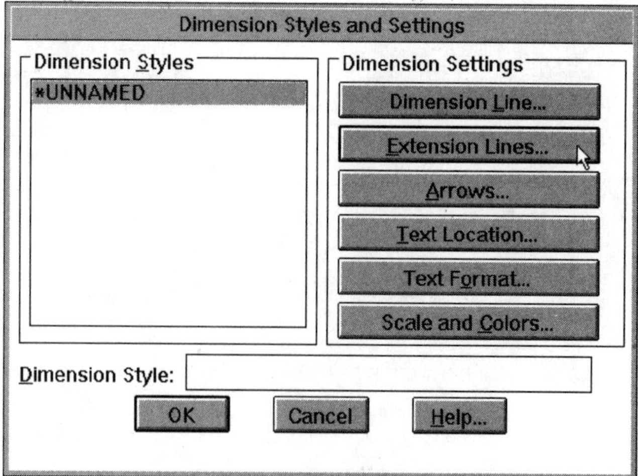

Figure 3.5 Dimension Styles and Settings box.

Figure 3.6 Extension Lines dialogue box.

Mark with Center Lines. The check box is on when it contains an X. Press the OK button in both dialogue boxes.

Add the center lines to the circle:

> `Draw` <pick> `Radial Dimensions` (see App. E, Fig. E.3.5) <pick> <pick> `Center Mark` <pick> `Select circle or arc:` Digitize a point on the circumference of the circle. <pick>

3.9 Exit

Choose `Save...` in the File menu to save your drawing to the default file C:\Drawings\Proj-3.Dwg. If you wish to save a backup copy to a floppy diskette, choose `Save As...` to save a copy to A:\Proj-3.Dwg. Choose `Exit...` to exit AutoCAD.

Chapter

4

Dimensioning

Objective. Dimension a drawing; calculate and set dimension scale; use linear, angular, and radius dimensioning; set dimension text controls; use Arc command; calculate text scale.

Drawing. Boot up AutoCAD LT and start a new drawing named Proj-4. Complete the drawing illustrated in Fig. 4.1, inserting all dimensions and text using the procedures outlined in this lesson.

4.1 Set Drawing Limits and Units

Set the limits of the monitor so that the 14 × 10 unit object will fit the screen and allow room for the dimensions. The lower-left corner of the *object* will be assumed as point 0,0, so the lower-left corner of the *monitor* will have negative coordinates. The limits can be reset later so you do not have to worry too much about the exact proper values for this initial setting. Refer to Chap. 3 for the procedure.

When the limits are set, use Zoom All to set the screen to the new limits:

`View` <pick> `Zoom` <pick> `All` <pick>

Set the units to decimal with one digit to the right of the decimal point. Refer to Chap. 3 if you have trouble. To return to the drawing editor, press the F2 key. Press Ctrl-D or F6 (see Fig. E-10) to activate the cursor coordinate display.

4.2 Draw Lines and Arc

Begin drawing lines using the lower-left corner of the plate as 0,0 and draw in a counterclockwise direction:

`Line` *(Toolbox)* <pick> `Line from point:` **0,0** <return> `To point:` **@8<0** <return> `To point:` **@1<90** <return> `To point:` **@4<0** <return>

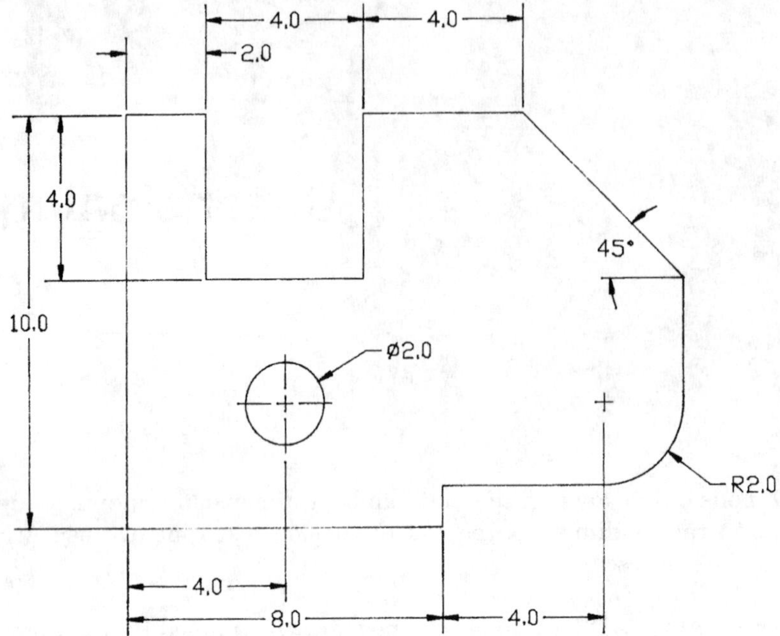

Figure 4.1 Project 4.

4.2.1 Last point

An arc is to be drawn starting from the end of the last line drawn. That point is the last point drawn.

When AutoCAD LT requests a point and the point is to be the same as the last point drawn, you can indicate that the last point is to be used by entering @ from the keyboard or buttons bar. This command will be used when drawing the arc because the start point of the arc is the end point of the last line drawn.

4.2.2 Draw arc

To draw an arc starting at the end of the last line and with a radius of 2 units, select Start, Center, End from the list of options. The arc will then be drawn in a counterclockwise direction starting at the last point, as illustrated in Fig. 4.2. The center is 2 units directly above the start point, so the relative command @2<90 is entered next. The end point is entered as 2 units to the right of the center @2<0:

```
Draw <pick> Arc <pick>  Start,Center,End <pick> Center/<Start point>: @
<return> Center: @2<90 <return> End point: @2<0 <return>
```

Arcs must always be drawn in a counterclockwise direction. Draw the remainder of the lines to complete the plate. If you draw a line incorrectly, use

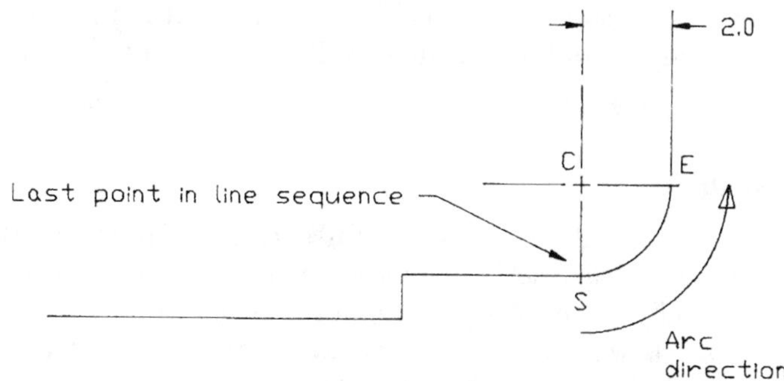

Figure 4.2 Arc drawing sequence.

Undo to erase it and then redraw the line. To start the line sequence at the end of the arc, use the relative @ command. When drawing the diagonal line, relative coordinates are used to locate the next point.

`Line` <pick> `From point:` @ <return> `To point:` **@3<90** <return> `To point:` **@-4,4** <return> etc.

Draw a circle with a diameter of 2.0 units at location 4,3.

4.3 Set Text Scale

When using AutoCAD LT, height or size refers to the number of drawing units. The number of units used for the size of text and dimension variables must reflect either the drawing limits set or the size desired for text and dimensions variables on the plotted drawing.

We will consider two methods to calculate the text height—the first based on a drawing not plotted to scale and the second based on a scaled plot.

4.3.1 Method 1—Drawing not plotted to scale

To calculate the text height, assume the following specifications for this drawing:

- Limits are set as –3,–3 and 17,13, giving a drawing size of 20 by 16 units.
- Plot size is to be an A-size sheet (8.5 by 11 in).
- Text height desired on plotted sheet is $\frac{3}{16}$ in (0.1875).

AutoCAD lettering height, h, is calculated by setting up a ratio of:

$$\frac{\text{Screen text height}}{\text{Screen dimension}} = \frac{\text{plot text height}}{\text{plot dimension}} \tag{4.1}$$

Based on the drawing height, h/16 = 0.1875/8.5, giving h = 0.35. Based on the drawing width, h/20 = 0.1875/11, giving h = 0.34.

The larger value governs. For lettering, set h = 0.35. When text is inserted into a drawing, AutoCAD LT requests the text height. If the drawing is not to be plotted to scale, enter 0.35.

4.3.2 Method 2—Drawing plotted to scale

If the drawing is to be plotted to scale, the text height is calculated based on the plot scale. Assume that this drawing is drawn in inch units and is to be plotted on an A-size sheet (8.5 by 11 in). A drawing plot scale of 1 in = 2 in, or ½ scale, should be satisfactory. If we wish the text height on the plotted drawing to be ³⁄₁₆ in (0.1875 in), the height (h) of the text on the monitor will be calculated as follows:

$$\tfrac{1}{2} \times h = 0.1875 \quad \text{giving } h = 0.375 \text{ drawing units (inches)}$$

Text will not be added to this drawing; however, the text height of 0.375 units will be used to calculate the height of dimension text and other dimension variables.

4.4 Dimension Scale

Dimension variables (arrow size, dimension text height, extension line offsets, circle and arc center lines and marks, etc.) can be set individually or by setting the scale factor for all dimensions using Dimscale. The default value for Dimscale is 1. AutoCAD's default size for dimension text is 0.18 drawing units multiplied by Dimscale, which has a default setting of 1.0.

In Sec. 4.3.2 it was determined that the text should be 0.375 units high on the monitor to obtain ³⁄₁₆-in text on the plotted drawing. Dimscale is calculated using the following formula:

$$\begin{aligned} &\text{Dimscale} \times 0.18 = \text{Text height} \\ &\text{Dimscale} \times 0.18 = 0.375 \qquad \text{giving Dimscale} = 2.1 \end{aligned} \tag{4.2}$$

To provide sufficient room for dimensioning, reset Limits to –3,–3 and 17,13:

`Settings` <pick> `Limits` <pick> `Lower-left corner <default>:` **–3,–3** <return> `Upper-right corner <default>:` **17,13** <return> `View` <pick> `Zoom` <pick> `All` <pick>

Set the dimension scale, Dimscale, as follows:

`Settings` <pick> `Dimension Style...` <pick>

The Dimension Styles and Settings box illustrated in Fig. 3.5 is displayed. Choose the `Scale and Colors...` box.

The Scale and Colors box illustrated in Fig. 4.3 is displayed. Enter the Dimscale value of **2.1** in the `Feature Scaling` box. Press the `OK` button and then choose the `Extension Lines...` box from the Dimension Styles and Settings box.

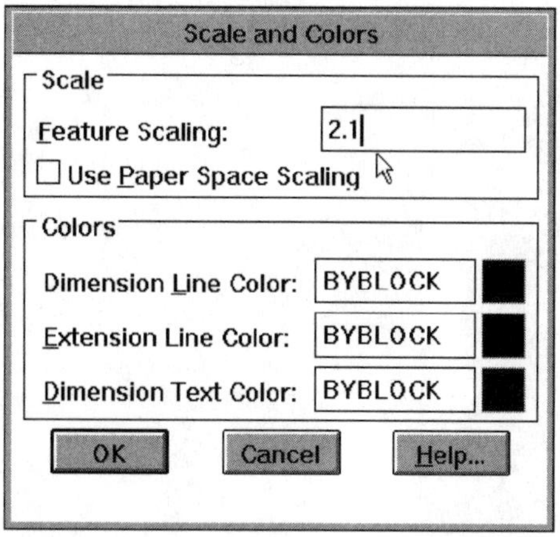

Figure 4.3 Setting the dimension scale.

4.5 Diameter Dimension

The 2.0-diameter circle is to have center lines to mark its center. Set the `Mark with Center Lines` check box on by moving the mouse into the box as illustrated in Fig. 3.6 and pressing the <pick> button. (The box is on when there is an X in it.) Exit the dimension settings dialogue boxes by selecting OK in each case.

When the 2.0-diameter circle is dimensioned center lines are added with the dimensions (see Fig. 4.4 and App. E, Fig. E.3.5):

> `Draw` <pick> `Radial Dimensions` <pick> `Diameter` <pick> `Select arc or circle:` Digitize a point on the top right side of the circumference of the circle, where you want the arrowhead for the diameter dimension to start (see Fig. 4.1). <pick> `Dimension text` <2.0>: Accept the default value of 2.0 by pressing <return> `Enter leader length for text:` Digitize leader length by moving the cursor to draw the leader. <pick>

When asked for the text, if the default value is not what is to be entered you can type in any value or text you want. Refer to App. A, item A.3 for other information on dimensioning circles.

4.6 Radius Dimension

The 2.0-radius arc is to have center marks. Select the following commands to change the Mark with Center Lines toggle box:

> `Settings` <pick> `Dimension Style...` <pick> `Extension Lines...` <pick>

Set the `Mark with Center Lines` toggle off, and exit the dialogue boxes. Dimension the arc and add the center mark as follows:

> `Draw` <pick> `Radial Dimensions` <pick> `Radius` <pick> `Select arc or circle:` Digitize the a point on the right side of the circumference of the arc, where you want the arrowhead for the radius dimension to start (see Fig. 4.1) <pick> `Dimen-`

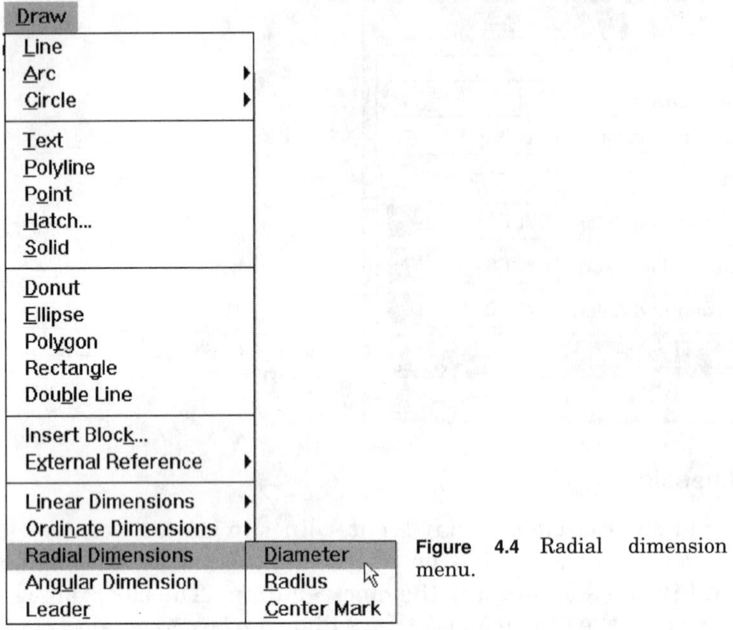

Figure 4.4 Radial dimension menu.

sion text <2.0>: Accept the default value of 2.0 by pressing <return> Enter leader length for text: Digitize leader length by moving the cursor to draw the leader. <pick>

Save the drawing before continuing.

4.7 Linear Dimensions

Linear dimensions can be horizontal, vertical, aligned (parallel to a diagonal line), or rotated (drawn at a specified angle, not necessarily parallel to the item being dimensioned).

When linear dimension commands are invoked, AutoCAD LT requests the `First extension line origin or RETURN to select:`.

If you select a point, it is taken as the first extension line origin (see Fig. 4.5), and you are then asked to select a second extension line origin. If you press Return instead of picking the first extension line origin, AutoCAD LT responds with `Select line, arc or circle:`. If a line or arc is selected, the first and second extension line origins are automatically taken by AutoCAD LT as the endpoints of the line or arc. If a circle is selected the diameter is used for the first and second extension line origins.

Once the first and second extension line origins are defined, you are asked for the `Dimension line location`. The point entered is where the dimension line will be drawn (see Fig. 4.5). AutoCAD LT then prompts you to enter the dimension text, using the distance measured between the first and second extension line origins as a default dimension.

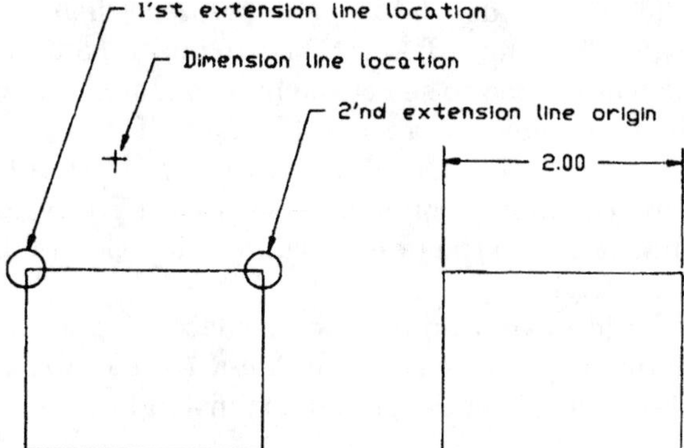

Figure 4.5 Dimensioning selection points.

Add the dimensions along the top of the figure as follows:

`Draw` <pick> `Linear Dimensions` <pick> `Horizontal` (see Fig. 4.6) <pick> `First extension line origin or RETURN to select:` <return> `Select line, arc or circle:` Pick a point on line a-b (Fig. 4.7) close to end a. <pick> `Dimension line location (Text/Angle):` Pick point c. <pick> `Dimension text <2.0>:` <return>

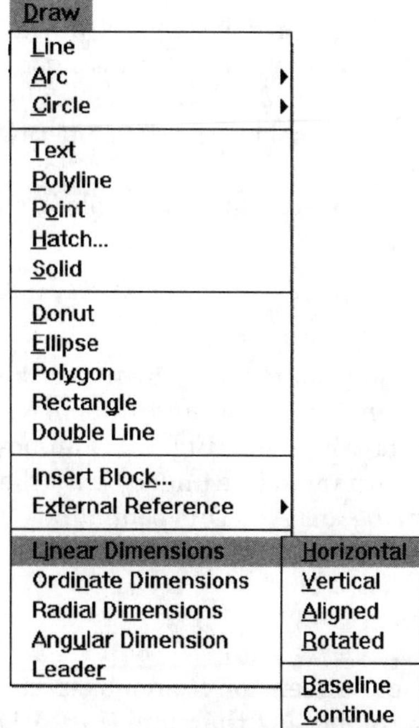

Figure 4.6 Linear dimension menu.

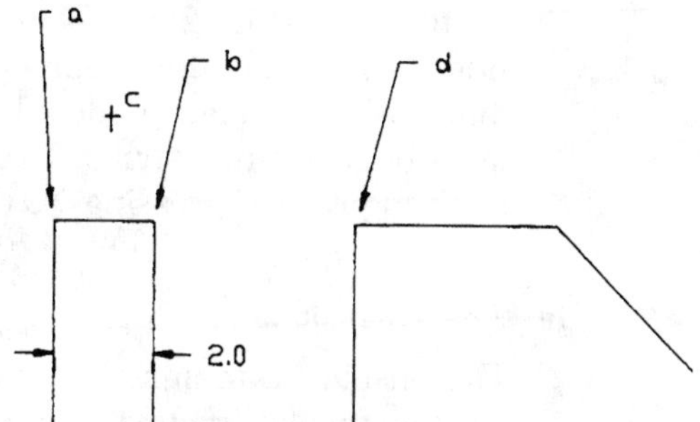

Figure 4.7 Dimensioning selection points.

In the previous set of commands, Return was pressed when asked for the first extension line origin. This forced AutoCAD LT into its automatic extension line mode and you were asked to select the line, arc, or circle to be dimensioned. By selecting line a-b near end a you told AutoCAD LT to use end a as the first extension line origin. This was necessary because the Continue option is to be used to continue the dimension string (see Sec. 4.7.1). Continue uses the second extension line origin in the previous dimension, point b in this case, as its first extension line origin.

The 2.0 dimension would have been crowded if placed inside the extension lines, so it was automatically placed outside by AutoCAD LT. Also note the 2.0 dimension was placed on the side of the second extension line.

4.7.1 Continuous dimensions

When dimensions are continuous as on the top of the plate being drawn, you can indicate that the next dimension is a continuation of the previous one by selecting Continue. The dimension will then be continued along the same line as the last set of dimensions and consequently you will only be asked to enter the second extension line origin, point d in Fig. 4.7.

To continue the dimension string select the following:

`Draw` <pick> `Linear Dimensions` <pick> `Continue` <pick> `Second extension line origin or RETURN to select:` **Pick point d (Fig. 4.7)** <pick> `Dimension text <4.0>:` <return>

If you did not select point d accurately the default dimension may not be 4.0. You can either type the proper value and press Enter, or enter u (undo) and try again.

Notice how AutoCAD LT moved the continuous dimension string up one row so it would not interfere with the 2.0 dimension.

Select Continue to complete the dimensions across the top of the plate as illustrated in Fig. 4.1.

4.7.2 Undo

If a dimension is inserted incorrectly, select Undo from the Edit menu or the buttons bar (Fig. 2.10) to undo the entire dimension (value and dimension line). If you undo the wrong entity, enter the Redo command (Fig. 2.11) immediately. If you select Undo while under the Dim command, it undoes only the last dimension in a string. To undo the entire string, exit the Dim command by selecting Exit or pressing ^C (Fig. 2.12) and then select Undo or enter U.

4.7.3 Baseline dimensions

The Baseline command is used to continue a linear dimension from a baseline, such as the 4.0- and 8.0-unit dimensions along the base of the plate (Fig. 4.1) which both use the left side of the plate as a baseline.

Add horizontal dimensions along the base of the plate as follows:

Draw <pick> Linear Dimensions <pick> Horizontal <pick> First extension line origin or RETURN to select: **Digitize point a in Fig. 4.8. <pick>** Second extension line: **Digitize point b in Fig. 4.8. <pick>** Dimension line location (Text/Angle): **Digitize point c. <pick>** Dimension text <4.0>: **(Type 4 if the default is not 4.0) <return>**

Draw <pick> Linear Dimensions <pick> Baseline <pick> Second extension line origin or RETURN to select: **Digitize point d. <pick>** Dimension text **<8.0>: <return>** Draw <pick> Linear Dimensions <pick> Continue <pick> Second extension line origin or RETURN to select: **Digitize point e. <pick>** Dimension text <4.0>: **<return>**

Insert the vertical dimensions on the left side of the plate. Because the Baseline command should be used and the baseline is the top-left corner of the plate, begin with:

Draw <pick> Linear Dimensions <pick> Vertical <pick> First extension line origin or RETURN to select: **Digitize the top-left corner. <pick>** Second extension line: **Digitize a point at the bottom-left corner of the cut; see Fig. 4.1. <pick>** Dimension line location: **Digitize the desired location of the dimension line. <pick>** Dimension text <4.0)>: **<return>** Draw <pick> Linear Dimensions <pick> Baseline <pick> (etc.)

4.8 Angular Dimension

An angular dimension is required for the slope of the right side of the figure. A horizontal extension line is required to be constructed with the angular dimension. This is indicated to AutoCAD LT by pressing Return when asked to Select arc, circle, line or RETURN:

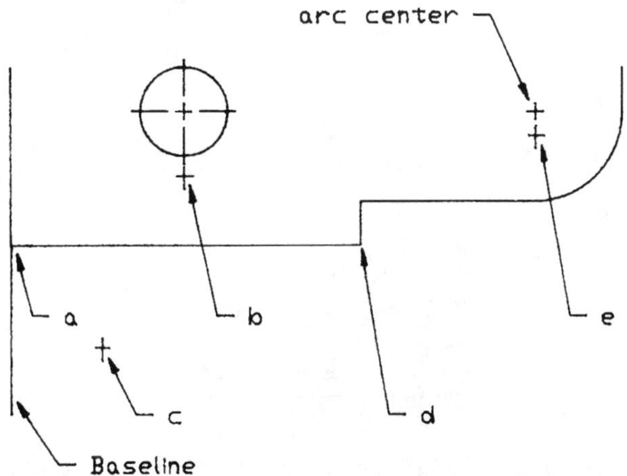

Figure 4.8 Dimensioning selection points.

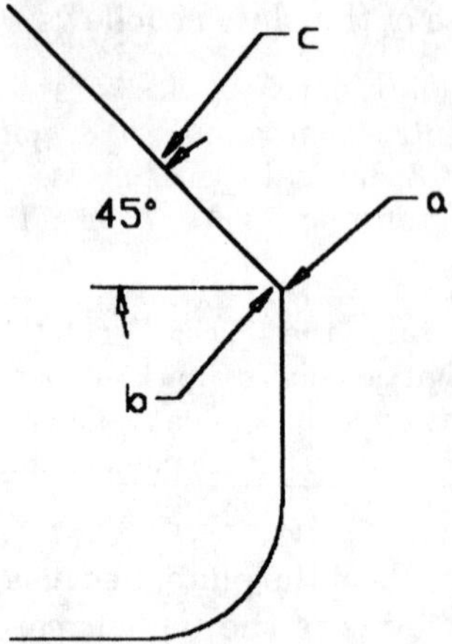

Figure 4.9 Angular dimensioning.

> `Draw` <pick> `Angular Dimensions` <pick> `Select arc, circle, line or RETURN:` <return> `Angle vertex:` **Digitize point a in Fig. 4.9.** <pick> `First angle endpoint:` **Digitize point b (slightly to the left of a).** <pick> `Second angle endpoint:` **Digitize point c.** <pick> `Dimension arc line location (Text/Angle):` **Digitize the point where you want the dimension line to be located.** <pick> `Dimension text <45>:` <return> `Enter text location (or RETURN):` **The angular dimension is visible and moves with the cursor. Select the desired location.** <pick>

Save the drawing to C:\Drawings\Proj-4.Dwg. Also save the drawing to a floppy diskette as a backup. Exit AutoCAD LT.

Chapter

5

Object Snaps

Objective. Use object snaps to select the nearest point, tangents, and intersections; use x/y/z filters; use the Aerial View window; set dimension scale; dimension a drawing; use a leader line; use dynamic text and control codes; change dimension text style; draw fillets; and practice using Break command.

Drawing. Boot up AutoCAD LT and choose the `New...` command in the File menu to name the drawing **c\drawings\proj-5.dwg.** Draw the control block illustrated in Fig. 5.1. This project is longer than previous ones, so you might want to complete it in two stages. If you do, exit AutoCAD LT using Exit . . . in the file menu and then select Save Changes from the drawing modifications dialogue box (refer to Chap. 1, Sec. 1.3.5). This saves your drawing using the file name entered with New . . . command. Continue the drawing later by booting AutoCAD LT and selecting Open . . . in the File menu. Select the drawing to be opened from the Open File dialogue box using procedures outlined in Chap. 1.

5.1 Set Drawing Limits and Units

Set the screen limits to –1,–1 and 10,8 (refer to Chap. 2, Sec. 2.2 if you have forgotten the commands). Enter the Zoom and All commands to reset the monitor to the new screen limits.

Set the units to decimal with three digits to the right of the decimal (refer to Chap. 2, Sec. 2.3). Press the F2 key (see App. E, Fig. E.10) to return to the drawing editor.

5.2 Draw Circles

The center point of the top view will be located at coordinates 3,5. The 1.125-unit-diameter circle will be drawn first. Next the Circle command is recalled

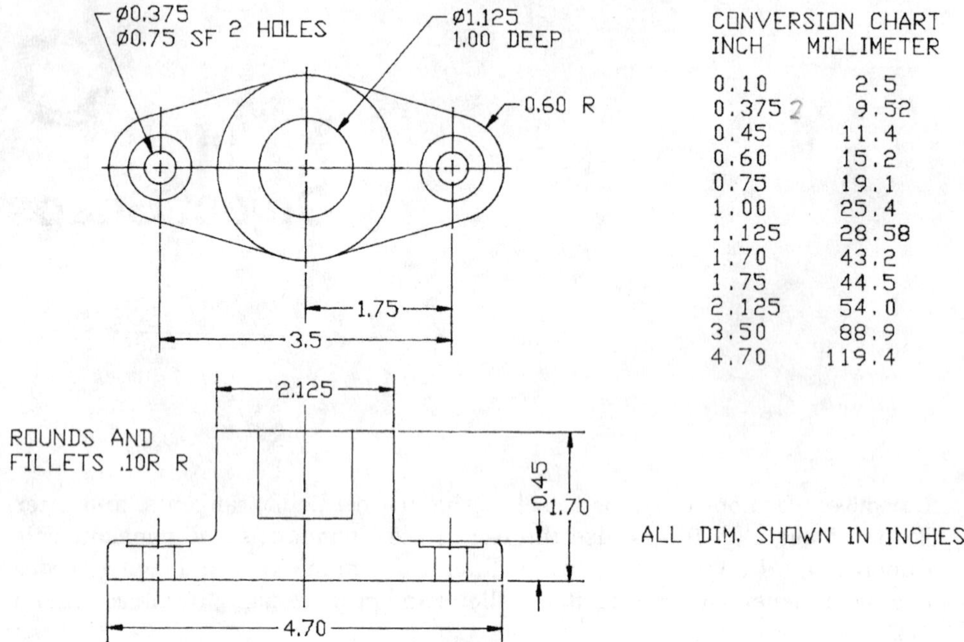

Figure 5.1 Project 5.

to draw the 2.125-unit-diameter circle by pressing Enter or the Space bar a second time. With AutoCAD LT you cannot draw circles using the diameter, and must use the circle's radius (1.125/2 = 0.5625 and 2.125/2 = 1.0625):

> `Draw` <pick> `Circle` <pick> `Center,Radius` <pick> `3P/TTR/<Center point>:` **3,5** <return> `Radius:` **0.5625** <return> <return> `CIRCLE 3P/TTR <Center point>:` **3,5** <return> `Radius:` **1.0625** <return>

Draw the 0.375- and 0.75-diameter circles on the left side of the block. A 0.60-unit-radius circle will also be drawn for the arc at the end of the block. Part of that circle will later be broken out when the tangent lines are drawn. Begin the commands by pressing the Space bar or Enter key to recall the circle command:

> <return> `CIRCLE 3P/TTR` <Center point>: **1.25,5** <return> `Radius:` **0.1875** <return> <return> `CIRCLE 3P/TTR <Center point>:` **@** (Select @ from the Buttons Bar—see App. E, Fig. E.11. Means same as last point.) <pick> `Radius:` **0.375** <return> <return> `CIRCLE 3P/TTR <Center point>:` **@** <pick> `Radius:` **0.3** <return>

Use the copy command (Chap. 3, Sec. 3.6) to copy the circular elements to the right side of the top view.

5.3 Tangent Lines

Before continuing, save the drawing done up to this point.

File <pick> Save... <pick>

Object snap is a mode that lets you refer to points already on the drawing. In this section you will use object snap to draw lines that are tangent to the circles previously drawn.

Object snap(s) can be turned on temporarily to assist in locating a point on the drawing by entering the object snap command when AutoCAD requests the point. Or a running object snap can be set which will be applied to all points selected until the object snap is turned off. The "running" object snap can be turned off temporarily by entering the None command. When object snap is on, an aperture (box) will be added to the intersection point of the cross hairs. To snap onto a line or other element, the aperture is placed on the line or elements. AutoCAD LT then searches within the aperture for the object snap location. The aperture appears only when a point, such as the start point of a line, etc., is to be located on the monitor.

In this drawing you are to draw tangent lines joining the center circle and the side circles. AutoCAD LT has an object snap command named Tangent which will be used to place the lines tangent to the circles.

Prior to drawing the tangent lines, enlarge the top view:

> View <pick> Zoom <pick> Window <pick> First corner: Digitize a point slightly to the left and below the top view. <pick> Second corner: Move the cursor up and to the right so that the window created encloses the entire top view. <pick>

A running Tangent object snap is set as follows:

Assist <pick> Object Snap... <pick>

The Running Object Snap dialogue box illustrated in Fig. 5.2 is displayed. Set the tangent object snap by placing the cursor in the Tangent box and pressing the <pick> button. An X will appear in the Tangent box. Press the OK button to exit.

With the help of the Tangent object snap, the line joining the two circles is drawn tangent to the circles with minimum effort:

> Draw <pick> Line <pick> From point: The cursor should now display a rectangular aperture box which is the object snap target. Place the aperture box on the top of the 2.10-unit-diameter center circle (point a in Fig. 5.3). If there is no aperture box, set the Tangent object snap as outlined above. <pick> To point: Place the object snap aperture box on the top of the right side circle, as illustrated in Fig. 5.3. <pick>

Notice that AutoCAD LT snaps the line tangent to the two circles. Object snaps should always be used when a line is to connect onto an entity. Never

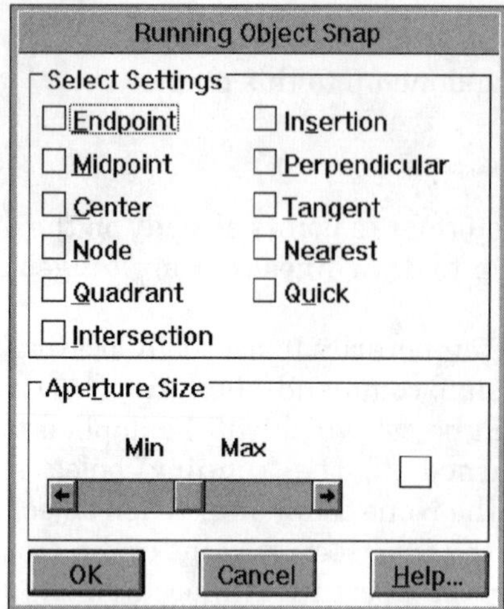

Figure 5.2 Running Object Snap dialogue box.

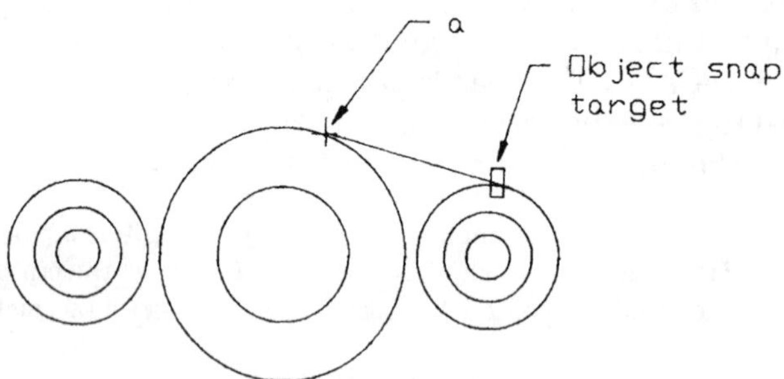

Figure 5.3 Tangent object snap location.

attempt to locate points by "eye" on an AutoCAD LT drawing. They may appear correct on the screen, but will invariably be off the desired point. Press <return> to exit the Line command.

Add the remaining four tangent lines to the drawing using the Line command. With AutoCAD LT you must press the <return> button on the mouse or keyboard to exit the line command after each line is drawn. If you have problems, use the Undo command and try again.

When you have completed the lines the running snap is turned off as follows:

```
Assist <pick> Object Snap... <pick>
```

The Running Object Snap dialogue box illustrated in Fig. 5.2 is displayed. Turn off the tangent object snap by placing the cursor in the Tangent box and pressing the <pick> button. The X will be removed indicating the object snap is off. Press the OK button to exit. Always turn running object snaps off when they are no longer required.

5.4 Break Circles at Tangents

Save the drawing before continuing. The 0.6-unit-radius circles will now be broken at the tangent points to delete the section of the circle inside the object. The point where each circle is to be broken is at the tangency point of the circles and the lines previously drawn. This point cannot be accurately selected visually; however, AutoCAD LT can accurately select the intersection point with the Intersection object snap command.

Remember that AutoCAD LT draws and breaks circles in a counterclockwise direction. If you make a mistake and break the wrong section of the circle, it can be restored with the Undo command.

When the Break command is used you will be asked to `Select the object.` This is done by digitizing a point on the circumference of the circle. Sometimes this point is also used as the first point of the break. This time, however, the first point of the break is the point of tangency of the line and circle. If this location is also used to select the object to be broken, AutoCAD LT would not know if you were selecting the circle or the line. The circle is to be selected by digitizing a point on its circumference clear of any other entities. Then, when AutoCAD LT requests `Enter second point (or F for first point)`, enter F (First) forcing AutoCAD LT to ask for the first point of the break:

> `Modify` <pick> `Break` <pick> `Select Object:` Digitize point a on the circumference of the circle to be broken, in Fig. 5.4. <pick> `Enter second point (or F for First point):` **F** <return> `Enter first point:`

The first point of the break is to be the intersection of the line and circle, shown as first target in Fig. 5.4. This point cannot be accurately selected by eye, and the Intersection object snap must be used. A temporary object snap is set by selecting it from the Toolbox or the floating object snap cursor menu. To invoke the floating object snap cursor menu illustrated in Fig. 5.5, hold down the shift key and click the second button—indicated as "`[Shift->2B]` <pick>" in the following:

> `Enter first point: [Shift->2B]` <pick> `Intersection` <pick> `of` Place the intersection object snap aperture box so the two entities for which the intersection

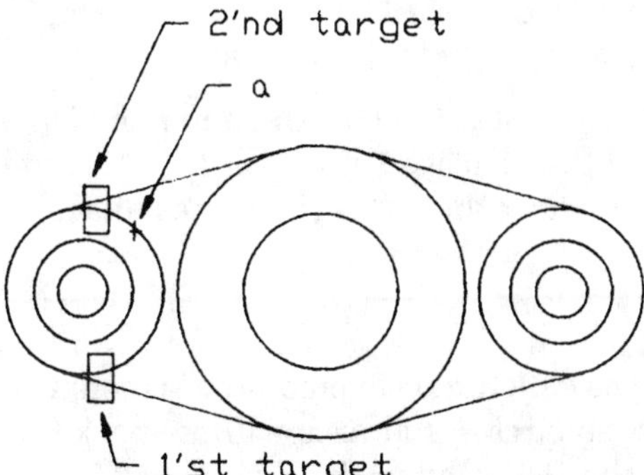

Figure 5.4 Intersection object snap locations.

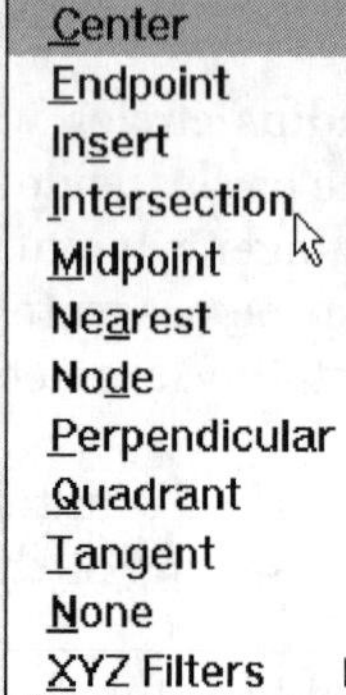

Figure 5.5 Floating object snap cursor menu.

is to be located are inside the box, shown as first target in Fig. 5.4. The bottom tangency is selected first since Break erases the circle in a counterclockwise direction. <pick> `Enter second point: [Shift->2B]` <pick> `Intersection` <pick> `of` Place the intersection aperture box so the line and circle at the top of the circle are inside the box, as illustrated. <pick>

The object snap used was set for only one selection and had to be recalled for the second point. Break the right-side circle following the same procedure. After completing the break, save the drawing.

5.5 Calculate Text Height and Set Dimension Settings

The plot will be done on an A-size sheet (8½ by 11 in) using a plot scale of ¾ in = 1 in. If the desired text height on the plotted drawing is ⅛ in (0.125), the text height (h) on the monitor should be:

$$\frac{3}{4} \times h = 0.125 \text{ in} \quad \text{which gives } h = 0.17$$

Dimscale is then calculated using equation 4.2:

$$\text{Dimscale} \times 0.18 = 0.17 \text{ in} \quad \text{which gives Dimscale} = 0.94$$

Set Dimscale using:

`Settings` <pick> `Dimension Style...` <pick> `Scale and Colors...` <pick> The Scale and Colors dialogue illustrated in Fig. 4.3 is displayed.

Move the cursor into the `Feature Scaling` box and enter the Dimscale value of **0.94.** Press the `OK` button and then choose `Extension Lines...` in the Dimension Styles and Setting box to display the Extension Lines dialogue box.

5.6 Draw Circle Center Lines

The Extension Lines dialogue box should be open on the screen. Click the `Mark with Center Lines` check box so circles and arcs will be marked with center lines rather than ticks. Press the `OK` button in the Extension Lines and Dimension Styles and Variable dialogue boxes.

Add center lines to the circles (also see Fig. 4.4 and App. Fig. E.3.4):

> `Draw` <pick> `Radial Dimensions` <pick> `Center Mark` <pick> `Select arc or circle:` Digitize a point on the circumference of the 2.125-unit-diameter center circle. <pick>

Add center lines to the side circles also. When selecting the circle, digitize a point on the circumference of the 0.60-unit outside circle so that the center lines extend to the extent of that circle, as illustrated in Fig. 5.1. Exit the Dim command.

5.7 Aerial View Window

Prior to dimensioning the top view it is necessary to change the size of the view on the screen to allow room to display the dimensions as they are drawn. The Aerial View window allows you to see the entire drawing in a separate window, locate a specific area and move to that area quickly. You can also zoom in on an area, change the magnification, and match the view in the graphics window to the one in the Aerial View window, or vice versa. If the Aerial View window is not displayed on your screen already, click on the Aerial View button (Fig. 5.6) in the toolbar (see App. E, Fig. E.11).

The Aerial View window illustrated in Fig. 5.7 is displayed on the screen. The window can be moved anywhere on the screen by moving the cursor into the window's title box, holding down the <pick> button and moving the cursor dragging the window across the screen. Release the pick button when you have the window in the desired location. Try the following using the Aerial View window:

Zoom using the Aerial View

1. Choose Zoom on the Aerial View window menu bar.
2. Move the cursor into the Aerial View screen and click one corner of a zoom window (see the dotted rectangle in Fig. 5.7).
3. Click the other corner of the zoom window.

Figure 5.6 Aerial view button.

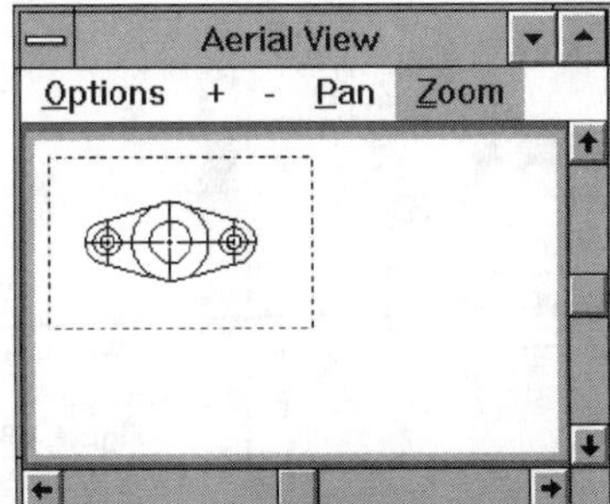

Figure 5.7 Aerial view window.

The object will zoom on the graphics screen to suit the zoom window selected. A blue box will appear around the object in the Aerial View window defining the zoom window displayed.

Pan using the Aerial View. Panning an object in AutoCAD LT is similar to moving a camera while viewing an object through the view finder—the object slides across the screen to a new location.

1. Choose Pan on the Aerial View window menu bar. The pan box is displayed as a dotted rectangle and appears the same size as the current zoom window box (created previously with the zoom command). If you can't see the outline of the pan box it is because it is the same size as the Aerial View window.
2. Move the pan box with the cursor and press the <pick> button when the object is panned to the desired area.

The graphics window displays the selected area.

Pan using the Aerial View scroll bars

1. Use the windows scroll bars along the right side and bottom of the Aerial View window to pan the aerial view.
2. Double-click the Zoom command to update the graphics area.

Pan and Zoom using Aerial View's Locate option

1. Choose Locate in the Options menu illustrated in Fig. 5.8.
2. Move the cursor into AutoCAD's graphics window as illustrated in Fig. 5.9. The Aerial View window displays a magnified view of the area under the cursor.
3. Press the <pick> button to display the magnified view in the AutoCAD's graphics window.

Locate magnifies the view eight times. The magnification can be changed by clicking the right mouse button while using the Locate command, to display a Magnification dialogue box.

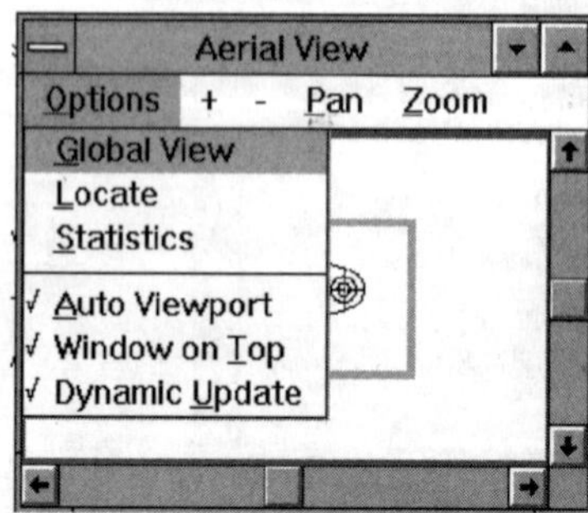

Figure 5.8 Aerial view options menu.

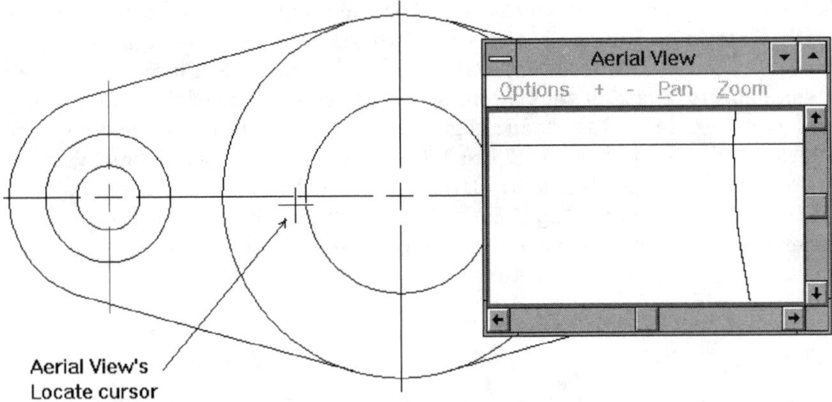

Figure 5.9 Using Locate.

The Aerial View window can be used transparently without cancelling AutoCAD commands that request the selection of points or entities. This is extremely useful in complex drawings. For instance you could invoke the Line command and use the Aerial View window to zoom in and select the first point of the line. When requested for the next point of the line you could once again use the Aerial View window to zoom into another part of the drawing and select the point. In each case the line command would not be interrupted.

5.8 Horizontal Dimensions

Prior to dimensioning the top view it is necessary to enlarge the size of the view on the screen to allow room to display the dimensions as they are drawn. Use the Aerial View window to zoom the view on the graphics screen as defined by the dotted rectangle in Fig. 5.7.

The horizontal dimensions in the top view originate from a baseline at the center line of the circles on the right side of the view. When dimensioning from a center line, the dimension extension lines should originate from, and act as an extension to, the circle center line. That point can be selected by placing the cursor on the end of the center line and digitizing the point or by using a temporary object snap Endpoint. Endpoint, in response to AutoCAD LT's request for a point, turns on a temporary object snap and places a target box over the cursor.

When the object snap target is placed on a line, AutoCAD LT searches for the end of that line which is closest to the target. A temporary object snap is used so the object snap command is in effect only for the point located immediately after Endpoint is entered. The floating object snap cursor menu is displayed by holding down the shift button & pressing the second button on the mouse.

`Draw` <pick> `Linear Dimensions` <pick> `Horizontal` <pick> `First extension line origin: [Shift->2B]` (Hold down the shift key and press the second button on the mouse.) Endpoint <pick> of Place the endpoint object snap aperture box on the bottom end of the center line of the right side circle. <pick> Second extension line origin: [Shift->2B] Endpoint <pick> of Place the endpoint object snap aperture box on the bottom end of the center line of the center circle. <pick> Dimension line location: Digitize the desired location of the dimension line. <pick> Dimension text <1.750>: **1.75** (Type 1.75 since the default value is 1.750) <return> Draw <pick> Linear Dimensions <pick> Baseline <pick> Second extension line: [Shift->2B] Endpoint <pick> of Place the endpoint object snap aperture box on the bottom end of the center line of the left side circle. <pick> Dimension text <3.500>: **3.5** <return>

5.9 Dimension Circles

The center marks have already been added to the circles. Set the value in the Center Mark Size box to **0** (zero) in the Extension Lines dialogue box so additional center lines are not added to circles as they are dimensioned:

Settings <pick> Dimension Style... <pick> Extension Lines... <pick> Set the center Mark size to 0 and exit the dialogue boxes.

Dimension the radius of the 0.6-unit right-side circle in the top view. Refer to Chap. 4, Sec. 4.6 for the procedure if you need assistance.

The Leader command will be used to dimension the 0.375 diameter circle on the left side of the top view. The Diameter command is not used because it places the text on the side its leader points to, which would be the left side of this leader (see Fig. 5.1). The text is forced on the other side by placing a short horizontal line at the end of the leader:

Draw <pick> Leader <pick> <pick> Leader start: Digitize a point on the top-left side of the circumference of the 0.375 diameter circle <pick> To point: Move the cursor up and to the left and select the first bend in the leader. <pick> To point: Move the cursor to the right drawing a short horizontal line. <pick> To point: <return> Dimension text <>: **%%c 0.375** <return>

The two percent signs, %%, in the text are a signal to AutoCAD LT that the next character is a control code. In this case the control code is the letter c, which prints the circle diameter symbol.

Dimension the 1.125 diameter center circle using the Diameter command.

Refer to App. A for more information on dimensioning circles and arcs.

The remaining text in the top view is added using AutoCAD LT's Text command. In Sec. 5.5 the text height was calculated as 0.17 units to get ⅛-in text on the plotted drawing. The "ϕ 0.75 SF" text is added as follows:

Draw <pick> Text <pick> Justify/Style/<Start point>: Digitize the start point of the text which is the lower-left corner of the text. <pick> Height <0.200>: **0.17** (Because the default value of 0.200 is incorrect.) <return> Rotation angle <0>: Select the default of 0. <return> Text: **%%c 0.75 SF** <return>

Add the remaining text to the top view using the Text command. The TEXT command can also be invoked from the Toolbox (see Fig. 3.4).

5.10 Draw Front View

Use the Aerial View window to zoom on the drawing from slightly above the horizontal center line in the top view and to the base of the drawing screen below it (see Fig. 5.10). This is done so that the front view will be as large as possible on the monitor and a sufficient amount of the top view will be displayed so that lines can be extended down to locate elements on the front view in relation to the top view.

The top-left corner of the 2.125-unit-diameter shaft in the front view will have a *Y* coordinate (vertical) of 2, which is determined by visually locating the screen cursor at the approximate vertical position desired and reading the vertical coordinate of that position from the coordinate display window (see Fig. E-11). The *X* coordinate (horizontal) is to be in line with the left side of the 2.125-unit-diameter circle in the top view.

5.10.1 X/Y/Z filters

When AutoCAD LT requests coordinates, they can be selectively entered by using filters. The format of filters is *.coordinate.* The filter coordinate is any one or two of the letters x, y, or z. This lets you build a 2D or 3D coordinate by entering coordinate values independent of each other. For example a 3D point can be entered by selecting the x,y coordinates by snapping onto the endpoint of an existing line and entering the z value from the keyboard. The .X and .Y filters can be selected from the buttons bar (see App. E, Fig. E.11) and the full filter list is available in the Floating cursor menu as illustrated in Fig. 5.11. To display the cursor menu hold down the Shift key and press the second button on the mouse (shown as `[Shift->2B]`).

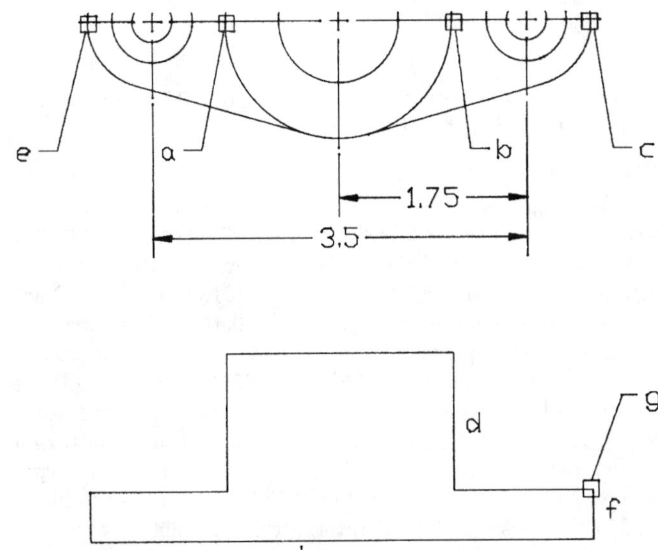

Figure 5.10 Front view.

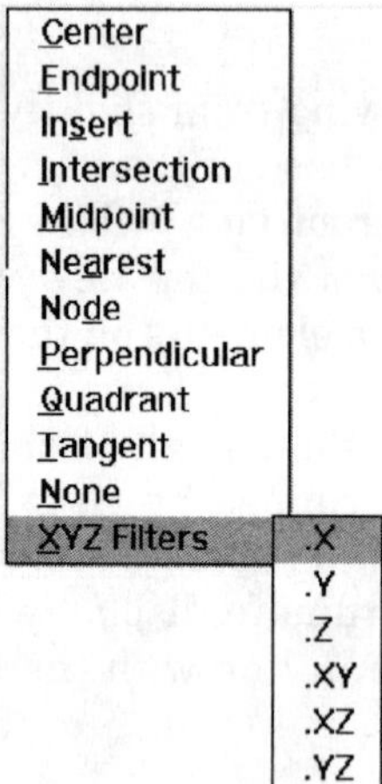

Figure 5.11 XYZ filters menu.

The use of filters is illustrated in the following (select LINE and INTERSECTION from the toolbox):

> LINE <pick> Line From point: [Shift->2B] XYZ Filters <pick> .XZ <pick> of INTERSECTION (Toolbox) <pick> of Locate the intersection object snap aperture box over point "a" in Fig. 5.10. <pick>

You have used an XZ filter to locate the *x* coordinate. The Intersection object snap was also used to accurately select the intersection. You have actually located x and z. The z coordinate happens to be 0. This is discussed in Chap. 10.

AutoCAD now requests the *y* coordinate, which we decided earlier was to be 2:

> (need Y) **2** <return>

XYZ filters are used in the continuation of the Line command below. Note that both .XY and .XZ filters are used in the following:

> To point: [Shift->2B] XYZ Filters <pick> .XZ <pick> of INTERSECTION (Toolbox) <pick> of Place the target over the intersecting entities at b in Fig. 5.10. <pick> (need Y): **2** <return> To point: **@1.25<270** <return> To point: [Shift->2B] XYZ Filters <pick> .XZ <pick> of INTERSECTION <pick> of Place the target over the intersecting entities at c. <pick> (need Y): ENDPOINT <pick> of Place the target near the bottom end of line d. <pick> To point: **@0.45<270** <return> To point: [Shift->2B] XYZ Filters <pick> .XZ <pick> of INTERSECTION <pick> of Place the target over intersection e. <pick> (66): ENDPOINT <pick> of Place the target near the lower end of line f. <pick> To point: [Shift->2B] XYZ Filters <pick> .YZ (Note YZ) <pick> of INTERSECTION <pick> of Place the target over the intersection at g. <pick> (need X): ENDPOINT <pick> of Place the target near the left end of line h. <pick> To point: [Shift->2B] XYZ Filters <pick> .YZ <pick> of INTERSECTION <pick> of Select intersection g. <pick> (need X) INTERSECTION <pick> of Select intersection a. <pick> To point: [Shift->2B]

XYZ Filters <pick> .YZ <pick> of ENDPOINT <pick> of Select the top end of line d. <pick> (need X): INTERSECTION <pick> of Select intersection a. <pick> To point: CLOSE (buttons bar) <pick>

Draw the 1.125-diameter hole in the 2.125-diameter shaft in the front view. The lines are to be continuous, rather than hidden, because the solid portion of the front view is to be hatched in Chap. 7, Sec. 7.4. The hole is started as follows:

LINE <pick> From point: [Shift->2B] XYZ Filters <pick> .XZ <return> [Shift->2B] Intersection <pick> of Place the object snap target on the left-side intersection point of the 1.125-diameter hole and the center line in the top view. <pick> (need Y) **2** <return> To point: (etc.)

When drawing the bolt and countersunk holes in the front view, it is important that the lines exactly meet object lines because of hatching to be done later. The Nearest object snap is used to *snap* onto a line, arc, or circle that is closest to the cursor object snap target as follows:

LINE (Tool bar) <pick> From point: [Shift->2B] XYZ Filters <pick> .XZ <pick> of INTERSECTION <pick> of Place the target on the intersection of the side of the countersunk hole and the center line in the top view. <pick> (need Y): NEAREST <pick> to Place the object snap target on the top of the plate in the front view where the countersunk hole is to start. <pick> To point:

The depth of the countersunk hole is drawn by eye. Continue the bolt holes in the front view. Use the .XZ filter to locate the x coordinate in the top view, when required, and the Nearest object snap to ensure that the y coordinate is selected exactly on an object line. When the bolt hole is completed on one side, use the COPY command to copy it 3.5 in horizontally to the other side.

5.11 Fillets

Fillets can be added by editing the drawing. When using the Fillet command for the first time, you must set the radius by entering the r (radius) option as illustrated below. Once the radius is entered, it need not be reentered unless the fillet radius is to be changed. Fillets are then drawn by recalling the Fillet command and digitizing the two lines that are to be joined by the fillet. When selecting the two intersecting lines to be filleted, remember that AutoCAD LT draws arcs in a counterclockwise direction.

Construct <pick> Fillet <pick> Polyline/Radius/<Select first object>: **r** <return> Enter fillet radius: **0.1** <return> <return> Polyline/Radius/<Select first object>: Digitize two intersection lines at a corner where a fillet is desired. <pick>

To insert other fillets, recall the Fillet command by pressing Enter or the Space bar, and select two points at the corner where the fillet is desired. The radius does not have to be reentered.

5.12 Dimension Front View

The horizontal dimension of the bottom of the front view can be done using AutoCAD's automatic extension line process:

Draw <pick> Linear Dimensions <pick> Horizontal <pick> First extension line origin or RETURN to select: <return> Select line, arc, or circle: Pick the bottom horizontal line in the front view. <pick> Dimension line location: Digitize a point indicating where you wish the dimension line to be located. <pick> Dimension text <4.700>: **4.70** <return>

Draw <pick> Linear Dimensions <pick> Vertical <pick> First extension line origin or RETURN to select: <return> Select line, arc, or circle: Pick the 0.45 unit line on the right side of the front view. <pick> Dimension line location: Digitize a point where you wish the dimension line to be located. <pick> Dimension text <0.350>: **0.45** <return>

Notice that the dimension is to the edge of the fillet—that is why AutoCAD LT read 0.35 instead of 0.45. Also the dimension text is horizontal. Select Undo to undo the dimension.

Because of the small space between the extension lines, AutoCAD LT will probably place the 0.45 units text outside the extension lines. If it does we would prefer that the text be printed aligned with the dimension lines rather than horizontal. This is set as follows:

Settings <pick> Dimension Style... <pick>

The Dimension Style and Settings dialogue box illustrated in Fig. 3.5 is displayed. Choose the Text Location... box to display the Text Location dialogue box illustrated in Fig. 5.12. Choose Alignment When Outside Only from the alignment drop-down box as illustrated in Fig. 5.12. Exit the dialogues boxes by pressing the OK buttons.

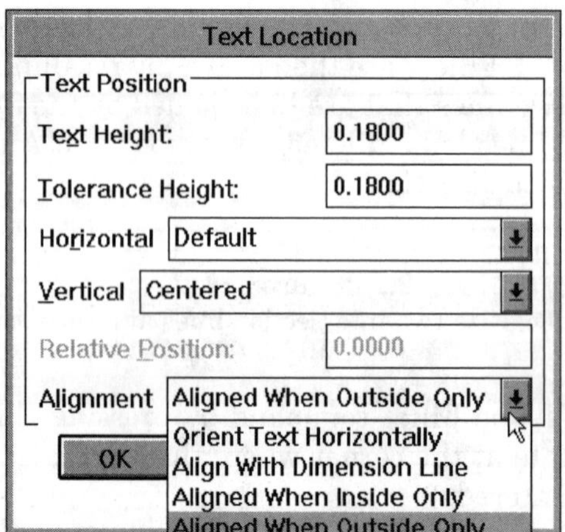

Figure 5.12 Setting text alignment.

As was noted, the automatic extension line process cannot be used because of the fillet:

> Draw <pick> Linear Dimensions <pick> Vertical <pick> First extension line origin: INTERSECTION <pick> of Place the target on the lower right corner of the front view. <pick> Second extension line origin: ENDPOINT <pick> of Place the target on the top end of the fillet. <pick> Dimension line location: Digitize the desired location: <pick> Dimension text <0.450>: **0.45** <return> Draw <pick> Linear Dimensions <pick> Baseline <pick> etc.

Add the remaining dimensions to the drawing.

5.13 Text

Add the "ROUNDS AND FILLETS .10 R" text to the right side of the front view.

> DRAW <pick> Text <pick> Justify/Style/<start point>: Digitize the location where text is to start. <pick> Height <0.17>: Select default value of 0.17 set earlier. <return> Rotation angle <0>: <return> Text: **ROUNDS AND** <return> Text:

Notice that the text appears on the drawing as it is being typed when Dynamic text is used. Also note that the Text: prompt is reissued after you have entered the text, and the cursor is positioned at the start of the next line below the current line of text. The next line of text will use the same specifications (height and angle). The Text command is canceled by pressing Enter without entering text, as illustrated in the following:

> Text: **FILLETS .10 R** <return> Text: <return>

Enter Zoom and All to set the monitor to the drawing limits.

Add the "Conversion Chart" text heading to the top-right side of the drawing. Prior to adding more text, move the cursor to the top far right of the drawing and read the coordinates of the location. If the chart plus a small border exceeds the current limits of 10,8, reset the Limits, providing a larger horizontal distance (possibly coordinates 11,8). Enter Zoom and All to reset the monitor to the new limits.

The standard AutoCAD LT text font is TXT. This font is not desirable when printing tables because the space used for letters is not uniform, making it impossible to align characters, as illustrated in the chart in Fig. 5.1. The MONOTXT font uses the same space for each character and is to be used for the chart. Prior to changing the current text font, the Style command is used to create the text style definition:

> Settings <pick> Text Style... <pick>

The Select Text Font dialogue box illustrated in Fig. 5.13 is displayed. Click on the Next box until the MONOTXT box illustrated is displayed as illustrated.

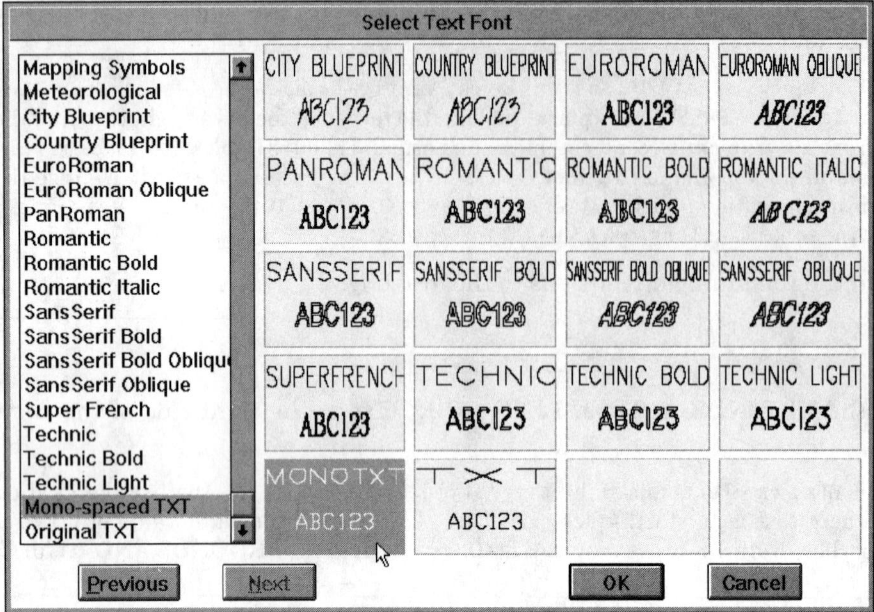

Figure 5.13 Selecting a text font.

This text is called Mono spaced TXT in the font file list. Click on the `MONOTXT` box as illustrated, and then press `OK`.

If the display box is not available, you can type in MONOTXT and press return to select the Mono spaced TXT font file. The remaining entries are indicated below. Notice the default text height of 0.00 is selected by pressing Return. If a numeric value is entered, it becomes the fixed text height and you are not asked for the text height when using the Text command.

`Height <0.00>:` <return> `Width factor <1.00>:` <return> `Obliquing angle <0>:` <return> `Backwards?<N>:` <return> `Upside-down?<N>:` <return> `Vertical?<N>:` <return> MONOTXT is now the current text style.

`Draw` <pick> `Text` <pick> <pick> `Justify/Style/<start point>:`

AutoCAD displays the previous text dotted indicating if you press return the text will be placed on the line below the dotted text using the same *style* as the previous text rather than the new Mono style. To use the new style the command must be invoked by selecting the text location on the monitor.

Pick the start point for the text on the monitor. <pick> `Height <0.17>:` <return> `Rotation angle <0>:` <return> `Text:` **0.10 2.5** <return> `Text:` **0.375 9.52** <return>

After the last entry in the list is entered press Return to complete the Text command. Codes, such as %%c, in the data entered are initially displayed in their code form on the monitor. When the Text command is completed, the codes are translated and the text is regenerated on the monitor.

Change the text style back to STANDARD by displaying the Select Text Font dialogue box and selecting Original TXT. Respond to the command line prompts as outlined above. Save the drawing and exit AutoCAD LT.

Chapter 6

Layers

Objective. Use Layer command for line type and colors in plot, Hatch command, set hatch and line type scale, and set dimension variables. Use associate dimensioning, updating dimensions and editing dimensions text; surveyor's units; Snap command, Text command options.

Drawing. Boot up AutoCAD LT and begin a new drawing with the name Proj-6. Draw the plot plan shown in Fig. 6.1, setting the screen limits to 0,0 and 70,50. Use decimal units with three digits to the right of the decimal point.

6.1 Using Layers

The concept of layering in CAD can be paralleled with overlays used in texts, where various components are drawn on transparent sheets and can be viewed individually or with any number overlaid to view the interaction of the parts. In AutoCAD LT any number of layers can be used. The layers all have the same drawing limits, coordinate system, and units. Zoom factors apply to all layers in the drawing. Layers can be viewed individually or any number or sequence of layers can be viewed at one time. Any one layer can be designated as the current layer on which new items drawn will reside.

The drafter designates a color and line type for each layer. All items on a layer will have the same color and line type. (The Entity Modes dialogue box in the Settings menu can be used to set different colors for entities residing on the same layer. It is recommended, however, that you do not mix the two methods, colors by layer and also by entities, to prevent confusion.) The color of a layer is used by the plotter to select pens. When plotting, each color can be given a pen number. As the colors change, the plotter will select the pen number designated for that color. The pens can have different colors and/or nib widths. This provides the drafter with the ability to control the line widths and colors on a plotted drawing. The layer colors can be displayed with a color monitor.

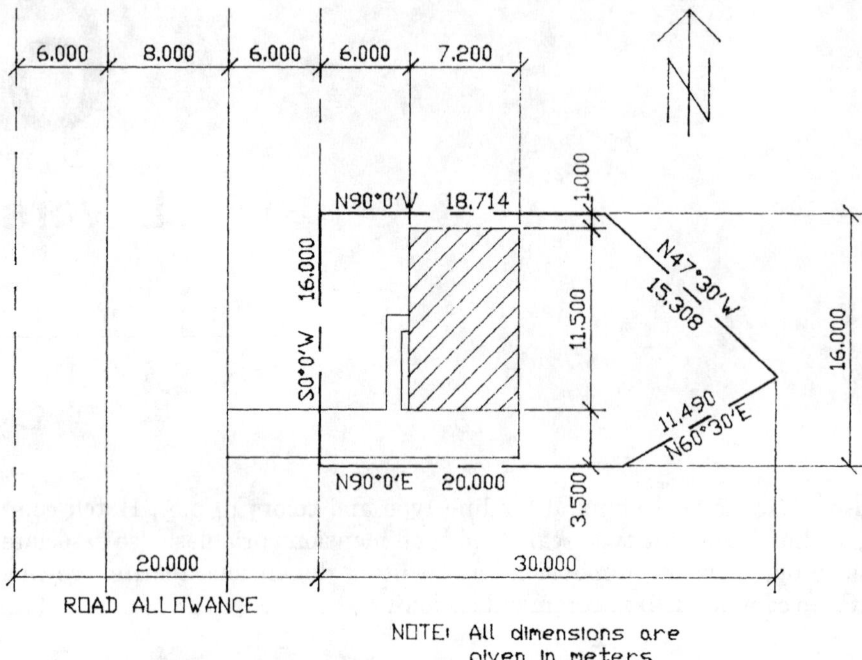

Figure 6.1 Proj-6 lot plan.

The layer that an item resides on can be changed at any time. If an item is moved to a layer with a different line type, the item's line type will change to that of the new layer.

6.1.1 Line types

Each layer is associated with a specific line type. A sample of line types supplied with AutoCAD LT is illustrated in Fig. 6.2. The default line type for a layer is continuous.

6.1.2 Colors

Each layer is assigned a specific color number, an integer between 1 and 255. The first seven color numbers are associated with specific colors:

1	Red
2	Yellow
3	Green
4	Cyan
5	Blue
6	Magenta
7	White

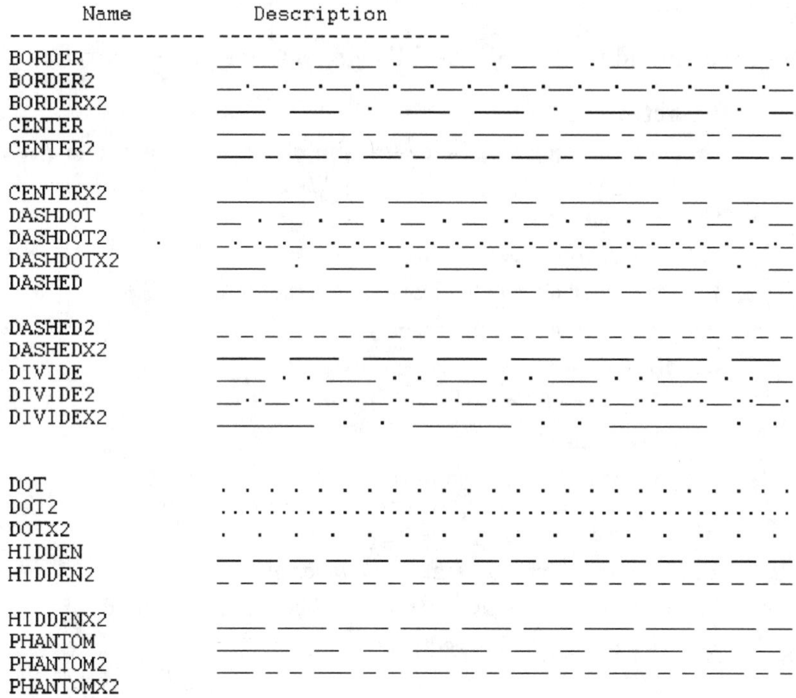

```
Name              Description
----------------  -------------------
BORDER
BORDER2
BORDERX2
CENTER
CENTER2

CENTERX2
DASHDOT
DASHDOT2
DASHDOTX2
DASHED

DASHED2
DASHEDX2
DIVIDE
DIVIDE2
DIVIDEX2

DOT
DOT2
DOTX2
HIDDEN
HIDDEN2

HIDDENX2
PHANTOM
PHANTOM2
PHANTOMX2
```

Figure 6.2 AutoCAD LT line types.

The color numbers can have a different effect with some systems; therefore, you should refer to the *AutoCAD LT User's Guide* for more information relating to your specific system.

Although the colors cannot be displayed with a monochrome monitor, you might want to use specific color numbers for layers to control the selection of pens by the plotter. When plotting, each color number can be associated with a specific pen number (if the plotter has more than one pen). The pens might vary in color and/or nib widths, thereby giving you control over the lines on the plotted drawing. The default color number for a layer is white (7).

6.1.3 Layer names

Each layer must be given an individual name. It can be up to 31 characters long and can contain letters, digits, and the special characters, $, _, and -. Do not include spaces in the layer name. It is better to pick descriptive names for a layer, such as roof, 1stfloor, etc.; however, the names can be as simple as 1, 2, 3, etc.

When AutoCAD LT is started, a layer named 0 is created with a continuous line type and a color number 7. This layer has specific properties, which are discussed in Sec. 10.2, and it cannot be deleted or renamed as other layers can.

6.1.4 Layer commands

When the Layer command is entered, the following options are displayed:

Command	Function
Make	Creates a new layer and makes it the current layer (a combination of New and Set).
New	Creates a new layer.
Set	Selects a current drawing layer.
ON	Layers turned on are displayed on the monitor.
OFF	Layers turned off are not displayed.
Color	Specifies a color number for specific layers.
Ltype	Specifies a line type for specific layers.
?	Lists layer data for specified layers.
Freeze	Frozen layers are ignored in the regeneration process, thereby speeding up the drawing regeneration. Freezing automatically turns a layer off.
Thaw	Used to turn the freeze state for a layer off.
Lock	Entities on a locked layer are visible but cannot be edited.
Unlock	Unlocks a layer to allow editing.

6.2 Set Layer Specifications

The lot plan to be drawn is to have file layers with the following specifications:

Object	Name	Color	Line type
Road and walk	0	White	Continuous
Road allowance	Center	Blue	Center
House	House	Red	Continuous
Dimensions and text	Dimens	White	Continuous
Property	Property	Red	Center

The current layer name is displayed in the upper-left corner of the monitor. Any new entities drawn will be displayed on that layer. Because the default layer set by AutoCAD LT is named layer 0, that name should be displayed in the upper-left corner of the monitor.

6.2.1 Loading linetypes

The default linetype for a new drawing is the Continuous linetype. If other linetypes, such as Center, are to be used they must be loaded into the drawing. The Center line is to be used for layers Center and Property, and is loaded as follows (see Fig. 6.3):

`Settings` <pick> `Linetype Style` <pick> `Load` <pick> `Linetype(s) to load:` **Center** <return>

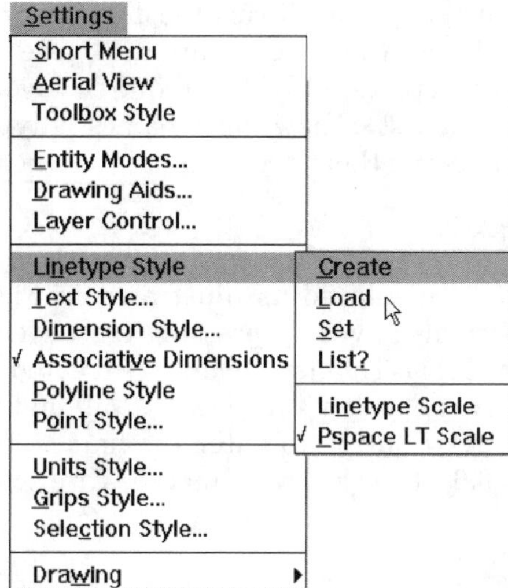

Figure 6.3 Linetype Style menu.

If you wanted to load all the linetypes you would enter * when asked for linetypes to load. AutoCAD LT displays the Select Linetype File dialogue box illustrated in Fig. 6.4. The file containing the desired linetypes is aclt.lin. Choose the aclt.lin file and press OK. AutoCAD LT responds at the command line with:

```
Linetype CENTER is loaded
?/Create/Load/Set:
```

If you wish to see a list of available linetypes (see Fig. 6.1) enter **?** <return>. To exit the request `?/Create/Load/Set:`, press <return>. To return to the graphics screen, press the F2 key.

6.2.2 Create the new layers

Prior to doing anything with the layers, they must be created. Layer 0 does not have to be created because it is the default layer created when AutoCAD LT is

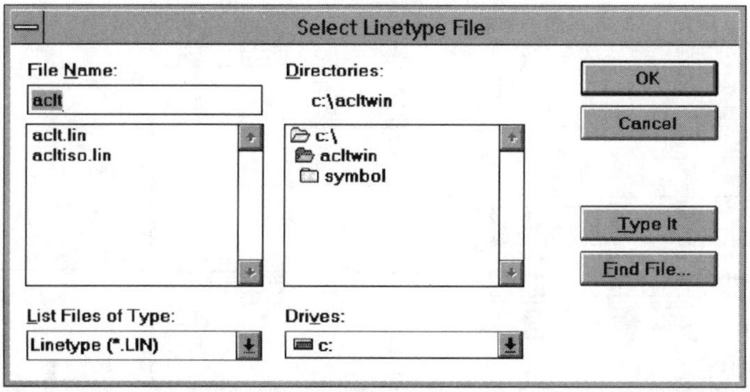

Figure 6.4 Linetype file dialogue box.

booted. New layers can be created at any time during the drawing process. The layers can be created individually as they are required or together at the beginning of the drawing. We will create all of the required layers for this drawing now (noting that when the list of new layer names is typed in, the names are separated with a comma and there are no spaces in the list):

Settings <pick> Layer control... <pick>

The Layer Control dialogue box is displayed as illustrated in Fig. 6.5. The Layer Control dialogue box is also displayed by pressing the Layer button in the buttons bar (see App. E, Fig. E.11). The new layers are created by placing the cursor in the layer name edit box (below the New button) and typing the names as illustrated. Press the New button to enter the names in the layer name list box illustrated in Fig. 6.6 (the colors and linetypes are set later).

6.2.3 Set the linetype for each layer

The default linetype for layers when they are created is Continuous. Entities drawn on layers Center and Property are to have a Center linetype. Choose layers Center and Property by clicking their names in the layer name list box. The layer names are highlighted as illustrated in Fig. 6.7.

Until a layer is chosen to work on, buttons on the right side of the Layer Control dialogue box such as On and Off are grayed (see Fig. 6.5). These buttons become active after a layer(s) is selected in the layer name list box (see Fig. 6.6). Click on the `Set Ltype...` box to display the Set Linetype dialogue box illustrated in Fig. 6.8.

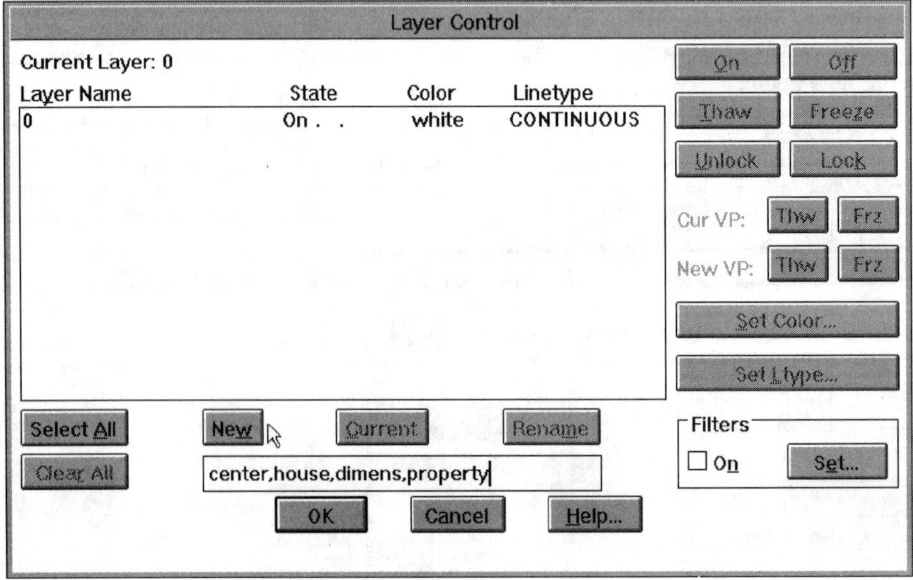

Figure 6.5 Creating new layers.

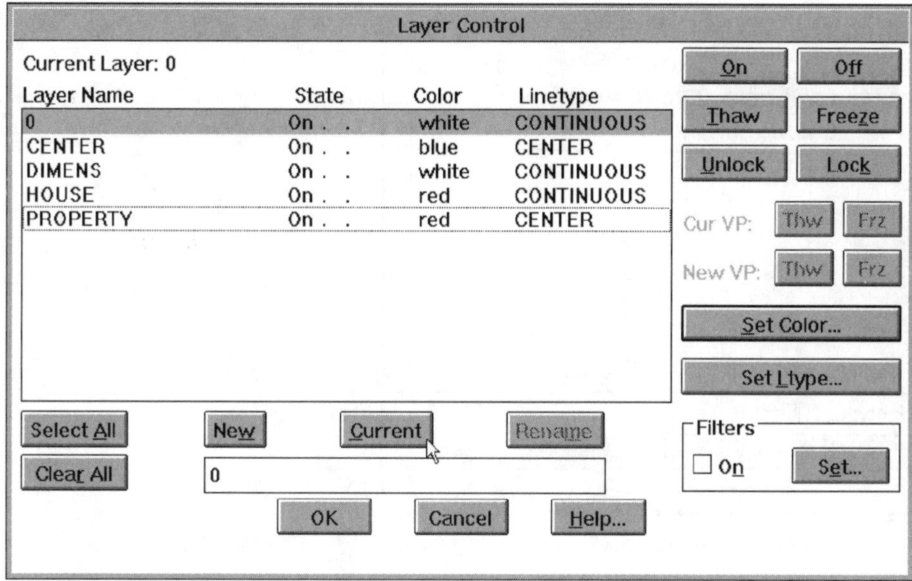

Figure 6.6 Setting the current layer.

Only the Center and Continuous linetypes were loaded in Sec. 6.2.1, so no other linetypes are available. Select the CENTER linetype as illustrated in Fig. 6.7 and press OK. Note that the Center linetype is now listed for layers Center and Property in the layer names list box.

6.2.4 Set the color for each layer

The color for each layer is to be defined. Remember that even if you do not have a color monitor, the color command is used because with it the plotter is instructed to select a different pen for each color in the drawing. Entities drawn on layer Center are to be blue. Currently layers Center and Property are highlighted. Deselect layer Property by clicking on its name in the layer

0	On . .	white	CONTINUOUS
CENTER	On . .	white	CONTINUOUS
DIMENS	On . .	white	CONTINUOUS
HOUSE	On . .	white	CONTINUOUS
PROPERTY	On . .	white	CONTINUOUS

Figure 6.7 Choosing layers.

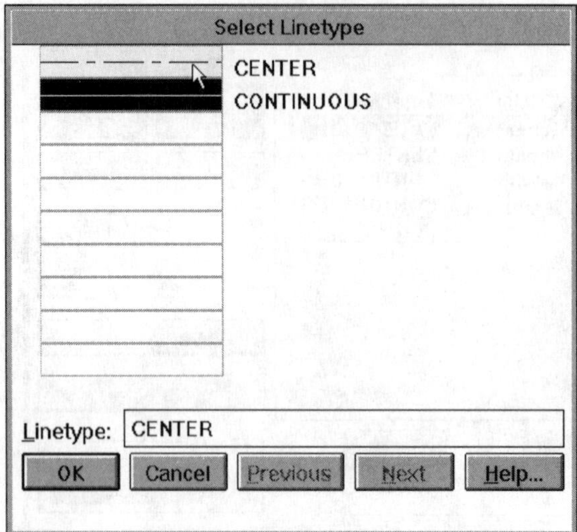

Figure 6.8 Selecting a linetype.

names list box. Only layer Center is to be highlighted as illustrated in Fig. 6.9. Click on the `Set Color...` button to display the Select Color dialogue box illustrated in Fig. 6.10. Then select the blue box in the Standard Colors box. The color is then listed in the Color box at the bottom of the dialogue box. Press the OK button.

Set the remaining layer colors as illustrated in Fig. 6.6. Then choose layer 0 in the layer names list box (it should be the only layer highlighted). Make it the current layer by pressing the `Current` button. This means that any entities drawn will be on layer 0. Press the OK button to exit the Layer Control dialogue box. Note that the layer 0 is displayed in the Current Layer name box, and its color is displayed in the Current Color box of the toolbar (see App. E, Fig. E.11).

0	On . .	white	CONTINUOUS
CENTER	On . .	white	CENTER
DIMENS	On . .	white	CONTINUOUS
HOUSE	On . .	white	CONTINUOUS
PROPERTY	On . .	white	CENTER

Figure 6.9 Deselecting a layer.

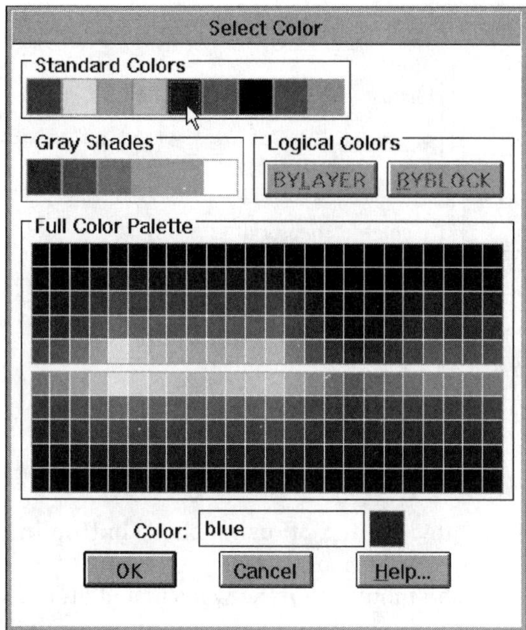

Figure 6.10 Selecting a color.

6.3 SNAP Command

Decimal units have been set with three digits to the right of the decimal for this drawing. The precision of the drawing, however, requires only one digit to the right of the decimal (note the 7.200 and 11.500 dimensions in Fig. 6.1). Because the dimension precision is 0.1, it is preferred to have 0.1 as the smallest cursor movements on the monitor. The Snap command is used to lock the cursor on an imaginary grid—in this case it is desired that the grid lines be 0.1 units apart. Snap sets the fine movement of the cursor. Larger steps can still be made. Choose the following:

Settings <Pick> Drawing Aids... <pick>

The Drawing Aids dialogue box is illustrated in Fig. 6.11. Move the cursor into the Snap X Spacing edit box and enter **0.1.** When the <return> button is pressed, AutoCAD LT sets the Y Spacing to 0.1. Turn snap on by clicking the On check box, which displays an X when on. Turn the Ortho (orthogonal) mode on by clicking its check box in the Modes block. Press the OK button to exit the dialogue box.

As the cursor is moved about the screen, the coordinates vary in steps of 0.1, if you have activated the coordinates with Ctrl-D or F6. The Snap function, once set, can be switched on or off by pressing the S (Snap) button in the toolbar (App. E, Fig. E.11).

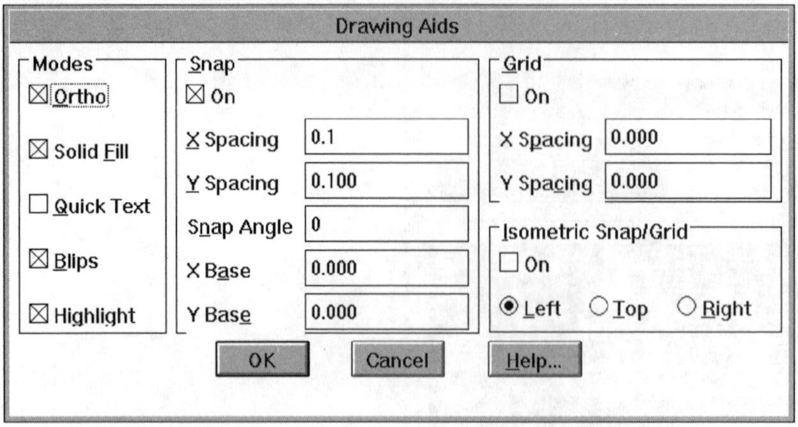

Drawing Aids

Modes
☒ Ortho
☒ Solid Fill
☐ Quick Text
☒ Blips
☒ Highlight

Snap
☒ On
X Spacing 0.1
Y Spacing 0.100
Snap Angle 0
X Base 0.000
Y Base 0.000

Grid
☐ On
X Spacing 0.000
Y Spacing 0.000

Isometric Snap/Grid
☐ On
◉ Left ○ Top ○ Right

OK Cancel Help...

Figure 6.11 Drawing Aids dialogue box.

The orthogonal mode is toggled on and off using the O button in the toolbar. When on, lines can only be drawn horizontally or vertically, thereby simplifying the selection of points on the monitor. Ortho was turned on in the Drawing Aids dialogue box.

6.4 Draw Road and Driveway

The road and driveway are to be drawn on layer 0 (see Sec. 6.2), which is the current layer as is indicated in the Current Layer box in the buttons bar (App. E, Fig. E.11). The line type for layer 0 is continuous; therefore, the lines will be drawn solid on the monitor.

The coordinates of the lower-left corner of the road will be assumed as 7,8. The road is then drawn using:

> `LINE` <pick> `Line from point:` **7,8** <return> `To point:` Move the cursor vertically to about point 7,45 and digitize the point. If the coordinate display at the top of the monitor does not change as the cursor is moved, press Ctrl-D. If the coordinate display shows relative distance < angle, press Ctrl-D again until it displays screen coordinates. <pick> `To point:` <return>

In the previous set of commands you should have noted that during the line command, Ctrl-D (or F6) is a toggle switch that is used to:

- Activate or deactivate the current coordinate display.
- Set the coordinate display to relative distance < angle.
- Set the coordinate display to current screen coordinates.

The Line command is next recalled to start a new line by pressing Enter or the Space bar. The other side of the road is drawn using:

> <return> `Line from point:` **@ 8<0** <return> `To point:` Move the cursor down drawing a line parallel with the first line. <pick> `To point:` <return>

Draw the driveway. The coordinates of the lower-left corner of the driveway are assumed as 15,16.5, and the driveway is 3 units wide:

<return> `Line from point:` **15,16.5** <return> `To point:` **@19.2<0** <return> `To point:` **@3<90** <return> `To point:` <return>

Draw the remainder of the driveway and walkway as illustrated in Fig. 6.12. Do not place any driveway lines along house lines because, when plotting this drawing (in Chap. 7), a different pen color will be used for the house and driveway.

6.5 Draw House on House Layer

The current working layer shown in the Current Layer box in the buttons menu is layer 0 (see App. E, Fig. E.11). The house is to be drawn on layer House, so the current layer is to be changed to layer House. This can be done using the Layer Control dialogue box (see Fig. 6.6). Alternatively clicking on the Current Layer box in the buttons menu displays the layer namer drop-down box illustrated in Fig. 6.13. Click on House in the list to make it current. House is now displayed in the Current Layer box and its color red is displayed in the Current Color box in the buttons bar. Presently all layers are on; however, House is set as the current layer so any new items drawn will be placed on layer House.

Draw the house lines starting at the top-right end of the driveway shown as point A in Fig. 6.12.

6.6 Hatching

AutoCAD LT is supplied with a good library of hatch styles. Refer to your AutoCAD LT manual for a listing of the patterns available. You can also create specific hatch pattern libraries for use by AutoCAD LT. Pattern creation is not discussed in this text.

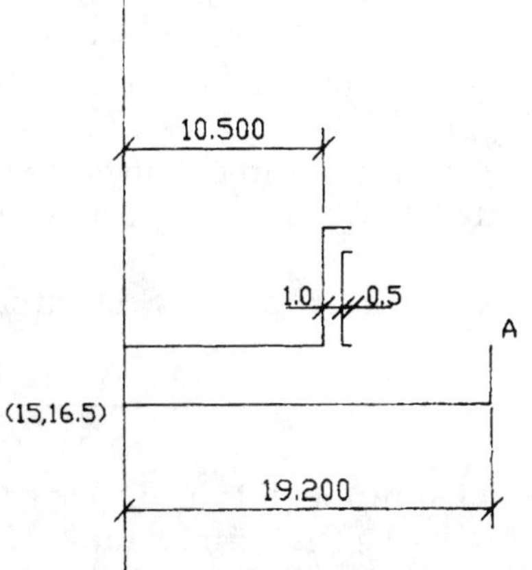

Figure 6.12 Driveway and walk.

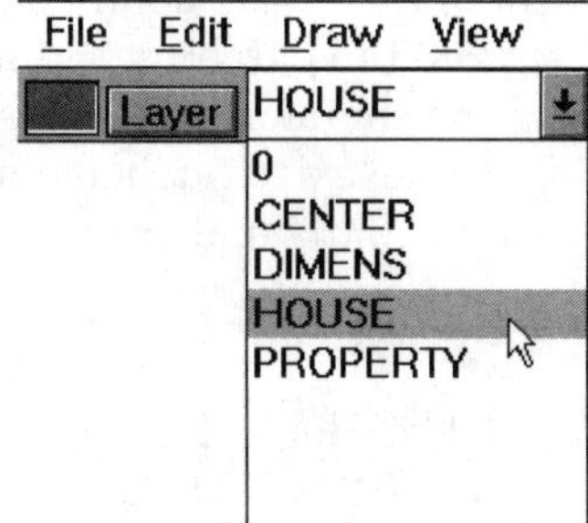

Figure 6.13 Setting current layer.

6.6.1 Hatch scale factor

All AutoCAD LT scale factors are based on a factor of 1 unit per 1 inch of plotted drawing; hence, the following formula can be used to determine any AutoCAD LT scale factor:

$$\text{Plot scale} \times \text{Hatch} = 1 \text{ in} \times \text{conversion} \tag{6.1}$$

where Plot scale = scale at which drawing is to be plotted
Hatch = hatch scale factor
conversion = factor to convert inches to drawing units.

This drawing is done in meter units and will be plotted using a scale of 1:300 to fit on an A-size sheet, which is measured in millimeters at 280 by 216 mm (11 by 8.5 in). Using 1 in = 25.4 mm and 1 m = 1000 mm:

$$\tfrac{1}{300} \times \text{Hatch} = 1 \text{ in} \times (25.4 \text{ mm}/1 \text{ in} \times 1 \text{ m}/1000 \text{ mm})$$
$$\text{Hatch} = 7.62$$

A hatch scale of 7.62 is then used.

Hatch scale factors are listed in App. C. Table C.2, item *A,* Drawing units: *Meters* shows the Hatch scale factor of 7.62 (as calculated above) for a drawing in meter units with a plot scale of 1:300. Tables in App. C list Hatch scales for other drawing units. For example, If AutoCAD LT's architectural units are used and a drawing is to be plotted with a scale of ⅛ in = 1 ft. 0 in, Table C.1, B-Drawing units: AutoCAD architectural or engineering units gives the hatch scale of 96. Using Eq. (6.1) the calculation is:

$$1/(8 \times 12) \times \text{Hatch} = 1 \text{ in}$$
$$\text{Hatch} = 96$$

6.6.2 Hatching the house

Objects hatched with AutoCAD LT must have boundaries of the area to be hatched clearly defined with single lines. For example if the left side of the box illustrated in Fig. 6.14 is to be hatched, lines A, B, D, and E must be drawn individually. If lines A–C and D–F are drawn as a continuous line, AutoCAD LT cannot hatch the left side of the box properly. In this drawing the four lines defining the house boundary were drawn as single entities without any extensions and the hatching boundary is not complicated. In Chap. 7 a procedure for hatching complex objects is discussed.

The house is hatched using the ANSI31 (American National Standards Institute) hatch pattern:

Draw <pick> **Hatch...** <Pick>

The Select Hatch Patterns dialogue box illustrated in Fig. 6.15 is displayed. Choose the ANSI31 pattern as illustrated and click the OK button. AutoCAD LT now requests the hatch scale. Enter the value of 7.62 calculated above:

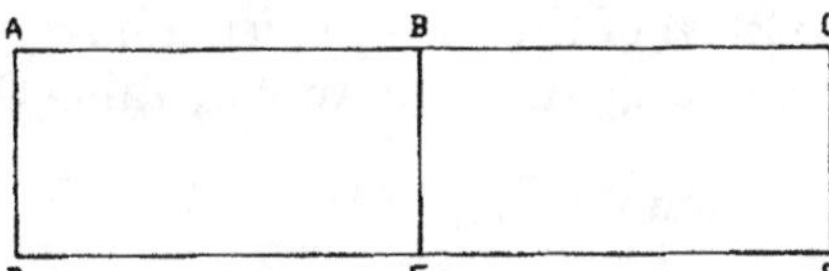

Figure 6.14 Hatch boundaries.

`Pattern (? or name/U,style): ansi31`
`Scale for pattern` <1>: **7.62** <return>
`Angle for pattern` <0>: <return>
`Select objects:` Digitize the four sides of the house and then press <return> to execute the Hatch command.

6.7 Draw Property Lines

Set the current drawing layer to Property. When the layer is set correctly, the Current Layer box in the buttons bar will show the layer name Property. Refer to Sec. 6.5 for the procedure used to set a new current layer.

6.7.1 Set line type scale

The center line type is used for the property layer. Because this line type is not a solid line, it must be scaled to suit our drawing. The scale factor for line types

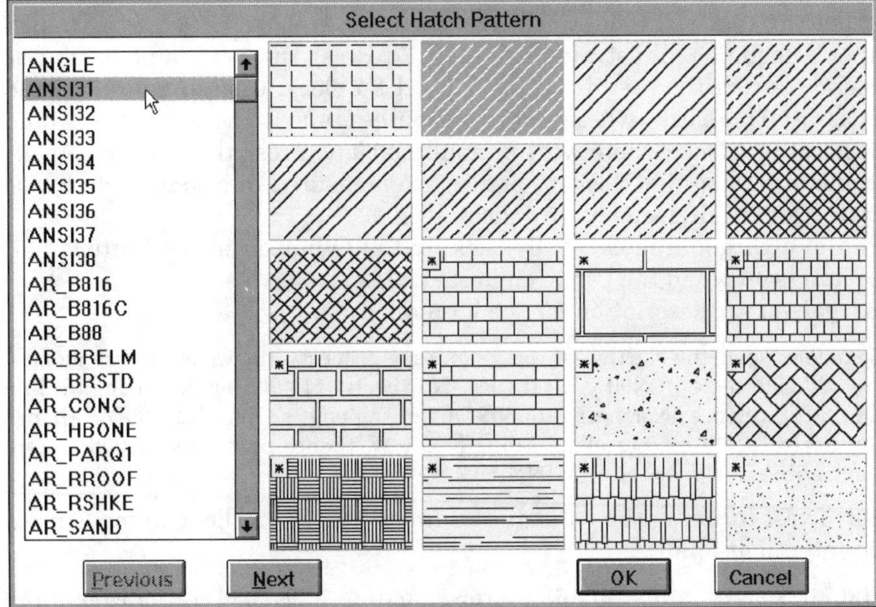

Figure 6.15 Selecting the hatch pattern.

(Ltscale) is calculated using Eq. (6.2) [¾ of the factor calculated by Eq. (6.1)]. The notations are the same as for Eq. (6.1). Also see App. C, Table C-2 A.

$$\text{Plot Scale} \times \text{Ltscale} = 1 \text{ in} \times \text{conversion} \times \tfrac{3}{4} \qquad (6.2)$$

$$\tfrac{1}{300} \times \text{Ltscale} = 1 \text{ in} \times (25.4 \text{ mm}/1 \text{ in} \times 1 \text{ m}/1000 \text{ mm}) \times \tfrac{3}{4}$$

$$\text{Ltscale} = 5.7$$

Settings <pick> Linetype Style <pick> Linetype Scale <pick> New scale factor <1.0>: **5.7** <return>

6.7.2 Surveyor's units

The property lines are defined in surveyor's units illustrated in Fig. 6.1. Bearing angles are always specified from the north or south direction toward the east or west direction; for instance a 45-degree angle is shown as N45°E, a 125-degree angle is shown as N35°W, and a 200-degree angle is shown as S70°W.

Because the degree symbol is not available on the keyboard, the letter D (upper- or lowercase) is used in place of the degree symbol (°) when entering angles in AutoCAD LT, so an angle is entered as 70d35′30″. This angle entered as a bearing is N70D35′30″E.

Angle units are set to surveyor's units as follows:

Settings <pick> **Units Style...** <pick>

The Units Control dialogue box illustrated in Fig. 6.16 is displayed. Click on the Surveyor Angles button. Then click on the down arrow in the Precision box to display the Precision drop-down box as illustrated. Set the precision to N0d00′E, so angles are displayed to the nearest minute. North is to be at 12 o'clock placing east at 3 o'clock. Click on the Direction Control... box to display the dialogue box illustrated in Fig. 6.17. Press the east radio button as illustrated, setting the east direction to be at 3 o'clock. Choosing north would place east at 12 o'clock (where north normally is), and choosing west would place east at 9 o'clock (where west normally is), etc. Press the Counter-Clockwise radio button so that positive angles are measured in a counterclockwise direction. Exit the dialogue box by clicking on OK.

Turn the orthogonal mode off by clicking the O button in the buttons bar. Orthogonal is off when the O button is shaded.

The legal survey description for the lot named Easy is

> Commencing at the Northwest corner of Easy property, thence Northerly along a line 20.000 meters N90°0′E, thence Northerly 11.490 meters along a line N60°30′E, thence Northerly 15.308 meters along a line N47°30′W, thence Northerly 18.714 meters along a line N90°0′W, thence Southerly 16.000 meters along a line S-°0′W to the BEGINNING.

The northwest corner of the lot is at coordinates 21,16 on the monitor. The lot data is entered as follows:

LINE <pick> From point: **21,16** <return> To point: **@20<N90D0′E** (*or* E) <return> To point: **@11.490<N60D30′E** <return> To point: **@15.308<N47D30′W** <return> To point: **@18.714<N90D0′W** (*or* W) <pick> To point: **@16<S** <return> To point: <return>

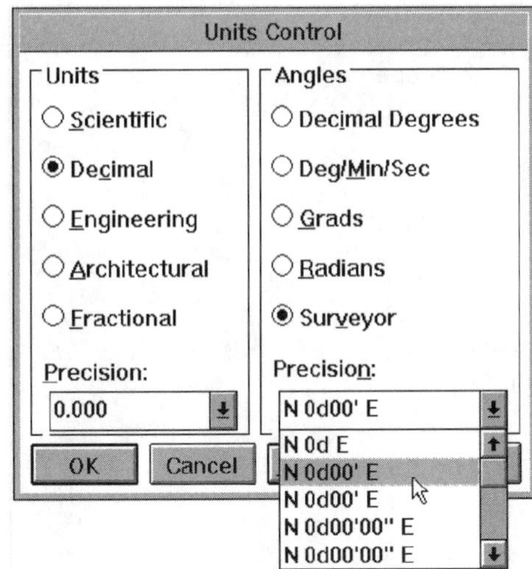

Figure 6.16 Surveyor units.

Figure 6.17 Angle direction control.

When AutoCAD LT's surveyor's units are used, angles can be entered as angles, i.e., 90, or as bearings, i.e., N, illustrated in this exercise.

6.8 Draw Road Allowances

The road allowances are to be drawn on the Center layer. Set Center as the current drawing layer. The line type scale does not have to be set again. Draw the road allowance as illustrated in Fig. 6.18. Do not overlap the previously drawn property line because a different color is used for the property line.

6.9 Dimension Drawing

Dimensioning is to be done on the Dimens layer. Set Dimens as the current drawing layer.

6.9.1 Calculate text height

The text and dimension text height will be calculated assuming that the drawing will be plotted on an A-size sheet (280 by 215 mm) using a scale of 1:300 (1 mm = 300 mm, or 0.3 m). The drawing units are meters, and the desired height for text on the plotted drawing is 3 mm.

The monitor text height (h) is then calculated as follows:

$$\frac{1}{300} \times h = 3 \text{ mm} \quad \text{giving } h = 900 \text{ mm, or } 0.9 \text{ m}$$

The dimension text variables scale, Dimscale, is calculated based on the default AutoCAD LT value for a dimension text height of 0.18 and the previous

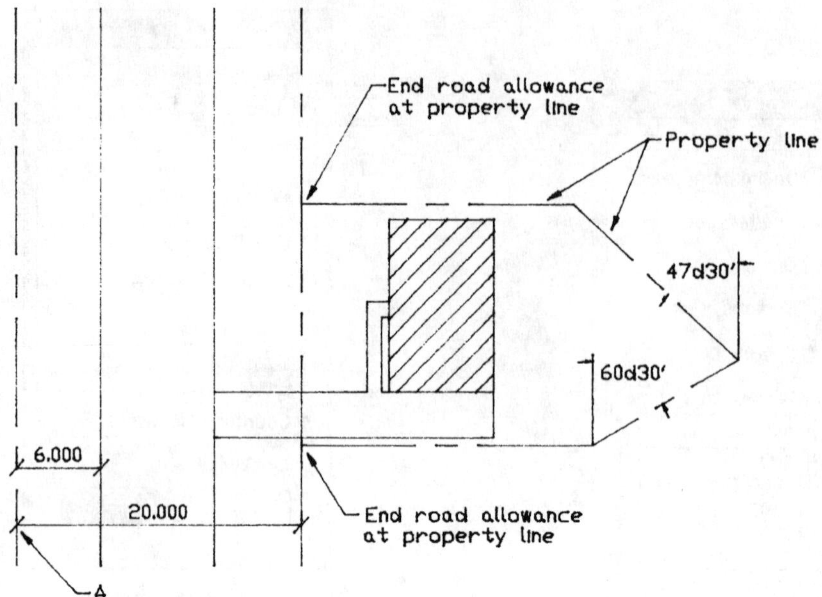

Figure 6.18 Road allowance and property line.

calculation from which we determined that the text height must be drawn 0.9 meters high to obtain a plotted text height of 3 mm when plotting the drawing using a scale of 1:300. Dimscale is calculated as follows using Eq. (4.2) (also see App. C, Table C.2 *A*):

$$\text{Dimscale} \times 0.18 = 0.9 \quad \text{giving Dimscale} = 5$$

Choose the following to set the dimension scale:

Setting <pick> **Dimension Style...** <pick>

The Dimension Styles and Settings dialogue box shown in Fig. 3.5 is displayed. Click on `Scales and Colors` to display the Scales and Colors dialogue box illustrated in Fig. 4.3. Move the cursor into the Feature Scaling box and enter the dimension scale of **5.** Click `OK` to exit.

6.9.2 Change dimension arrows to ticks

The Dimension Style dialogue box (Fig. 3.5) is on the screen. Choose `Arrows` to display the Arrows dialogue box illustrated in Fig. 6.19. Change the dimension arrows to ticks by pressing the `Tick` radio button. Set the `Arrow Size` (tick size) to **0.09,** giving dimension ticks about one-half the dimension text height which by default is 0.18. Remember that all numerical dimension variables are multiplied by the dimension scale of 5. The dimension text is then 0.9 units (5 × 0.18) on the screen as specified in Sec. 6.9.1, and the ticks will be 0.45 units. The Tick Extension allows you to specify an amount the dimension line is to

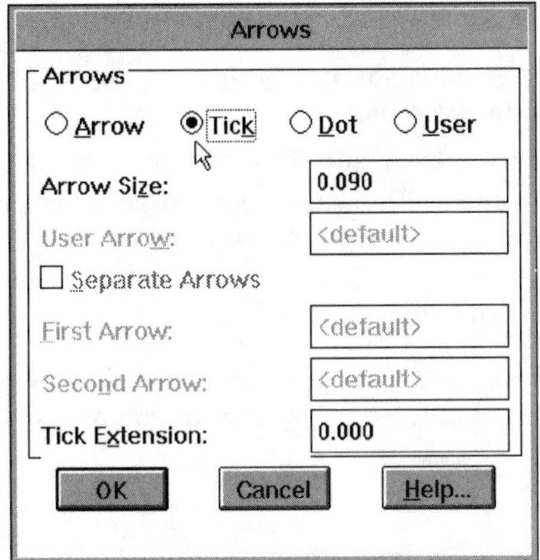

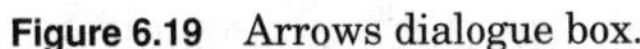
Figure 6.19 Arrows dialogue box.

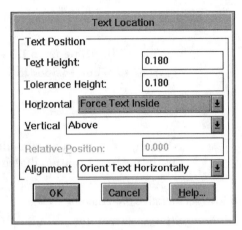

Figure 6.20 Text location settings.

extend past the extension line. It will be left at the default value of 0. Click on `OK` to exit the Arrows dialogue box.

6.9.3 Set dimension text location

The Dimension Style dialogue box is on the screen. Choose `Text Location...` to display the Text Location dialogue box illustrated in Fig. 6.20. Note the default Text Height of 0.18. This is not changed since it is controlled by the dimension scale (Feature Scaling) factor of 5. The settings displayed in Fig. 6.20 are made by clicking on the down arrow to the right of each box displaying the options. Also see App. A.

The `Horizontal` setting is: `Force Text Inside.` Options are:

Default — Results will vary. For linear and angular dimensions, text is placed inside extension lines if there is sufficient room. For radius and diameter dimensions, text is placed outside the circle or arc.

Force Text Inside — Forces text between extension lines.

Text, Inside Arrows — Forces text and arrows between extension lines. Suppresses the arrows and dimension line if the extension lines are close together.

The `Vertical` setting is: `Above.` Options are:

Centered — Splits the dimension line for the text, centered between extension lines.

Above — Places the text above the dimension line.

Relative — Places the text relative to the dimension line at a distance governed by the value entered in the Relative position box (and the dimension scale).

The Alignment setting is: Orient Text Horizontally. Options are:

Orient Text Horizontally	Draws text horizontally regardless of the alignment of the dimension line.
Align With Dimension Line	Draws text aligned with the dimension line.
Aligned When Inside Only	Text is aligned with the dimension line only when text is inside the extension lines.
Aligned When Outside Only	Text is aligned with the dimension line only when text is outside the extension lines.

Complete the settings as illustrated in Fig. 6.20 and then choose OK to exit both the Text Location dialogue box and the Dimension Style dialogue box.

6.9.4 Associative dimensions

If associative dimensioning is enabled (by setting the Dimaso dimension variable on) you can edit dimensions as single entities, and the dimensions are linked to the object so that as the features of the object are modified the dimension will change accordingly (see Chap. 13, Sec. 2.5).

When Dimaso is off, dimensions lines, extension lines, arrows, leaders, and dimension text are individual entities.

Associate dimensioning is set to on by default. Verify this by displaying the Settings menu. When associative dimensioning is on there is a tick mark beside Associative Dimensions. If there is no tick mark beside Associative Dimensions click on it to turn the associative dimensioning feature on. All projects in *Easy AutoCAD LT* are to be dimensioned with the associative dimensioning feature on.

6.10 Horizontal Dimensions

The horizontal text at the bottom of the drawing is added:

> Draw <pick> Linear Dimensions <pick> Horizontal <pick> First extension line origin or RETURN to select: [Shift->2B] Nearest <pick> to Digitize point A in Fig. 6.21 <Pick> Second extension line origin: **@20<0** <return> Dimension line location: **@** <return> Dimension text <20.000>: <return> Draw <pick> Linear Dimensions <pick> Continue <pick> Second extension line: [Shift->2B] Intersect <pick> of Digitize point c. <pick> Dimension text <30.000>: <return>

@ is a relative command—when no values are entered, this point is the same as the last point. It is used here because no extension line is desired. Notice how the second extension line origin and the dimension line location were made at the same point by using the relative @ command. By doing that, the size of the dimension extension line is reduced. There is a way to completely eliminate it, but that is discussed in a later project.

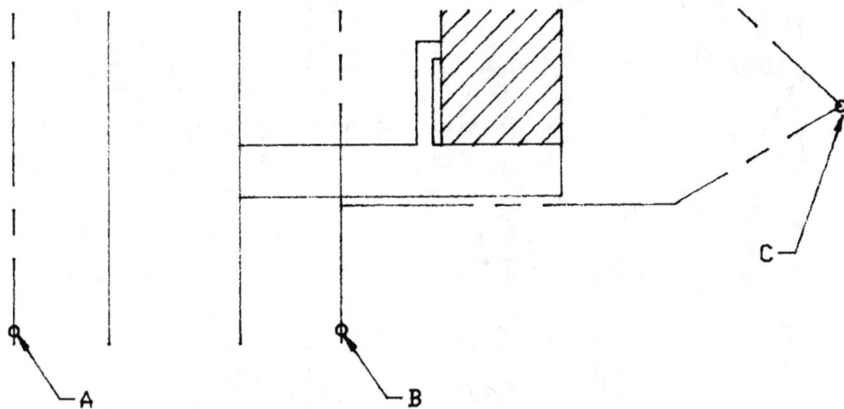

Figure 6.21 Horizontal dimension points.

The horizontal text across the top of the drawing is added:

Draw <pick> Linear Dimensions <pick> Horizontal <pick> First extension line origin or RETURN to select: [Shift->2B] Nearest <pick> To Digitize point A in Fig. 6.22 <Pick> Second extension line origin: [Shift->2B] Nearest <pick> to Place the target on B with the horizontal cursor line aligned with point A. <pick> Dimension line location: @ <return> Dimension text <6.000>: <return> Draw <pick> Linear Dimensions <pick> Continue <pick> Second extension line: [Shift->2B] Nearest <pick> *to* Place the target on C with the cursor aligned with B. <pick> etc.

Continue the horizontal dimensions along the top of the lot plan. Use the Intersection object snap to locate the corners of the house as shown in Fig. 6.22. Be careful when locating the object snap target so that you do not get the intersection of one of the hatch lines and the side the house. If the default dimension text is not correct, that is probably what happened. Accept the erroneous value and after it is printed enter Undo (Toolbar) and retry the continue command being more careful with the selection of the intersection point.

6.11 Vertical Dimensions

The Vertical dimensions along the right side of the house are entered as follows:

Draw <pick> Linear Dimensions <pick> Vertical <pick> First extension line origin or RETURN to select: [Shift->2B] Nearest <pick> to Digitize point A in Fig. 6.23 <Pick> Second extension line origin: [Shift->2B] Intersect <pick> of Place the target on the bottom right corner of the house, being careful to select the intersection of the house walls and not an intersection of a hatch line and the house wall. <pick> Dimension line location: Select point A. <pick> Dimension text <3.500>: <return>

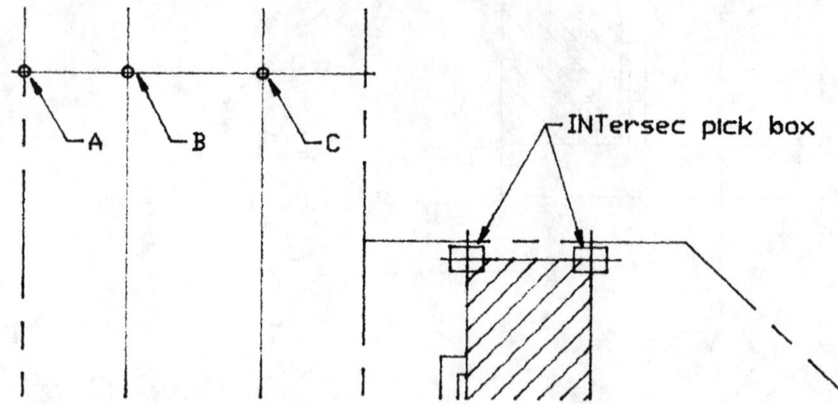

Figure 6.22 Horizontal dimension points.

If you get a default dimension other than 3.500 you might have selected an intersection of a hatch line and the house wall. Enter Undo and retry the dimension.

The next dimension is continued as follows:

Draw <pick> Linear Dimensions <pick> Continue <pick> Second extension line origin: [Shift->2B] Intersect <pick> of Pick the upper right corner of the house. <pick> Dimension text <11.500>: <return>

Because the last dimension extended beyond its extension lines, AutoCAD LT incremented the dimension lines as illustrated in Fig. 6.23. Setting the dimension line Baseline Increment to 0 will prevent AutoCAD LT from incrementing the dimension lines. Undo the last two dimensions and set the Baseline Increment to 0:

Edit <pick> Undo <pick> Undo <pick> Settings <pick> Dimension Style... <pick>

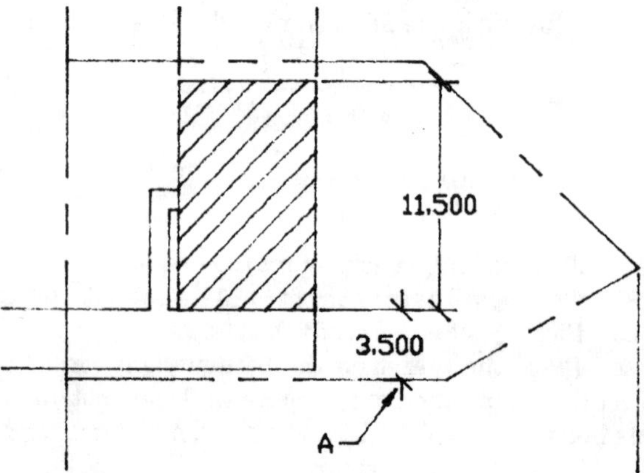

Figure 6.23 Vertical dimension points.

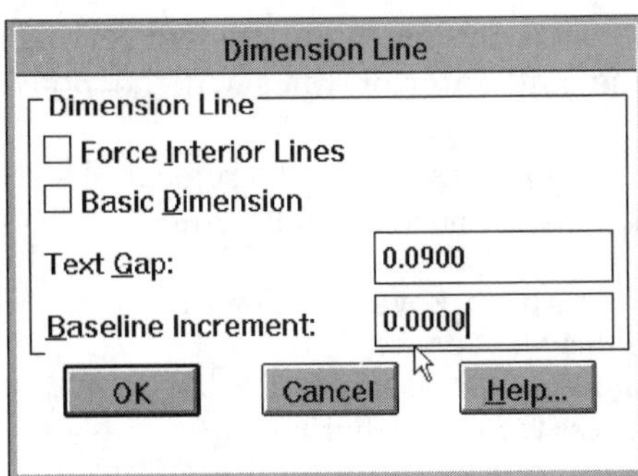

Figure 6.24 Dimension Line dialogue box.

Choose `Dimension Line...` from the Dimension Styles and Settings dialogue box to display the Dimension Line dialogue box illustrated in Fig. 6.24. Move the cursor into the Baseline Increment edit box and change the value from 0.38 to 0. Select OK in each dialogue box to exit and return to the graphics screen.

Redraw the vertical dimensions along the right side of the house, continuing the dimension string to the edge of the property as illustrated in Fig. 6.1. The dimension text is horizontal, and will be edited later to appear exactly as illustrated in Fig. 6.1.

When the dimensions along the right side of the house are completed set the Baseline Increment back to the default value of 0.38.

Complete the remaining dimensions on the drawing.

6.11.1 Editing associative dimensions

Because associative dimensioning is on, the dimensions can be edited as single entities. For example, the vertical dimension text is horizontal, and the dimension line does not appear between the extension lines. Make the following dimension setting:

`Settings` <pick> `Dimension Style...` <pick>

Choose `Text Location...` from the Dimension Style and Settings dialogue box to display the Text Location dialogue box illustrated in Fig. 6.20. Display the drop-down menu for the `Alignment` box and change the Alignment setting from Orient Text Horizontally to `Align with Dimension Line`. Press `OK`.

Next, choose `Dimension Lines...` from the Dimension Styles and Settings dialogue box to display the Dimension Line dialogue box illustrated in Fig. 6.24. Click the `Force Interior Lines` box on (it displays an X when on). Press OK in both dialogue boxes to exit to the graphics screen. Both of these settings could have been done prior to doing the original dimensioning. They were not done so you could learn how to edit dimensions after they are completed. Choose the following commands:

`Modify` <pick> `Edit Dimensions` <pick> `Update Dimensions` <pick> `Select dimensions`: Digitize each of the vertical dimensions. When selected they become dotted on the screen. <return>

The dimensions will be updated to the new dimension setting, becoming aligned with the dimension line and interior lines will be placed between extension lines.

Now the 3.500 and 1.000 dimension texts need to be relocated so they are not crowded between the extension lines. Choose the following:

> `Modify` <pick> `Edit Dimensions` <pick> `Move Text` <pick> `Select dimension:` Click on the 3.500 dimension. <pick> `Enter text location (Left/Right/Home/Angle):` Move the cursor noting the text moves on the screen with it. When the text is in the desired location press the <pick> button.

Move the other text as required. Entering L (left) in response to Enter text location, moves the text left. Try the other responses. If you don't like the results choose Undo and try again. If you end up with a bunch of dots on the screen, choose Redraw in the Edit menu to redraw the screen, cleaning it up.

6.12 Text

The text is to be on layer Dimens, which should be the current layer. In Sec. 6.9.1 the text height was calculated as 0.9 units. Normally the start point of the text is selected when entering text. To center the bearing text above a lot line the center option is used which allows entry of the bottom center point for the text.

The bearing requires a degree symbol, which is not available on the keyboard. AutoCAD's code to print a degree symbol is the lowercase letter d preceded by two percent symbols, %%d.

The N60°30′E bearing text is entered as follows:

> `Draw` <pick> `Text` <pick> `Justify/Style/<Start point>:` **J** (Justify) <return> `Align/Fit/Center/Middle/Right:` **C** (Center) <return> Pick the bottom center point for the N60°30′E text below the lot line allowing room for the height of the text. <pick> `Height <0.200>:` **0.9** <return> `Rotation Angle` <E>: Pick a point so the "rubber band" cursor line is parallel with the lot line <pick> `Text:` **N60%%d30′E** <return>

The Justify option to the Text command allows you to enter a variety of alignment options:

Align AutoCAD LT requests the start and endpoints of the text, and aligns the text along the given line, adjusting the height so the text fits between the two points.

Fit Fit is like align except the text height is requested from the drafter, and only the text width is adjusted to fit between the two points entered.

Center AutoCAD LT requests the center point of the baseline of the text, and centers the text horizontally on the given point.

Middle AutoCAD LT requests the middle point of the line of text, and centers the text horizontally and vertically on the given point.

Right Right justifies the text.

Add the remaining text to the drawing. If you forget the bearing or length of a line, the List command can be invoked to display the line data as follows:

> `Assist` <pick> `List` <pick> `Select objects:` Pick a line for which you want to view the data. <pick> `Select objects:` <return>

The data for the N60°30′E line is as follows:

```
LINE      Layer: PROPERTY
   Space: Model space
from point,          X= 41.000 Y= 16.000 Z= 0.000
    to point,        X= 51.000 Y= 21.658 Z= 0.000
Length = 11.490,     Angle in X-Y Plane = N 60d30'E
   Delta X = 10.000, Delta Y = 5.658, Delta Z = 0.000
```

6.12.1 North arrow

> `Text` <pick> `Justify/Style/<Start point>:` Digitize the point where you wish the right side of the arrowhead for the north arrow to be. <pick> `Height <0.900>:` 4 <return> `Rotation angle <default>:` **90** *(or N)* <return> `Text:` > <return> `Draw` <pick> `Line` <pick> Draw a line for the arrow shaft. <pick> `Text` <pick> `Justify/Style/<Start point>:` **J** (Justify) <return> **M** (Middle) <return> `Middle point:` Pick the middle point for the N text on the arrow shaft. <pick> `Height <4.000>:` <return> `Rotation angle <N>:` **E** *(or 0)* <return>

6.13 Measurement System

Exercises in this text use AutoCAD LT's English measurement system. AutoCAD LT's metric measurement system is set as follows:

> `File` <pick> `Preference` <pick>

The Preferences dialogue box illustrated in App. A, Fig. A.1.1 is displayed. Choose Metric in the Measurement drop-down box and then press OK. AutoCAD LT responds with "`Measurements changes take effect when hatch patterns, linetypes, and new drawings are initially loaded.`" When a new drawing is loaded, the default limits are 297 by 420 (versus 17 by 11) and the default dimension text height is 2.5 units (versus 0.18). Default scale factors are based on 1 unit per 1 mm of plotted drawing. This changes equations 4.2, 6.1, and 6.2 as follows:

$$\text{Dimscale} \times 2.5 = \text{Text height} \tag{4.2M}$$

$$\text{Plot Scale} \times \text{Hatch} = 1\text{ mm} \times \text{conversion} \tag{6.1M}$$

$$\text{Plot Scale} \times \text{Ltscale} = 1\text{ mm} \times \text{conversion} \times \tfrac{3}{4} \tag{6.2M}$$

With AutoCAD LT set for metric measurements Dimscale, Hatch, and Ltscale, settings in this chapter would be:

$$\text{Dimscale} \times 2.5 = 0.9 \qquad \text{(Sec. 6.9.1)}$$
$$\text{Dimscale} = 0.36$$

$$\tfrac{1}{300} \times \text{Hatch} = 1\ \text{mm} \times 1\ \text{m}/1000\ \text{mm} \qquad \text{(Sec. 6.6)}$$
$$\text{Hatch} = 0.3$$

$$\tfrac{1}{300} \times \text{Ltscale} = 1\ \text{mm} \times 1\ \text{m}/1000\ \text{mm} \times \tfrac{3}{4} \qquad \text{(Sec. 6.7.1)}$$
$$\text{Ltscale} = 0.23$$

Metric drawings can be done with AutoCAD LT set for English measurement. That is done throughout this text. The measurement system is irrelevant since a unit of measurement in AutoCAD LT is in whatever units you want it to be. When the default measurement system is set to English, AutoCAD LT loads a prototype drawing named ACLT.DWG (see Fig. 1.15), and when set to metric, AutoCAD LT loads a prototype drawing named ACLTISO.DWG. These prototype drawings have different linetype, hatch, and dimension scale factors. Otherwise the drawing process is the same.

If you have set the measurement unit to metric, change it back to English for the remaining exercises in this text.

Chapter

7

Plotting/Printing

Objective. Plot a drawing; set system printers using Windows Print Manager; setting plot specifications; hatching objects.

Drawing. Proj-5.dwg and Proj-6.dwg will be plotted.

7.1 Plotting Drawings

Drawings are plotted/printed by choosing `Print/Plot...` from the `File` menu (App. E, Fig. E.1) or choosing the print/plot button in the Buttons bar (App. E, Fig. E.11). AutoCAD LT displays the Plot Configuration dialogue box illustrated in Fig. 7.1.

7.1.1 Print/plot setup

With AutoCAD LT, clicking on the `Print/Plot Setup and Default Selection...` displays a Device and Default selection box illustrated in Fig. 7.2. To choose a printer, click on `Print/Plot Setup...` which displays the Print setup dialogue box illustrated in Fig. 7.3.

The default printer in Fig. 7.3 is the Windows System Printer. To display other printers/plotters that are available, click the radio button beside Specific Printer. Then click the down arrow to the right of the printer list box to display the drop-down box listing other printers configured through Windows Print Manager. If your plotter is not in the list, it must be added through Windows Print Manager.

7.2 Windows Print Manager

AutoCAD LT uses the Windows System Printer for all hard-copy output. Any printer or plotter you want to use must first be installed through Windows Print Manager.

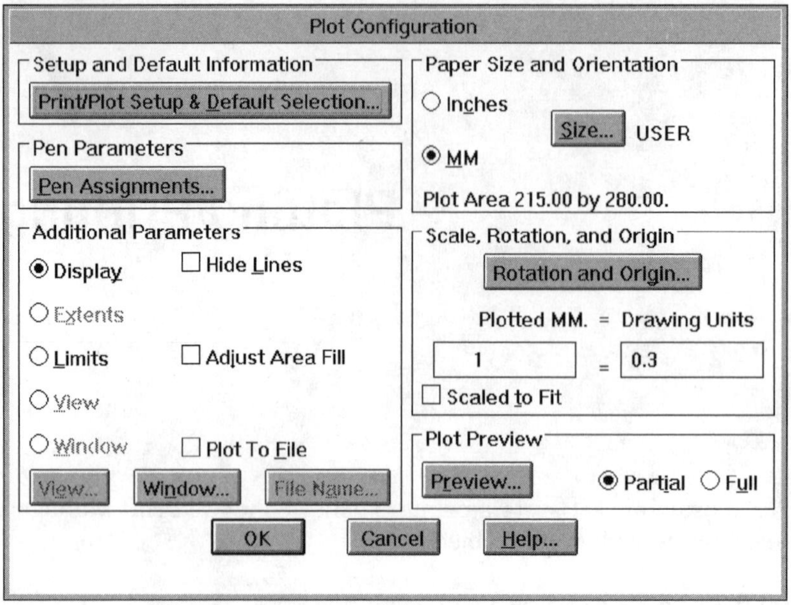

Figure 7.1 Plot Configuration dialogue box.

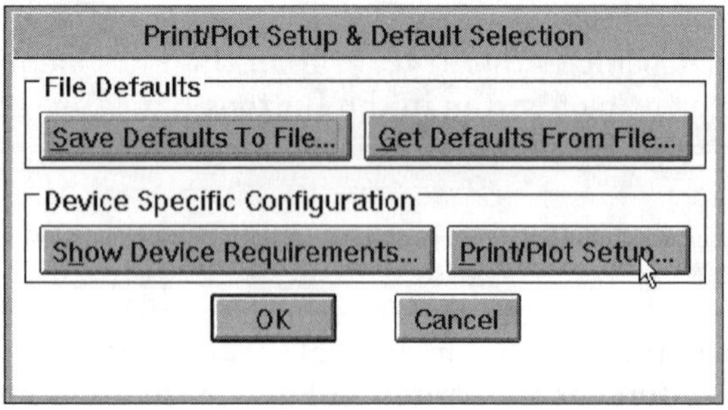

Figure 7.2 Print/Plot setup.

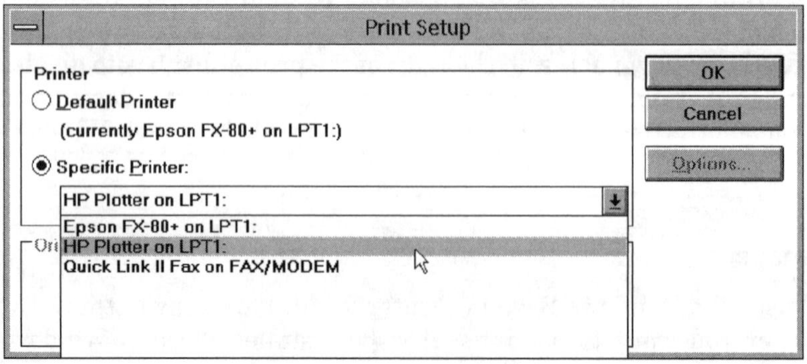

Figure 7.3 Selecting a plotter.

To install a printer/plotter, exit AutoCAD LT to Windows (see Fig. 1.1). Bring the Main Window group to the front by clicking on it, and then choose the Print Manager icon. The Print Manager Window (Fig. 7.4) is displayed. Choose `Printer Setup...` from the menu. The Printer selection box illustrated in Fig. 7.5 is displayed.

Click the `Add>>` button in the Printers selection box to display the List of Printers as illustrated in Fig. 7.5. Then select the printer/plotter you wish to add from the drop-down box. Install the device by clicking `Install`. You may be asked to insert the disk that contains the printer driver file. This is one of your original Windows diskettes or a diskette provided by your printer manufacturer. If you are prompted for other files, insert the diskette and then press the OK button. Choose the Close button when through installing printers/plotters. The printers/plotters installed can now be accessed as Windows System Printers. (*Note:* The original Microsoft Windows 3.1 HPGL printer/plotter may not print correctly. Refer to App. A.5, Printer Problems, for more information.)

7.3 Plotting/Printing Proj-6

Boot AutoCAD LT and choose `Open...` in the File menu to edit C:\DRAWINGS\PROJ-6. The full drawing should be displayed on the screen. If it is not,

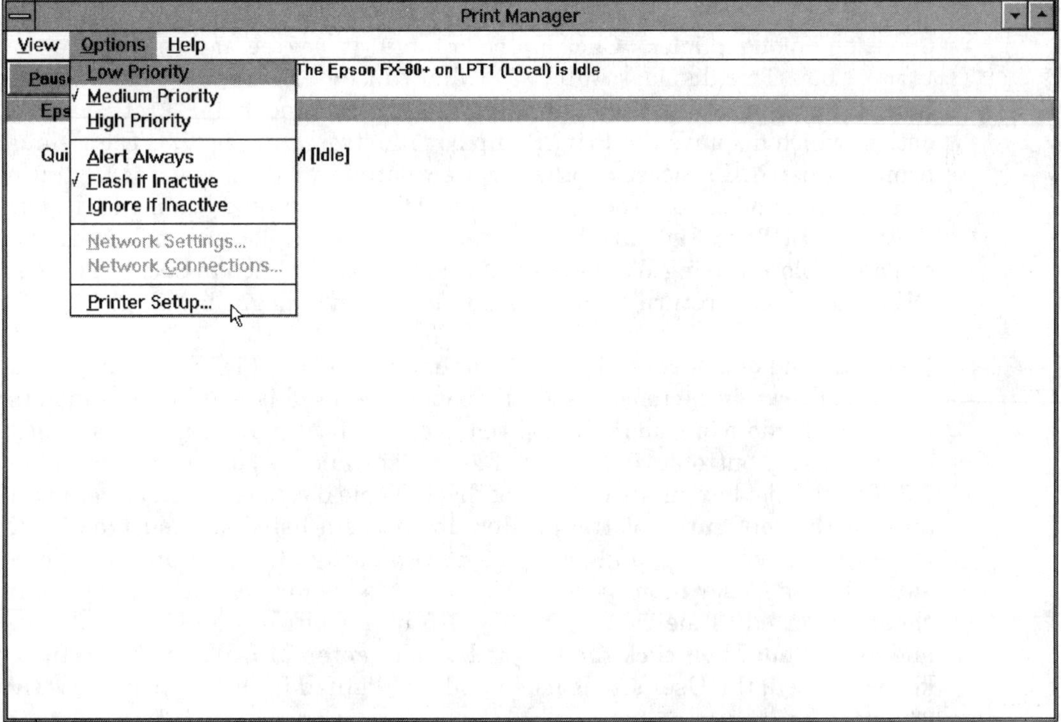

Figure 7.4 Print Manager window.

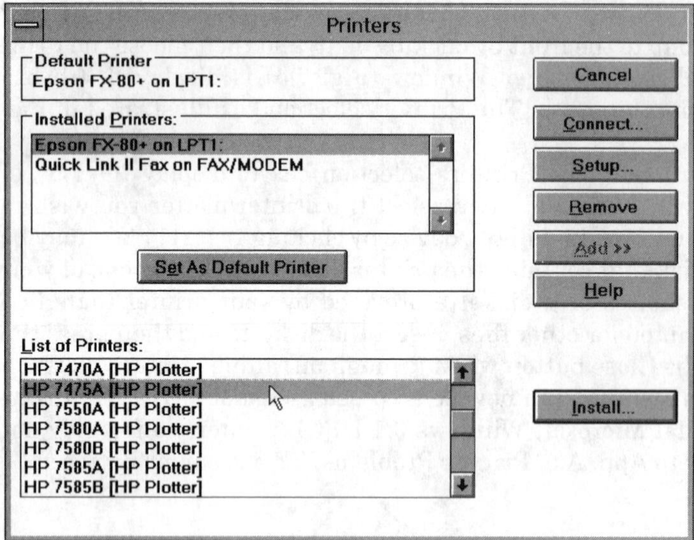

Figure 7.5 Printer selection box.

enter the Zoom and All commands. Select `Print/Plot...` in the File menu. The Plot Configuration dialogue box illustrated in Fig. 7.1 is displayed.

Choosing a plotter/printer. Click on the `Print/Plot Device and Default Selection...` box. This displays AutoCAD LT's Print/Plot Setup and Default Selection dialogue box illustrated in Fig. 7.2. Choose the `Print/Plot Setup...` option, which displays the Print Setup box illustrated in Fig. 7.3. The Default printer is listed. To choose another printer/plotter, press the `Specific Printer` radio button and choose the desired plotter from the drop-down menu, ie., HP Plotter on LPT1 in Fig. 7.3 (also see App. A.5). If your plotter is not listed, you can add a plotter using Windows Print Manager as outlined in Sec. 7.2. Choose OK in each box to return to the Plot Configuration dialogue box (Fig. 7.1).

Paper size and orientation. The Plot Configuration box (Fig. 7.1) is displayed. Proj-6 is drawn in meter units so the paper size used is to be in millimeters. Press the `MM` radio button in the top-right corner of the dialogue box. Then click on the `Size...` button to display the Paper Size dialogue box illustrated in Fig. 7.6. The size list box on the left side of the dialogue box lists the plot sizes available for the configured plotter/printer. To choose a listed size, such as MAX, move the cursor onto it and press the <pick> button. Other user sizes can be entered in the User input boxes. This plot is to be done on an 11 in by 8.5 in sheet converted to metric 280 mm by 215 mm. Click on the User `Width` box and enter **280.** Then click the `Height` box and enter **215.** When the <return> key is pressed, the User size is listed and highlighted in the list box. Press the `OK` button.

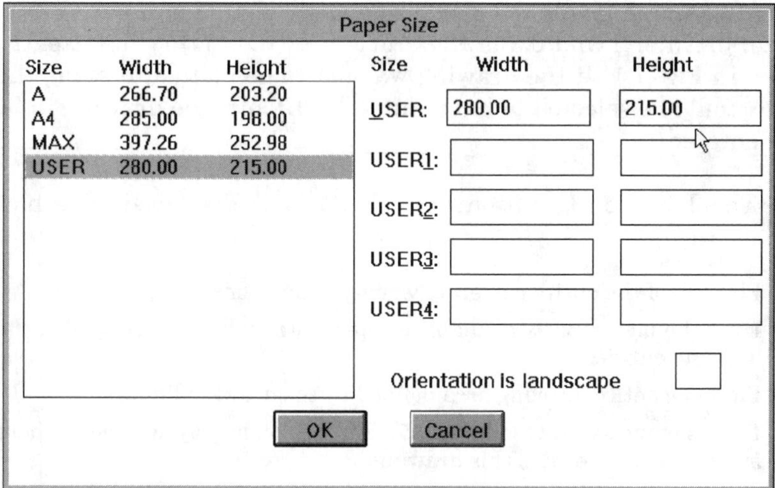

Figure 7.6 Setting the paper size.

Plot rotation and orientation. The Plot Configuration box (Fig. 7.1) is displayed. Click on the `Rotation and Origin...` box to display the Plot and Rotation dialogue box illustrated in Fig. 7.7. Press the `0` Plot Rotation button (with a standard width printer you will have to rotate the plot 90 degrees). The 0.00 X origin and 0.00 Y Origin will be accepted. If you wish to start the plot at some other location on the sheet, measure the X and Y distance from the plotter's home position using the paper size units (mm in this case) and enter the desired coordinates in the input boxes. You will have to experiment with your plotter to see what settings are best. Press the `OK` button.

Plot scale. The Plot Configuration box (Fig. 7.1) is displayed. Proj-6 is drawn in meter units, and is to be plotted using a scale of 1:300. This means that 1 millimeter (mm) of the plot is to equal 300 mm of the drawing. Since the drawing is in meter (m) units the 300 mm is converted to drawing units by dividing

Plot Rotation and Origin
Plot Rotation
0 90 180 270
Plot Origin
X Origin: 0.00 Y Origin: 0.00
OK Cancel

Figure 7.7 Setting the plot rotation and origin.

by 1000 (1 m = 1000 mm), giving 0.3 m. This means 1 plotted mm = 0.3 drawing units (meters). Enter **1** and **0.3** in the `Plotted MM = Drawing Units` entry boxes as shown in Fig. 7.1. If the drawing was not to be plotted to scale, the Scale to Fit box could be selected to have AutoCAD LT plot the drawing to fit the paper size entered.

What to plot. The Plot Configuration box (Fig. 7.1) is displayed. The plot options available are:

Display Plots all of the entity currently visible on the monitor.

Extents Plots the largest view available of the drawing that contains all of the drawing entities.

Limits Plots the entire drawing area defined by the drawing limits

View Plots a named view (see Chap. 15). This option is grayed because there are no named views in this drawing.

Window Plots an area enclosed by a user-defined window. Pressing this radio button displays the dialogue box illustrated in Fig. 7.8. The window to enclose the area to be plotted can be defined two ways: by entering a First Corner `X` and `Y` coordinate, and a Second Corner `X` and `Y` coordinate in the input boxes, or by Clicking the `Pick<` button which displays the drawing allowing you to place a window around the plotted area using the cursor.

Press the `Display` radio button to plot the view currently displayed on the monitor. Press the `OK` button to exit.

Pen assignments. The Plot Configuration box (Fig. 7.1) is displayed. Click on the `Pen Assignments...` box to display the Pen Assignments dialogue box illustrated in Fig. 7.9. The pen list box shows the following (if you are using a printer you may not have any options available, or you may be able to set dots/mm depending on your printer):

Color The color of an entity on the drawing, defined by the layer or entity color.

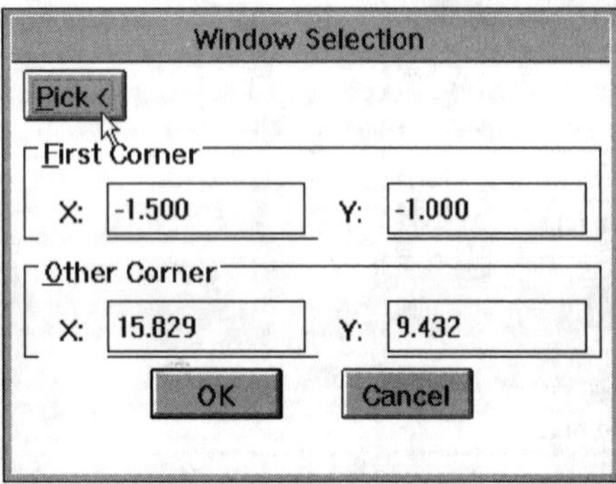

Figure 7.8 Defining a plot using a window.

Pen No. The number of a pen slot in the pen holder of the plotter. Setting this number tells AutoCAD LT what pen to select for a specified entity color.

Linetype The linetype defined by the plotter. Normally linetype of entities is controlled by the layer linetype setting in AutoCAD LT, and the plotter line type is set to 0, which is a continuous linetype. Mixing linetypes such as using a center linetype on a layer, and setting a dotted linetype on the plotter gives unexpected results. To list the linetypes available on the plotter, and their associated number click on the Feature Legend . . . box.

Pen Speed The speed of movement of the plotter. You may want to reduce the pen speed for a pen that skips.

Pen Width The width of the pen being defined. This is critical when an object is being filled (see Chap. 10) since it tells the AutoCAD LT how far apart to place the stokes of the pen to fill something in. The number on a pen, i.e., .3, is usually in millimeters. Setting a pen width too large, such as giving a pen size of 0.3 (mm) rather than 0.1 (inches) for an Imperial units drawing often causes strange output from the plotter.

Layer colors used in Proj-6 (see Chap. 6, Sec. 6.2) are black (color no. 7), blue (5), and red (1). Set the pens for those colors as illustrated in Fig. 7.9. For example, to set color 7, move the cursor onto color 7 and press <pick>, highlighting that color in the selection box. When a color's data is highlighted in the list box, its Pen No., Linetype, etc. can be modified in the Modify Value entry boxes on the right side of the dialogue box. The color box changes to black, and 7(white) is printed. Move the cursor into the `Pen:` entry box and type **1** and press <return>. Set the `Ltype:` to **0,** and `Width:` to **0.3** as shown. As the values are entered they change in the list box. Click color 7 in the list box to deselect it, and then click color 5. Color 5 is highlighted and the Modify Values color box

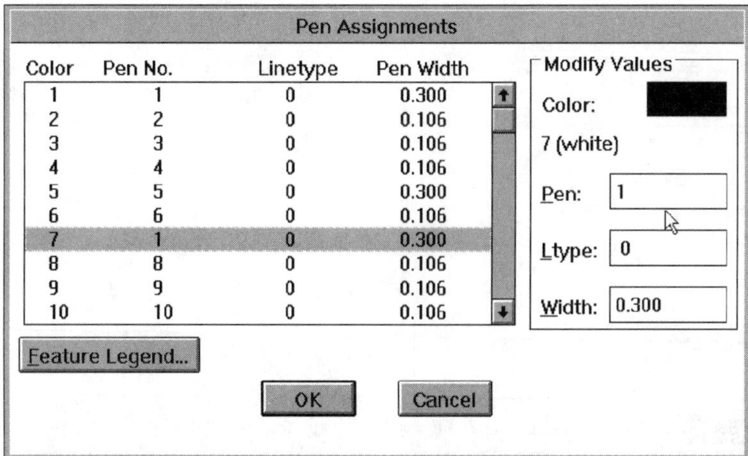

Figure 7.9 Setting pen assignments.

changes to blue. Modify the settings for color 5 as shown in Fig. 7.9. Then deselect color 5 and select color 1 (red), and modify its settings as shown. Since other colors are not used in the drawing their settings are not necessary. When the plot is being done the plotter will select pen 1 for red entities, pen 5 for blue entities, and pen 1 for white entities. The pens in these holders can be whatever color or width of pen you want to be selected for each color. Press the OK button when through.

Plot preview. A preview of the plot can be obtained prior to actual plotting. To obtain the partial preview illustrated in Fig. 7.10 press the `Partial` radio button in the lower-left corner of the Plot Configuration dialogue box (Fig. 7.1) and then click the `Preview...` box. The rotation icon (pointed to in Fig. 7.10) marks the lower-left corner of your drawing. Since the rotation of the drawing was set to 0 degrees, it appears in the lower-left corner of the display. If the plot is rotated 90 degrees (clockwise) the rotation icon would appear in the upper-left corner, etc. If the plot is not oriented correctly on the paper, exit and click the Rotation and Origin . . . box and rotate the plot 90 degrees. The warning in Fig. 7.10 indicates that the plotter is unable to plot to the full 280 mm by 215 mm entered for the sheet size. This warning is not a problem in this case. Press the `OK` button.

To obtain the full preview illustrated in Fig. 7.11 press the `Full` radio button and then click on the `Preview...` box. Try the pan and zoom options and then end the preview by clicking the End preview box. Change the plot origin to better center the plot on the sheet by clicking on the Rotation and Origin . . . box. Preview the plot and, if necessary, reset the plot origin again.

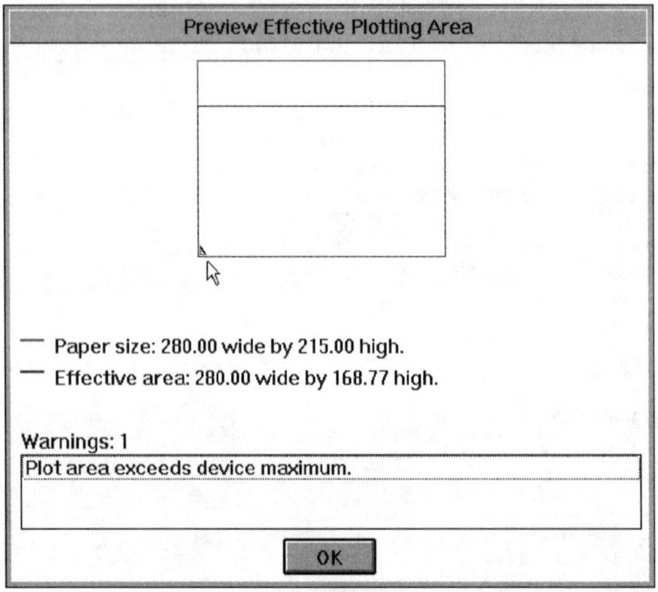

Preview Effective Plotting Area

— Paper size: 280.00 wide by 215.00 high.
— Effective area: 280.00 wide by 168.77 high.

Warnings: 1
Plot area exceeds device maximum.

OK

Figure 7.10 Partial plot preview.

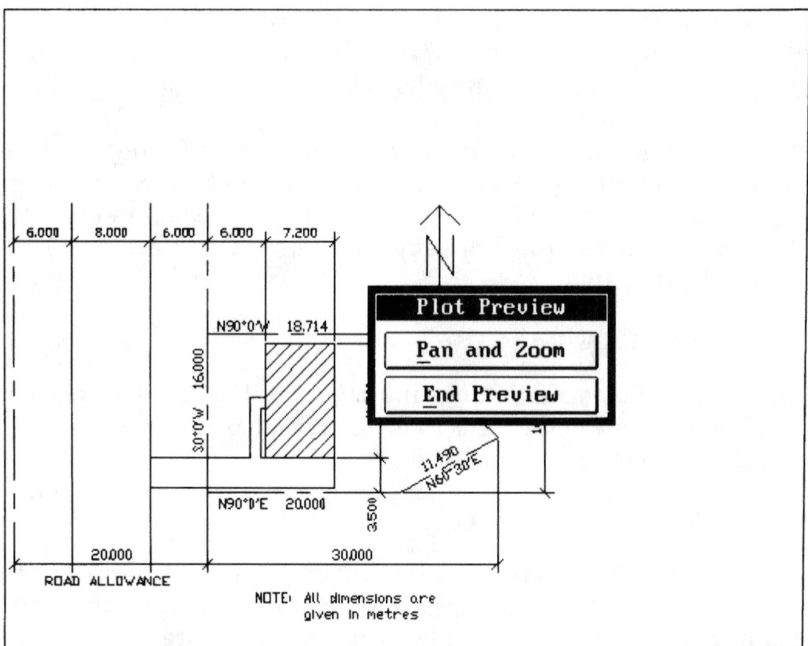

Figure 7.11 Full plot preview.

Readying the plotter. When the plot is centered properly and all the plot settings are completed, send the drawing to the plotter by pressing the OK button of the Plot Configuration dialogue box. AutoCAD LT will show the plot area and request that you position the paper and `Press RETURN to continue or S to Stop for hardware setup`. Press <return> and the drawing is plotted. The plot can be paused at any time by pressing S. Refer to App. A.5 for information on printer/plotter problems.

7.4 Hatch Proj-5

Boot AutoCAD LT and Open drawing Proj-5. Display the Layer Control dialogue box (Fig. 6.6) by clicking on the Layer button in the buttons bar (App. F, Fig. F.11). Following the procedures in Chap. 6, Sec. 6.2.2, create a new layer for the hatching named Hatch, colored red, and having a Continuous linetype. Also create a new layer for the hatch boundary named Boundary, colored yellow, and having a continuous linetype. Then click on layer Boundary in the layers list box (Fig. 6.6) so that its row is highlighted (if other rows are highlighted click on them do deselect them). Set Boundary as the current layer by pressing the `Current` button. The Layer named DEFPOINTS listed contains AutoCAD LT's definition points for associative dimensions (see Chap. 6, Sec. 6.9.4). Items on this layer may be visible on the monitor but are not plotted, so you should never make this layer the current layer. Press `OK`.

The Layer button on the left side of the buttons bar (App. E, Fig. E.11) shows Boundary as the current layer and the Current Color box is yellow. If not, display the Layer Control dialogue box and check the layer settings.

Hatch boundary. Use the Zoom and Window commands (App. E, Fig. E.4.1) to enlarge the front view of the object on the monitor. You are to draw lines over the existing front view lines outlining the objects to be hatched (see Fig. 7.12). To assist in locating the intersecting lines at the corners of the object, set a running Intersection object snap:

Assist <pick> **Object Snap...** <pick>

The Running Object Snap selection box illustrated in Fig. 5.2 is displayed. Select Intersection (it is on when an X is in its selection box). Press OK.

Choose the LINE command from the toolbox:

LINE <pick> From point:

The Intersection aperture box is visible at the crossing point of its vertical and horizontal axes. When asked to select a point, AutoCAD LT will search for the intersection of lines within this aperture box when <pick> is pressed. Proceed around the object <pick>ing the corners using the Intersection object snap. When you come to a fillet there is no intersection so you must temporarily turn the Intersection object snap off before you digitize that corner. To do this hold down the Shift key on the keyboard and press the 2nd button on the mouse to display the floating temporary object snap menu (Fig. 5.5). Choose `None` to turn off the object snap for that one selection. Select the point where the vertical and horizontal lines would intersect if there were no fillet, by carefully lining up the cursor axis along the vertical and horizontal edges of the object. If you are having trouble selecting the "intersection" use the Aerial View Window to assist you (read Chap. 5, Sec. 5.7). The new lines defining the boundary of the object are yellow (over the existing lines). The desired boundary is illustrated in Fig. 7.12.

When the three sections are drawn, fillet the corners by following the procedures outlined in Chap. 5, Sec. 5.10.

Prior to hatching, the objects layers are set by clicking on the Layer button in the buttons bar to display the Layer Control dialogue box. Click on layer 0 in the layer list box highlighting its row, and then press the Freeze button on the right side of the dialogue box. A dot (.) will appear in its listing in the layer list box in place of On, indicating the layer is frozen. Next click layer 0 in the list box to deselect it and then select layer Hatch to highlight its listing. Click the Current button to make Hatch the current layer. Press the OK button.

The Current Layer button in the buttons bar (App. E, Fig. E.11) should show layer Hatch as the current layer. Its color, red, should be in the Current Color box. Layer 0 is frozen so all entities on that layer are not visible on the screen. Only the yellow outline (Fig. 7.12) on layer Boundary should be visible. If

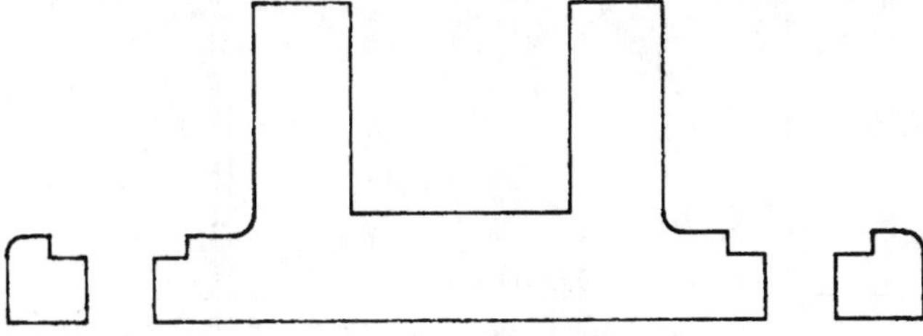

Figure 7.12 Hatch boundary.

Hatch is not the current layer, and/or entities on layer 0 are visible, repeat the layer settings outlined above.

Hatching. The hatch scale is calculated using Eq. (6.1). The object is to be plotted on an A-size sheet using a ¾ scale:

$$\text{Plot scale} \times \text{Hatch} = 1\text{ (inch)} \times \text{conversion}$$
$$\tfrac{3}{4} \times \text{Hatch} = 1 \times 1$$
$$\text{Hatch} = 1.33$$

Hatch the three areas using the ansi31 pattern and following the procedures outlined in Chap. 6, Sec. 6.6.2. When asked to `Select objects` to be hatched using a window selection box, pick a point in a clear space to the left and below the three entities to be hatched. Then when asked for the `Other corner` move the cursor to the right creating a window box enclosing all three entities. When selected correctly all entities should appear dotted. Pressing <return> completes the selection and hatches the objects. If the hatch is incorrect, enter Undo and retry the hatching. If hatching problems persist, zoom on each of the corners of the objects, checking that lines at the corners actually meet. If there is a gap at any corner, hatching will not work properly. Fix the gap and retry the hatching.

When the hatching is complete, use the Layer Control dialogue box to Thaw layer 0 and make it the current layer. Then Freeze layer Boundary to turn the hatch boundary off.

7.5 Plotting Proj-5

Choose `Print/Plot...` from the File menu. The Plot Configuration dialogue box is illustrated in Fig. 7.13. If you want to use a plotter other than your System printer (such as the HP7475 plotter) you will probably have to set it. To change the printer/plotter follow the procedure outlined in Chap. 7, Sec. 7.2.

The plot scale to fit Proj-5 on an A-size sheet (11 × 8.5) is to be ¾ in = 1 in. Set the plot configuration as illustrated in Fig. 7.13, using inches units and an A-size sheet. Press the `Size...` button and set the sheet size to a A-size (10.5 by 8.0). Only black and red colors are used in the drawing. Press the `Pen`

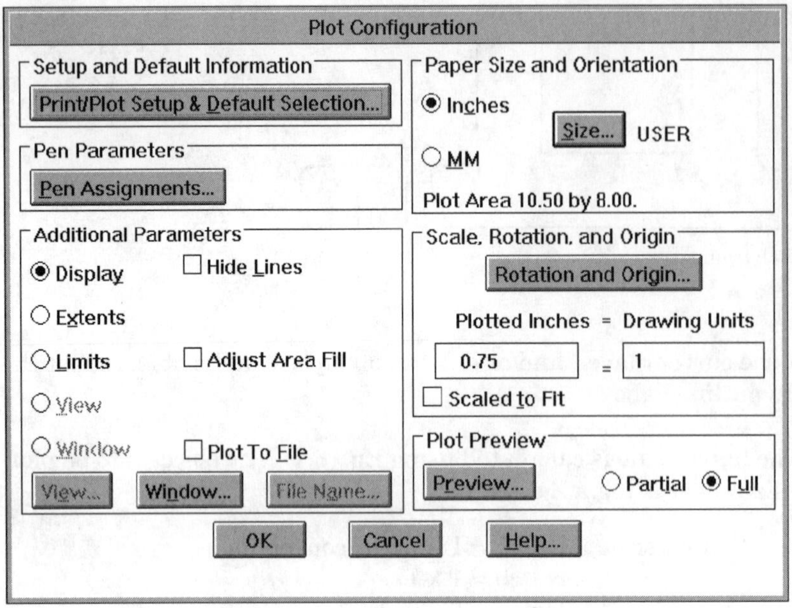

Figure 7.13 Plot configuration.

`Assignments...` button and set the pens (refer to Fig. 7.9) as: color 1 (red) is to select pen number 2, and color 7 (black) is to select pen 1. Press `OK` to return to the Plot Configuration Dialogue box. Place a black pen in your pen holder slot 1, and a red pen in your pen holder slot 2. `Preview...` the plot before pressing OK. If the paper orientation is incorrect, press `Rotation and Origin...` and rotate the paper 90 degrees. Press OK when the settings are correct, and the plot is executed.

Chapter

8

Isometric Drawing

Objective. Use Snap mode and Ellipse command to draw an isometric drawing; display a grid of reference points on the monitor; set drawing aids using the dialogue box; change isoplanes; locate intersection points, midpoints, and nearest points of lines with the temporary object snap mode; and edit with the Trim command.

Drawing. Boot up AutoCAD LT and begin a new drawing named Proj-8. Set the screen limits to –6,–0.5 and 6,8.5 so that the coordinates of the lower-front corner are 0,0. Use decimal units with two digits to the right of the decimal. The 4- by 4-unit "isobracket" illustrated in Fig. 8.1 is to be drawn.

8.1 Isometric Snap/Grid

The Snap command is used to align the cursor movements to an invisible grid. The snap resolution defines the spacing of the grid points. When Snap is on, the smallest movement of the cursor is from grid point to grid point. The user has two snap styles to select from—standard and isometric. In the standard mode the invisible grid is on a rectangular *x,y* plane. In the isometric style the grid is rotated to a 30-degree isometric plane.

When the snap style is set to isometric, the cursor movements vary depending on whether one is drawing on the top, front, or right side view of an object. When isometric snap is activated, the isoplane is "left" (the left side of the cube). As the cursor is moved about the drawing screen, the movements will be either in a vertical direction or along a line acting at 150 degrees to the horizontal, as illustrated in Fig. 8.2.

The isoplane can be changed by selecting a new plane from the screen menu or by pressing Ctrl-E or F5. The new plane will be specified in the command line at the bottom of the drawing screen.

When isoplane "right" is activated, the cursor movements are in a vertical direction or along a line at 30 degrees to the horizontal, as illustrated in

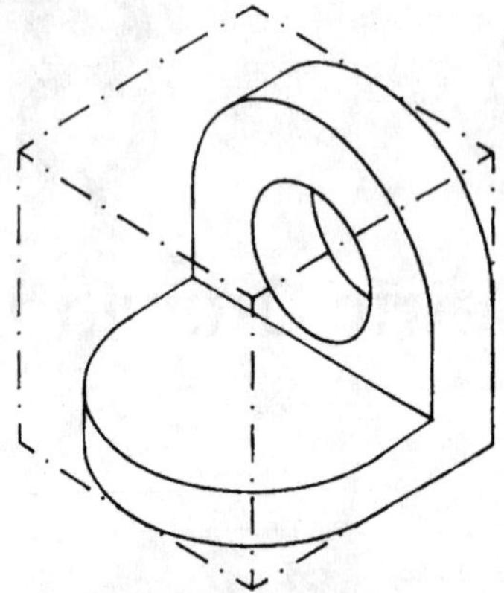

Figure 8.1 Isobracket.

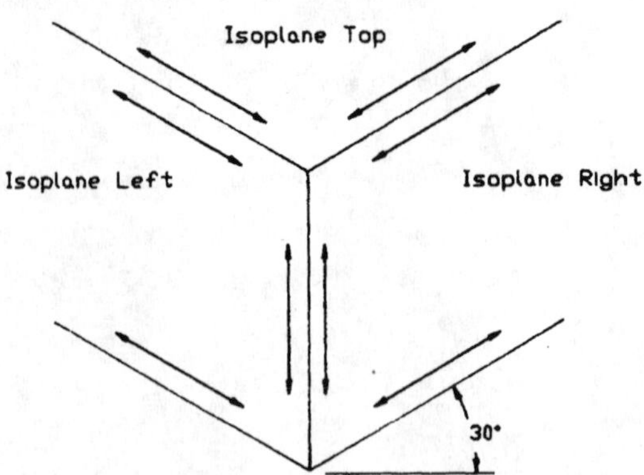

Figure 8.2 Isometric snap cursor movement.

Fig. 8.2. In the isoplane top mode the cursor movements are along a line at 30 degrees to the horizontal or a line at 150 degrees to the horizontal, as illustrated in Fig. 8.2.

The isometric mode is used only to assist the drafter in drawing isometric views and has no other effect on the drawing. The user can reset AutoCAD LT to the standard mode at any time and continue drawing with the cursor movements acting along the standard horizontal and vertical lines.

The snap style is set to isometric as follows:

`Settings` <pick> `Drawing Aids...` <pick>

The Drawing Aids dialogue box illustrated in Fig. 8.3 is displayed. Press the `On` button in the `Isometric Snap/Grid` box to set the isometric mode on. An X appears in the box when isometric is on. The Isoplane can be set to Left, Top,

Drawing Aids

Modes
☒ Ortho
☒ Solid Fill
☐ Quick Text
☒ Blips
☒ Highlight

Snap
☒ On
X Spacing 0.17
Y Spacing .1
Snap Angle 0
X Base 0.00
Y Base 0.00

Grid
☒ On
X Spacing 0.87
Y Spacing .5

Isometric Snap/Grid
☒ On
◉ Left ○ Top ○ Right

OK Cancel Help...

Figure 8.3 Drawing aids settings.

or Right by pressing the appropriate radio button. Isoplanes are also toggled from the drawing window by pressing the Ctrl and E buttons together or pressing the F5 key. Press the `Left` radio button. Do *not* press OK.

8.1.1 Snap

The snap setting defines the smallest numerical movement of the cursor on the monitor, and defines the accuracy of the drawing. For this drawing a snap setting of 0.1 is to be used. In the standard (nonisometric) mode X and Y snaps can have different values defining a rectangular invisible grid. In the isometric mode, however, the Y axis (90 degrees) snap value is entered and AutoCAD LT calculates the X value based on the isometric angle of 30 degrees. Consequently when a value of 0.1 is entered for the Y snap (see Fig. 8.3) AutoCAD LT enters a value of 0.17 for the X snap. Click on the `Snap` box to turn Snap on, and enter the Y snap value of **0.1.** AutoCAD LT enters the X snap value of 0.17. Snap may be toggled on/off from the drawing editor by pressing the Snap button in the buttons bar (see App. E, Fig. E.11). Do *not* press OK yet.

The Snap Angle entry box allows you to rotate the 0 base angle. The X Base and Y Base entry boxes allow you to define the base point for the rotated snap.

8.1.2 Grid

The Grid settings allow you to define a reference grid of dots, with a specified spacing, on the drawing editor screen. The grid is visible on the monitor only and is not plotted with the drawing. When isometric is on, the grid follows the isometric planes. If the grid spacing specified is too dense, AutoCAD displays a message indicating so, and the grid is not drawn. The grid is drawn only within the screen limits. Like snap, a different X and Y grid value can be entered in the standard (nonisometric) mode. In the isometric mode the Y value is entered and AutoCAD calculates the X (30 degree) value. Click on the `Grid` box to turn Grid on, and enter the Y grid value of **0.05.** AutoCAD enters the X grid value of 0.87. Grid may be toggled on/off from the drawing editor by pressing the Ctrl and G keys together or the F7 key (see App. E., Fig. E.10). Do *not* press OK yet.

8.1.3 Orthogonal (Ortho) mode

When the Ortho mode is turned on, lines are snapped to the drawing planes. This means that if the snap mode is set to standard and Ortho is on, all lines will snap to either a vertical or horizontal axis. In the isometric mode, the lines snap along a vertical, 30-degree, or 150-degree axis depending on the current isoplane. Click on the `Ortho` box to turn Ortho on. Ortho may be toggled on/off from the drawing editor by pressing the Ortho button in the buttons bar. Press `OK` to exit the Drawing Aids dialogue box.

The screen will now display a grid of dots 0.5 units c/c on an isometric grid. Move the cursor around the screen noting the X,Y coordinate values in the Coordinate Display Window of the buttons bar indicate the cursor moving along an invisible grid with steps of 0.1, the snap setting. If the values in the

Coordinate Display Window do not change as the cursor is moved, press Ctrl-D or F6 (see App. E, Fig. E.10). Also note that the Snap and Ortho buttons in the buttons bar are pressed (on).

8.4 Draw the Cube

The bracket object lines are to be drawn on layer 0 and the construction lines on layer Constr. Using the Layer Control dialogue box, complete the following layer settings:

Object	Name	Color	Line type
Bracket object lines	0	White	Continuous
Construction lines	Constr	Yellow	Continuous

Set Constr as the current layer. If the current isoplane is not the right-side plane, toggle Ctrl-E or F5 to set the isoplane. The Ortho button in the buttons bar should be pressed on. Draw the right side of the cube using the following commands—data can be entered via the keyboard as illustrated or by digitizing the points on the screen using the distance<angle coordinate position displayed at the top of the screen.

`LINE` <pick> `From point:` **0,0**<return> `To point:` **@4<30**<return> `To point:` **@4<90** <return> `To point:` **@4<210** <return> `To point:` **c** <return>

Notice that when drawing on isoplane right, the cursor moves along a 30-degree and 90-degree line on the right-side view.

Prior to drawing the lines for the left side of the cube, toggle Ctrl-E or F5 to set the snap plane to isoplane left. The current isoplane is specified in the command line at the bottom of the monitor.

The left side of the cube is drawn as follows:

`LINE` <pick> `From point: [Shift->2B] Intersection` <pick> `of` Place the intersection object snap on the lower-front corner of the current right-side view. <pick> `To point:` **@4<150** <return> `To point:` **@4<90** <return> `To point: [Shift->2B] Intersection` <pick> `of` Close the left-side view by placing the object snap target on the top-front corner of the right-side view. <pick> `select objects:` <return>

Use the Ctrl-E or F5 toggle switch to set the snap style on isoplane top, and draw the top view of the cube. Use the temporary object snap command to start the lines from a corner of the cube.

8.5 Ellipse Command

When drawing an ellipse, the center point of the ellipse must be entered. Toggle to isoplane left and draw the lines illustrated in Fig. 8.4 to locate the center of the back side of the cube—Ortho must be on:

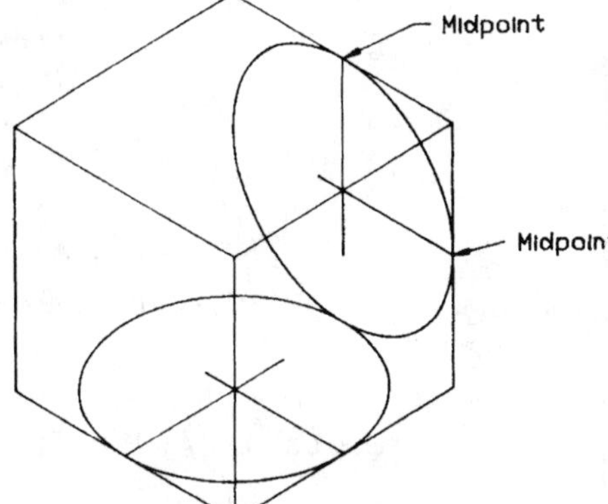

Figure 8.4 Ellipse.

> LINE <pick> From point: [Shift->2B] Midpoint <pick> of Place the target on one of the midpoints indicated in Fig. 8.4. To point: Draw the line as illustrated. To point: <pick> select objects: <return> <return> Line From point: Draw the next midpoint line.

Toggle to isoplane top and draw the construction lines to locate the center point of the bottom of the cube.

Prior to drawing the ellipses, set the current layer to 0. The first ellipse is drawn on the bottom of the cube as follows—the current plane should be isoplane top, and the layer should be 0:

> Draw <pick> Ellipse <pick> <Axis Endpoint 1>/Center/Isocircle: **I** (Isocircle) <return> Center of circle: [Shift->2B] Intersect <pick> of Place the Intersection aperture box on the midpoint intersecting lines in the bottom view of the cube. <pick> <Circle radius>/Diameter: **2** <return> (Or you could drag the cursor to the edge of the cube and pick the radius.)

Toggle Ctrl-E or F5 until the isoplane is the left side and draw the ellipse on the back face of the cube.

The thickness of the back of the cube is 1 unit. The Copy command is used to draw a second ellipse 1 unit in front of the back of the cube. Choose COPY from the Toolbox (Fig. 3.4):

> COPY <pick> Select objects: Digitize a point on the circumference of the ellipse which is on the back of the cube. <pick> <return> <Base point or displacement>/Multiple: Pick a point on the ellipse. Second point of displacement: **@1<210** <return>

The bottom of the bracket is to be 0.75 units thick. Toggle to isoplane-right and copy the bottom ellipse 0.75 units above the base of the cube. Freeze layer constr.

Use the Aerial View Window (see Chap. 5, Sec. 5.7) to enlarge a view as illustrated in Fig. 8.5. In isoplane left, draw line *a* in the upper-left corner tangent

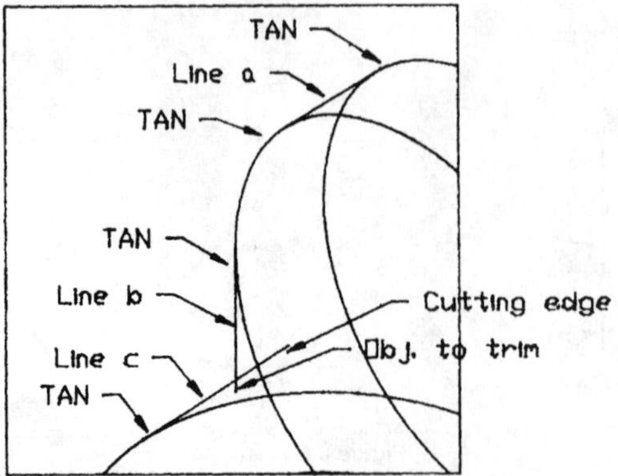

Figure 8.5 Tangent lines.

to the two ellipses using the Tangent object snap to pick each point. If AutoCAD LT indicates a tangency could not be found, press Ctrl-C and redo the line, placing the Tangent object snap target closer to where the point of tangency should be. This can happen because the ellipse is drawn as a polyline (see Chap. 15) using four arc segments, and the tangent target might not be on the proper segment.

Toggle to isoplane right and draw lines *b* and *c* (Fig. 8.5) as follows:

> `LINE` <pick> `From point: [Shift->2B] Tangent` <pick> `to` Digitize the Tangency point for line *b*. `To point:` **@2<270** <return> `To point:` <return> `LINE From point [Shift->2B] Tangent` <pick> `to` Digitize the tangency point for line *c*. <pick> `To point:` **@2<30** <return>

In the preceding the second point is entered from the keyboard because the orthogonal mode is disabled by AutoCAD LT when the Tangent object snap is used to select the first point.

8.6 Trimming Lines

The Trim command is used to trim lines to a specified cutting edge. Lines *b* and *c* in Fig. 8.5 are to meet at a point; hence each line acts as a cutting edge for the other. The lines are trimmed as follows:

> `Modify` <pick> `Trim` <pick>
> `Select cutting edges.....`
> `Select objects:` Select the cutting edge for line *b* as illustrated in Fig. 8.5. <pick> `Select objects:` <return>
> `Select object to trim:` Select the end of the line *b* to trim as illustrated in Fig. 8.5. <return>

Repeat the Trim command to trim line *c*. Line *b* is the cutting edge. When picking the object to be trimmed, remember to pick the side of line *c* that is to be trimmed off. If you make a mistake and trim the wrong side, use the U (undo 1) command to fix the mistake and try again.

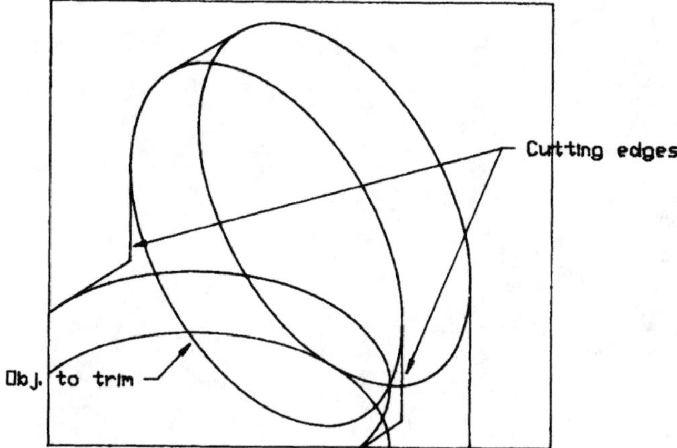

Figure 8.6 Trimming.

Zoom the back- and right-side lower-right corner of the cube and add in the necessary lines following the same procedures.

Sections of the ellipses must now be removed. Zoom on a view as illustrated in Fig. 8.6. To trim the ellipse on the front of the vertical portion of the bracket, two cutting edges are selected as illustrated in Fig. 8.6. The object to trim is then the bottom of the ellipse as shown. When trimming the ellipse at the back of the cube, the cutting edges are line *a* in Fig. 8.5 and the vertical line in the lower-right corner of the back of the cube.

Complete the cube as illustrated in Fig. 8.1. The hole in the back upright is two units in diameter. Turn the Constr layer off and plot the drawing using a scale of ½ = 1.

Chapter

9

Entity Controls

Objective. Use entity controls—Move, Copy, Array, Stretch, and Mirror; change layer an entity resides on; set grid and snap mode; set layers for separate drawing elements; plot specific layers; locate circle center with object snap command; select entities using WPolygon.

Drawing. Draw and dimension the octagonal and rectangular plates illustrated in Fig. 9.1. Begin a new drawing named Proj-9. Initially set the screen limits to 0,0 and 13,9 (don't forget to use Zoom and All). Use decimal units with two digits to the right of the decimal.

9.1 Define Layers

Four layers will be required with the following specifications:

Item	Name	Color	Line type
Construction lines	0	White	Continuous
Objects	Object	White	Continuous
Center lines	Center	Red	Center
Dimensions and text	Dimens	Red	Continuous

Normally only the continuous linetype is loaded when AutoCAD LT is booted. Prior to using the Center linetype, it must be loaded. Load the Center linetype as outlined in Chap. 6, Sec. 6.2.1.

Using the Layer Control dialogue box, create the new layers illustrated at the beginning of this section and set their colors (see Chap. 6).

9.1.1 Set snap and grid

Display the Drawing Aids dialogue box illustrated in Fig. 9.2 and set snap and grid as shown. Enter an X Snap value of 0.1. AutoCAD LT uses the same value for the Y Snap. If the Y Snap was to be a different value it could be entered.

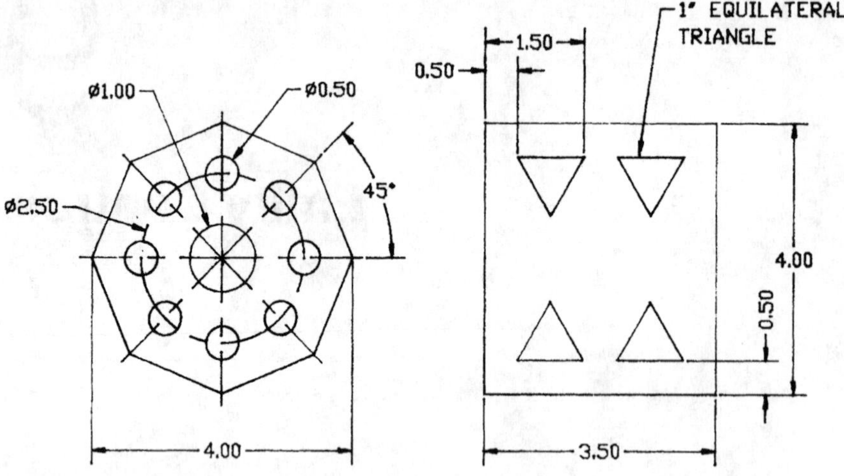

Figure 9.1 Project 9.

Enter the X Grid value of 0.5. Press the Snap and Grid buttons to turn them on. Press OK.

9.2 Set Line Type Scale Factor

Because a center line type is being used, the line type scale (Ltscale) will have to be set to suit the final plot size of this drawing. It will be assumed that the drawing units are inches and that the final drawing will be plotted on an A-size sheet (8½ by 11 in) using a ¾ scale. Using Eq. (6.2), the scale factor is calculated as:

$$\text{Plot scale} \times \text{Ltscale} = 1 \text{ in} \times \text{conversion} \times \tfrac{3}{4}$$
$$\tfrac{3}{4} \times \text{Ltscale} = 1 \text{ in} \times \tfrac{3}{4}$$
$$\text{Ltscale} = 1$$

Drawing Aids

Modes
☐ Ortho
☒ Solid Fill
☐ Quick Text
☒ Blips
☒ Highlight

Snap
☒ On
X Spacing 0.1
Y Spacing 0.10
Snap Angle 0
X Base 0.00
Y Base 0.00

Grid
☒ On
X Spacing 0.5
Y Spacing 0.50

Isometric Snap/Grid
☐ On
◉ Left ○ Top ○ Right

OK Cancel Help...

Figure 9.2 Setting snap and grid.

Since the linetype scale (Ltscale) is 1, which is the default value, it does not have to be set. Review the procedure in Chap. 6, Sec. 6.7.1 to refresh your memory on the procedure.

9.3 Octagon Plate

To construct the octagon, a 4-unit-diameter circle with its center at coordinates 3.5,4.5 is to be drawn. Lines are then drawn through the circle at 45-degree intervals. The points where the lines intersect the circle will be the corners of the octagon. Later the layer that these construction lines reside on will be changed to place them on the center layer, which has a center line type. These lines will then change line type and become center lines.

The circle on this layer is for construction purposes and will not be displayed with the final drawing.

The current layer, indicated in the left corner of the Buttons bar, should be layer *0*.

Press Ctrl-D or F6 to display the cursor coordinates:

Draw <pick> Circle <pick> Center, Radius: <pick> Center point: **3.5,4.5** <return> Radius **2** <return>

9.3.1 Draw an array of lines

The construction lines crossing the circle will be drawn using the Array command.

The Array command is used to draw a cluster of similar items. The array can be rectangular or circular. In a rectangular array, the items are repeated in rows and columns in a block or rectangular pattern, as illustrated in Fig. 9.3. That array has four columns and three rows. The original item is in the lower-left corner of the array. The unit cell distance between rows is illustrated as *a* and the unit cell distance between columns is distance *b*. If the unit cell distances are entered as positive numbers, the array "grows" upward and to the right (positive cartesian coordinates). To replicate the objects to the left, enter a negative-unit cell distance for the columns. To replicate the objects downward, enter a negative-unit cell distance for the rows.

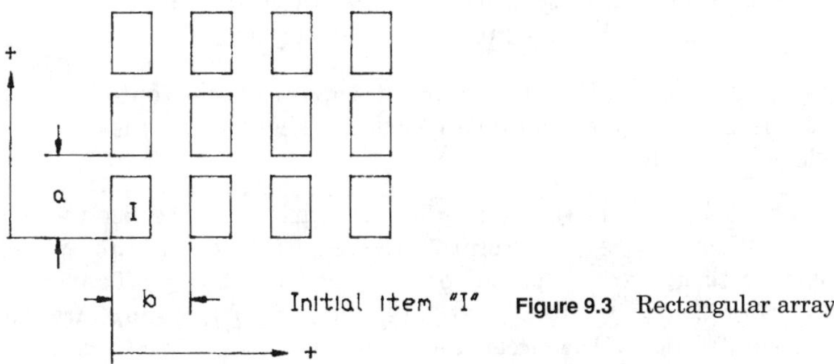

Figure 9.3 Rectangular array.

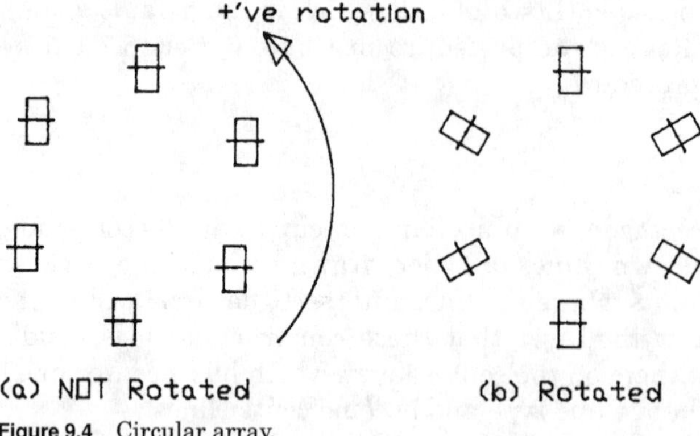

Figure 9.4 Circular array.

In a circular array the items are repeated along the circumference of a circle, as illustrated in Fig. 9.4. AutoCAD LT will ask if the items are to be rotated as they are copied. The items in Fig. 9.4*a* were not rotated whereas the items in Fig. 9.4*b* were rotated as they were copied. If the angle between items is entered as positive, AutoCAD LT copies the objects by rotating about the circle center in a counterclockwise direction.

If the entity to be repeated in a circular array is made up of a number of entities, such as the rectangle in Fig. 9.4*b*, and the entities are not to be rotated as they are copied, the entity will have to be saved as a block (see Chap. 10) before the array is constructed. That is necessary because AutoCAD LT will locate each entity in the item about the center point of the array and, consequently, the relative position of the entities with respect to each other might change. If the entities are part of a block, the item becomes a single entity and the item does not become disjointed. This is not a problem when the items are rotated as they are copied.

To use the Array command a single item is drawn first. The Array command is then invoked and a rectangular or circular pattern is selected. The items will then be repeated in the pattern selected and spaced as specified.

To begin the array a horizontal line will be first drawn across the center of the circle. The Array command is next invoked to draw an array of lines around the circle at 45-degree intervals. The lines will have to be rotated as they are copied so that each line is at a 45-degree interval from the previous line and passes through the center of the circle, as illustrated in Fig. 9.6.

`Line` <pick> `From point:` Using the cursor, draw a horizontal line across the center of the circle. Ensure that the line extends slightly past the circumference of the circle on each side.

`Construct` <pick> `Array:` <pick> `Select objects:` Digitize the horizontal line <pick> `Select objects:` <return> `Rectangular or Polar array (R/P):` **P** (Polar) <return> `Center point of array: [Shift->2B] Center` (*To invoke the center object snap*) <pick> `Center of:` Place the object snap target anywhere on the circumference of the circle. <pick> `Number of items:` **4** <return> `Angle to` fill (+=CCW, -CW) <360>: **0** (Zero is a no response, forcing a request for angle between items.) <return> Angle between items (+=CCW, -CW): **45** <return> Rotate objects as they are copied <N>: **y** <return>

9.3.2 Draw octagon

Click on the Current Layer Name box (see Fig. 6.13) in the buttons bar to display the Layer Name drop-down box. Click on Object to make it the current layer.

The Polygon command is to be used to draw the octagon (an eight-sided polygon). The polygon is to be inscribed in a 4-unit diameter circle; however, with AutoCAD LT there is no option for drawing a polygon inscribed in a circle. The polygon will have to be circumscribed around a 4-unit circle and then scaled to fit inside the circle. In the following select the Center and Intersection object snaps from the Toolbox:

Draw <pick> Polygon <pick> Number of sides <4>: **8** <return> Edge/Center of polygon: Center (Toolbox) <pick> of Place the target on the circumference of the circle. <pick> Radius of circle: **2** <return>

Scale command. The polygon must now be scaled to fit with the 4-unit circle. Select the Scale command and the Center and Intersection object snaps from the Toolbox (Scale is also in the Modify menu bar):

Scale <pick> Select objects: Digitize a point on the polygon. <pick> Select objects: <return> Base point: Center <pick> of Place the Center object snap aperture box on the circumference of the circle. <pick> <Scale factor>/Reference: **r** (Reference) <return> Reference length <1>: Center <pick> of Place the Center object snap aperture box on the circumference of the circle. <pick> Second point: Intersect <pick> of Place the Intersection object snap aperture box on a corner of the polygon—see Fig. 9.5. <pick> New length: **2** <return>

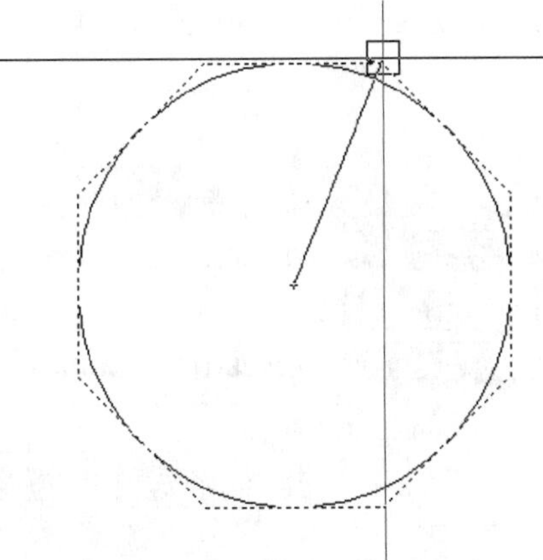

Figure 9.5 Stretching the polygon.

The Reference option of the Stretch command was used. The Reference length used was from the center of the octagon to its corner, and the new length was the radius of the circle. The octagon was then stretched (shortened) by that ratio.

The octagon is now to be rotated by 22.5 degrees:

> `Modify` <pick> `Rotate` <pick> `Select objects:` Digitize a point on the octagon <pick> `Select objects:` <return> `Base point: Center` <pick> `of` Pick the circumference of the circle <pick> `Rotation angle/reference:` **22.5** <return>

Draw the 1.0-unit-diameter circle in the center of the octagon. When the center of the circle is asked for, use the Center object snap and place the target on the circumference of the previous circle.

9.3.3 Change command

The Change command will be used to change the layer the lines crossing the center of the circle reside on to the Center layer. When the lines are changed to the Center layer, which has a Center linetype, the lines change to center lines:

> `Modify` <pick> `Change Properties` <pick> `Select objects:` digitize lines 1, 2, 3, and 4 in Fig. 9.6. <pick> `Select objects:` <return>

The Change Properties dialogue box (Fig. 9.7) is displayed. Click on the `Layer...` box to display a Change Layer dialogue box. Click on Layer `Center` and then click `OK`. The Change Properties dialogue box is redisplayed with the layer Center, colored red, listed. Click `OK` and the center lines are changed to layer Center.

Click on the Current Layer Name box in the buttons bar to display the Layer Name drop-down box, and change the current layer to `Center`. Then draw a circle with a diameter of 2.5 units (radius of 1.25 units). This circle forms the center line for the 5-unit diameter (2.5 unit radius) circles, which will be drawn later. Remember to use the Center object snap to pick the center of the main circle when asked for the location of the center of the 2.5-unit-diameter center line circle. Try using the Center object snap command in the Toolbox.

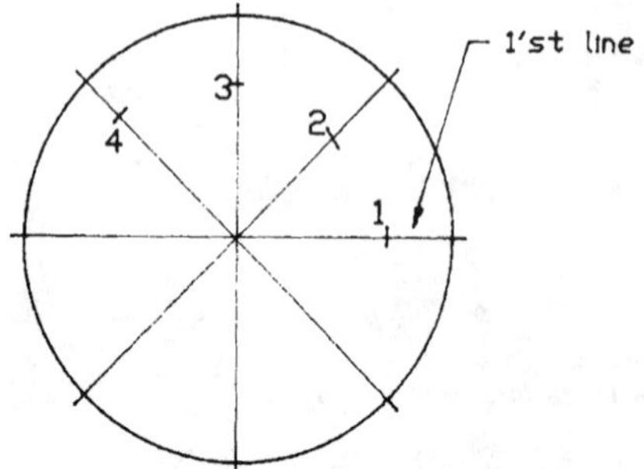

Figure 9.6 Circular array lines.

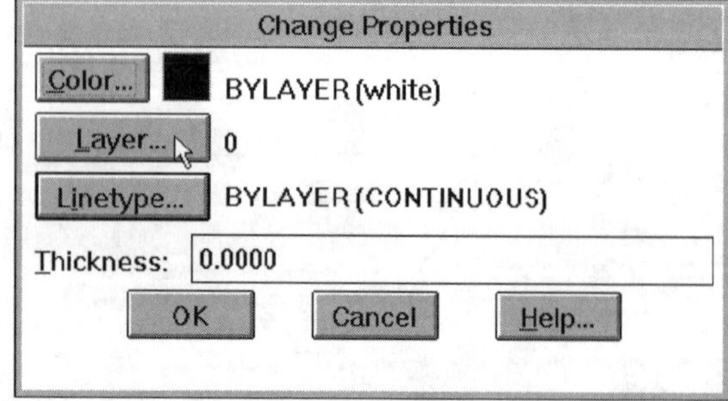

Figure 9.7 Change Properties dialogue box.

9.3.4 Draw array of 0.5-diameter circles

Set the current layer to `Object`. The circle which is to be used as the entity in the array is first drawn at the top of the octagon. Its center is at the intersection of the 2.5-unit-diameter center circle just drawn and the vertical center line. That point is located by using the Intersection object snap. Draw the circle with a diameter of 0.5 units (0.25 radius).

> `Draw` <pick> `Circle` <pick> `Center,Radius` <pick> `Center point: Intersection` (Toolbox) <pick> `of` Place the Intersection aperture target over the intersection point shown in Fig. 9.8. <pick> `Radius:` **0.5** <return>

Draw the circular array of 0.5-diameter circles as follows:

> `Construct` <pick> `Array` <pick> `Select objects: Assist` <pick> `Select` <pick> `Last` <pick> `Select objects:` <return> `Rectangular or polar array (R/P):` **P** (Polar) <return> `Center point: [Shift->2B] Center` <pick> `of` Place the object snap target on the circumference of the large circle. <pick> `Number of items:` <return> `Angle to fill (+=CCW, -=CW) <360>:` Select default **360** <return> `Angle between items (+=CCW, -=CW):` **45** <return> `Rotate objects as they are copied <Y>:` <return>

Note the two different methods used to draw an array of items. For the lines, the number of items was entered, but an "Angle to fill" of 0 was used. This forced AutoCAD LT to ask for the angles between items. For the circles, because the number of items was not entered, the angle to fill (360 degrees) had to be entered.

The construction lines were drawn on layer 0. That layer is turned off by pressing the Layer button in the buttons bar to display the Layer Control dialogue box. Highlight layer 0 in the layer list and then press the Freeze button. Press OK to return to the drawing screen.

9.3.5 Dimensions and text

Determine the text height and set the dimension scale. The drawing units are inches. It is to be plotted at a ¾ scale. Assume ⅛-in-high text is desired on the plotted drawing:

$$\tfrac{3}{4} \times h = \tfrac{1}{8} \quad \textit{gives } h = 0.20$$

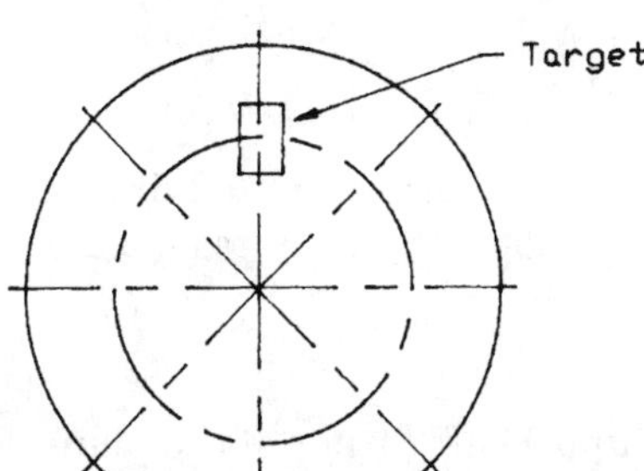

Figure 9.8 Intersection object-snap target location.

The dimension scale, Dimscale, is calculated using Eq. (4.2):

$$Dimscale \times 0.18 = text\ height$$
$$Dimscale \times 0.18 = 0.20\ gives\ Dimscale = 1.11$$

Set Dimscale as follows:

Settings <pick> **Dimension Style...** <pick>

The Dimension Styles and Settings box (Fig. 3.5) is displayed. Choose the `Scale and Colors...` box. Enter the Dimscale value of **1.11** in the `Feature Scaling` box (Fig. 4.3) and then press `OK`. Also press OK in the Dimension Style and Settings box.

Before continuing, set Dimens as the current layer.

Angular dimensioning. The Angular dimension subcommand is used to add the 45-degree dimension on the right side of the octagon plate as follows:

`Draw` <pick> `Angular Dimensions` <pick> `Select arc, circle, line or RETURN: Endpoint` (Toolbox) <pick> `of` Place the Endpoint object snap aperture on the right side end of line 1 in Fig. 9.6. <pick> `Second angle endpoint: Endpoint` <pick> `of` Place the Endpoint object snap aperture on the right side end of line 2 in Fig. 9.6. <pick> `Dimension arc line location (Text/Angle):` Digitize the point where you want the dimension line to be located. <pick> `Dimension text <45>:` <return> `Enter text location (or RETURN):` The angular dimension is visible and moves with the cursor. Select the desired location. <pick>

Compare the procedure used here to draw an angular dimension with that used in Chap. 4, Sec. 4.8. In Chap. 4, Sec. 4.8 when asked to Select arc, circle, line or RETURN: the <return> key was pressed. This prompted AutoCAD LT to request the angle vertex. In the preceding set of commands a point on a line was selected instead. AutoCAD LT then asked for a second line and their point of intersection was used as the vertex for the angular dimension.

Diameter dimensioning. Dimension the 2.5-diameter circle as follows:

`Draw` <pick> `Radial Dimensions` <pick> `Diameter` <pick> `Select arc or circle:` Digitize point a illustrated in Fig. 9.9. <pick> `Dimension text <2.5>:` <return> `Enter leader length for text:` Select the leader visually on the screen <pick>

9.4 Rectangular Plate

Set the current layer as `Object`. Using the `Line` command draw the rectangular plate starting with the lower-left corner at coordinates 7.5,2.5.

9.4.1 Draw and copy triangles

Draw one equilateral triangle in the upper-left corner of the plate. The Id command will be used to locate the cursor on the upper-left corner, and relative coordinates are then used to locate the top-left corner of the triangle:

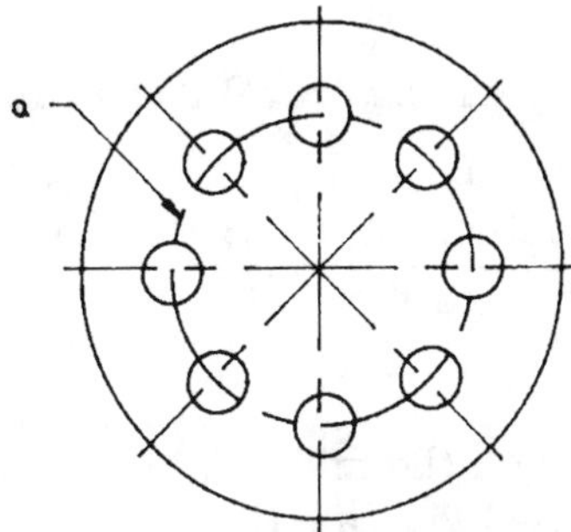

Figure 9.9 Diameter dimension location.

> `Assist` <pick> `ID Point` <pick> `Point: Intersection` (Toolbox) <pick> `of` Place the Intersection aperture over the top-left corner of the rectangle. <pick> `X=7.50 Y=6.50 Z=0.00`
>
> `Line` <pick> `From point:` **@0.5,–0.5** <return> `To point:` **@1<0** <return> `To point:` **@1<240** <return> `To point:` **c** <return>

The triangle is now copied to the right a distance of 1.5 units. When asked to `Select objects` the WPolygon (Window Polygon) is used to draw a polygon window around the triangle. All entities enclosed by the window are selected:

> `COPY` (Toolbox) <pick> `Select objects: Assist` <pick> `Select` (see App. E, Fig. E.5) <pick> `WPolygon` <pick> `First polygon point:` Digitize point a in Fig. 9.10. <pick> `Undo/<Endpoint of line>:` Digitize point b. <pick> `Undo/<Endpoint of line>:` Digitize point c. <pick> `Undo/<Endpoint of line>:` <return> `Select objects:` <return> `Base point or displacement:` Digitize a point anywhere on the monitor to act as a reference point. <pick> `Second point of displacement:` **@1.5<0** <return>

Prior to continuing, Choose the `Save...` command in the File menu to save your drawing. You may also wish to use Save As . . . to save a backup copy onto another diskette in another drive.

A copy of the first triangle will now appear on the monitor, 1.5 units to the right of the initial triangle. Notice that the first displacement point was selected anywhere on the drawing. This is possible because the second point selected is relative to the first, defining the amount of movement and the direction rather than the location of the copied object.

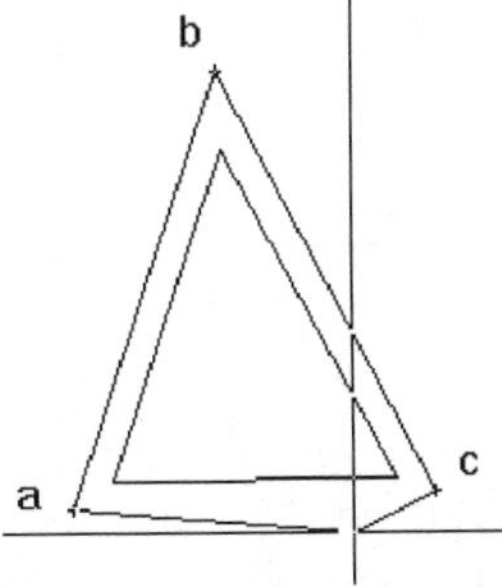

Figure 9.10 Selecting entities using WPolygon.

9.4.2 Draw mirror image of triangles

The two bottom triangles will be drawn by having AutoCAD LT draw a mirror image of the two top triangles as follows:

> `Construct` <return> `Mirror` <return> `Select objects:` Digitize the lower-left corner of the window as illustrated in Fig. 9.11. <pick> `Other corner:` Digitize the upper-right corner of the window <pick> `Select objects:` <return> `First point of mirror line:`

The mirror line is a horizontal line through the midpoint of the rectangular plate. The Midpoint object snap will be used to locate the midpoint of the side of the rectangle as illustrated in Fig. 9.11.

> `Midpoint` (Toolbox) <pick> `of` Locate target on the left side line. <pick> `Second point: Midpoint` (Toolbox) <pick> `of` Locate target on the right side line. <pick> `Delete old objects? <N>: n` <return>

Because the top two triangles are not to be deleted, n (no) was entered in response to the last question. Notice how a selection window was invoked by picking the lower-left corner of the window in space.

9.4.3 Dimension rectangular plate

Set the Dimens layer as the current layer and dimension the rectangular plate, as illustrated in Fig. 9.1.

9.5 Plotting

Choose `Print/Plot...` from the File menu. The Plot Configuration dialogue box is illustrated in Fig. 7.13. If you want to use a plotter other than your System printer (such as the HP7475 plotter) you will probably have to set it. To change the printer/plotter follow the procedure outlined in Chap. 7, Sec. 7.2.3.

The plot scale to fit Proj-9 on an A-size sheet (11 × 8.5) is to be ¾″ = 1″. Set the plot configuration as illustrated in Fig. 7.13, using inches units and an A-

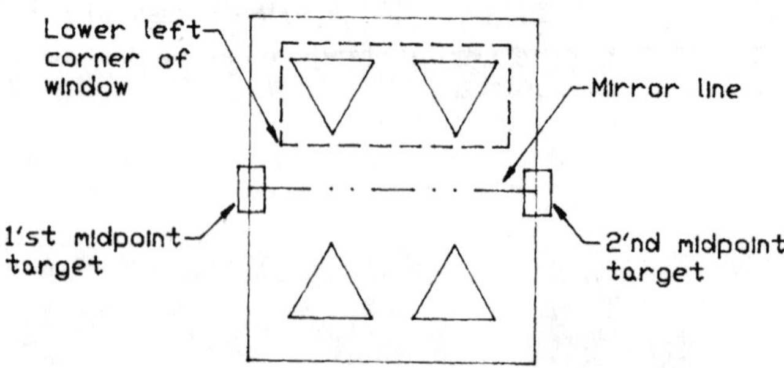

Figure 9.11 Mirror selection points.

size sheet. Press the Size... button and set the sheet size to an A-size (or a User size of 11 by 8.5). Only black and red colors are used in the drawing. Press the Pen Assignments... button and set the pens as: color 1 (red) is to select pen number 2, and color 7 (black) is to select pen 1. Press OK to return to the Plot Configuration Dialogue box. Place a black pen in your pen holder slot 1, and a red pen in your pen holder slot 2. Preview... the plot before pressing OK. If the paper orientation is incorrect, press Rotation and Origin... and rotate the paper 90 degrees. Press OK when the settings are correct, and the plot is executed.

Choose Exit... in the File menu to exit AutoCAD LT.

Chapter

10

Blocks

Objective. Create block files to be inserted as components in another drawing, use coordinate and dynamic insertion, Block command, Insert command, Block Out to file, block revisions, Solid command. Complete an electronic circuit drawing.

Drawing. Create a block drawing file for each of the electrical components. Complete the electronic circuit drawing illustrated in Fig. 10.1 by inserting the electronic component block files into the circuit drawing.

10.1 Blocks

Blocks are entities grouped together to form a complex object which is then defined as one entity. If the block is repeated in a number of locations on the drawing, there is a considerable saving in disk space because the block entities are not redefined with each use. The use of blocks also speeds up the drawing process by allowing the insertion of complex block units into the drawing.

Making revisions to components on drawings is often very tedious. If a component was drawn as a block, all copies of the component are altered by revising the original block, with a considerable saving of time.

When a block is created, AutoCAD LT asks the user for an insertion point for the block. The operator then specifies a point on the block, which is to be used as the point of insertion for that block on any subsequent drawings. Often the lower-left corner of the block or coordinate 0,0 is selected as the insertion point.

When blocks are inserted into drawings, AutoCAD LT asks for x and y scale factors. This allows the drafter to input multipliers of the x and y axes, modifying the x and y dimensions of the block being inserted. The program also asks for the rotation angle for the block, allowing the drafter to draw the block at any angle. The drag mode can be used for any of these items, allowing the drafter to visually insert the component into the drawing.

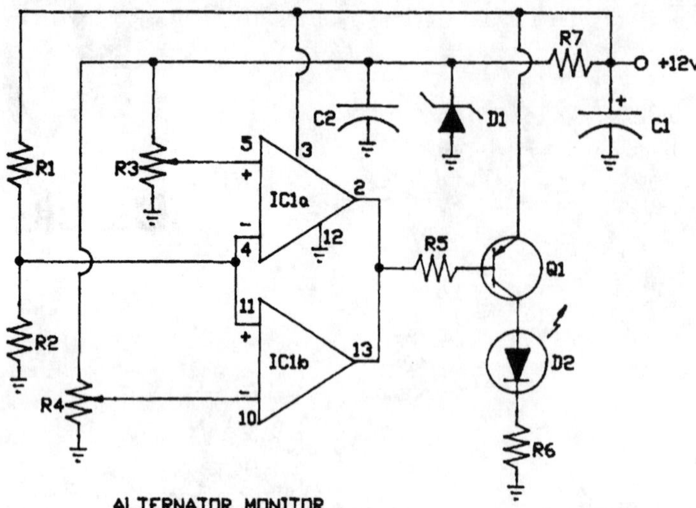

Figure 10.1 Project 10 Electronic drawing.

If components are to be stored in a drawing file for insertion into different drawings or if the component might have different *x-y* dimensions on the drawing, a useful convention is to draw the component in a 1- by 1-unit block. When the block is inserted into the drawing, the *x* and *y* scale factors then become the actual dimensions in drawing units.

After a block is initially defined on a drawing and saved as a block, it is erased by AutoCAD LT. If the initial location of the block is desired, it can be recalled into that location by immediately using the oops command.

When a block is created, it is defined as a block on the current drawing only. To create a drawing file of the block for utilization on other drawings, the WBlock (Block Out) command must be used. The electronic components used on this project will be stored as drawing files for use on other drawings. If the blocks are to be stored on the data disk in drive A, you must remember to use A: in front of the file name.

Block names can be up to 31 characters long and can contain letters, digits, and the characters - and _>. File names for blocks are subject to the same restrictions as are drawing file names (eight characters maximum). If a block is to be stored as a file, you will usually want to use the same block and file name; hence, the more stringent restrictions of the file name will be used when naming the block.

Blocks can be composed of other blocks. This is referred to as *nesting* of blocks.

10.2 Blocks and Layers

Information about the layer on which the entities of a block were initially drawn is part of the block information that is stored with the block on the disk.

When the block is inserted into a drawing, the entities of the block remain on their original layer regardless of what layer the block is inserted into on the drawing.

One exception to the layer rule for blocks is that entities that were drawn on layer 0 in a block will become part of the layer that is set when the block is inserted into the drawing.

10.3 Draw Resistor Block

Each of the electronic components shown in Fig. 10.2 is to be drawn as a block and stored as a file for later insertion into a drawing. Draw each component as a 1- by 1-unit block to allow modification of the size as desired when the block is inserted into the drawing. The insertion point should be selected on the left side of the component at a point where it would be connected to the electronic circuit. The following procedure is used to draw the resistor.

Start a new drawing named Proj-10. Use the default screen limits of 0,0 and 12,9.

Set the units to decimal with two digits to the right of the decimal.

The Grid command is very useful when working with blocks. The blocks should be drawn in a grid that will be used in the final drawing. Points on the block entities will then coincide with the grid on the final drawing, facilitating the connection of entities on the main drawing. This procedure is illustrated in this chapter.

Set Snap to 0.1 and set the Grid to 0.2 and turn both snap and grid on.

The blocks will be drawn in a 1-square-unit box starting at coordinate 1,1. Zoom on a box around 1,1 and 2,2:

View <pick> Zoom <pick> Window <pick> First corner: **0.2,0.2** <return> Next corner: **2.8,2.8** <return>

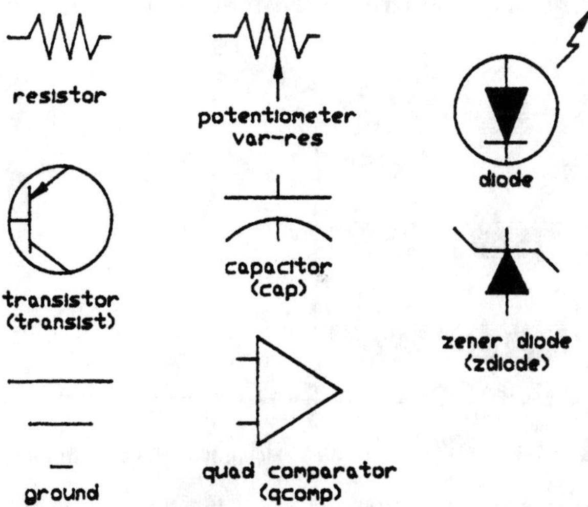

Figure 10.2 Electronic components.

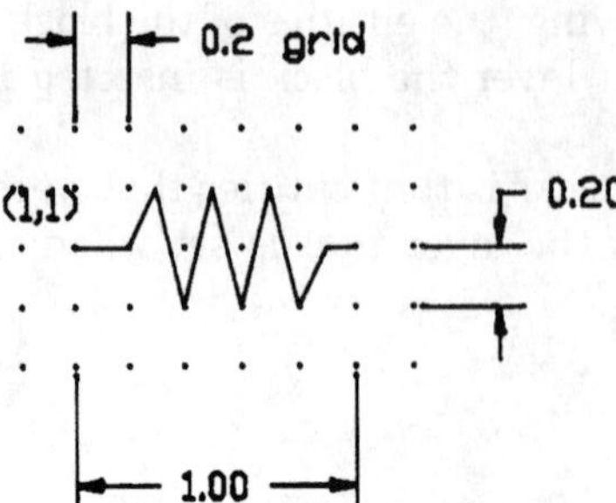

Figure 10.3 Resistor.

Draw the resistor 1 unit long using the cursor snap and the grid, as illustrated in Fig. 10.3.

10.3.1 Save resistor as a block

Designate the resistor as a block (remember that the left end of the resistor lead is coordinate 1,1):

`Construct` <pick> `Make Block...` <pick>

The Block Definition dialogue box illustrated in Fig. 10.4 is displayed. Move the cursor into the `Block name:` edit box and enter the name `Resistor`. The left end of the resistor was started at coordinates 1,1. Enter the insertion point of the Resistor in the Base Point dialogue boxes as `X:` **1.0** and `Y:` **1.0** as illustrated. Alternatively you could press the Select Point< button and then use the Endpoint object snap to select the left end of the resistor. Click the `Retain Entities` check box to turn it off—there should not be an X in it. When retain entities is off, entities are not removed from the screen when they are blocked. If it is on, entities remain on the screen after they are blocked. Next, press the

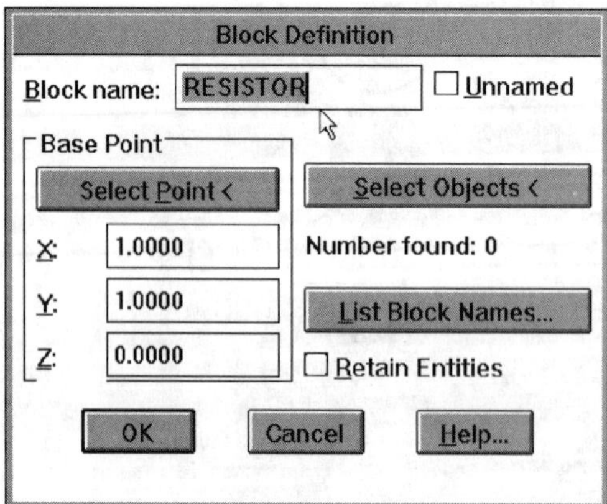

Figure 10.4 Block definition.

`Select Objects<` button. The dialogue box is removed from the screen and the resistor is visible. The command line prompts are:

> `Select objects:` Place a selection window around the resistor by clicking the lower-left corner of the selection window, and then the upper-right corner. If the resistor is selected properly it will become dotted. If it is not dotted reselect it. <Pick> `Select objects:` <return>

The Block Definition dialogue box is returned to the screen. Press the `OK` button to execute the Block command.

The resistor will be erased from the screen. If you want to have the resistor returned to the screen, the Oops command can be used. That is not desired now, however.

The block can be recalled to this drawing at any time with the Insert command. If you want to use this block in other drawings, it must be saved in a drawing file using the Block Out command. If the block is to be used only in the current drawing, it should not be saved in a drawing file because that would be a waste of disk space. To write the block to a drawing file, enter the following commands:

> `File` <pick> `Import/Export` (Fig. 10.5 and App. E, Fig. E.1) <pick> `Block Out...` <pick>

The Create Drawing File dialogue box illustrated in Fig. 10.6 (and Fig. 1.17) is displayed. Following the procedures shown in Fig. 1.17 and Fig. 1.18, using the slider bar, change the Directory to `c:/drawings` (see Fig. 10.6). Then move the cursor to the `File Name:` edit box and enter the file name as **resistor.dwg.** Press OK to open the file. Blocks written to file are regular AutoCAD LT drawings, as indicated by the file extension, .dwg.

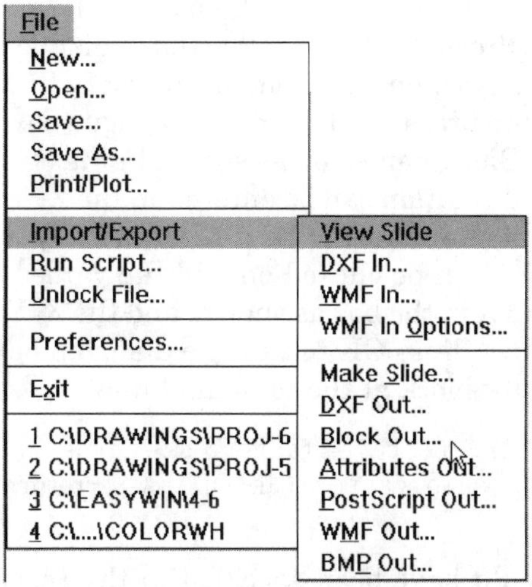

File
New...
Open...
Save...
Save As...
Print/Plot...
Import/Export
Run Script...
Unlock File...
Preferences...
Exit
1 C:\DRAWINGS\PROJ-6
2 C:\DRAWINGS\PROJ-5
3 C:\EASYWIN\4-6
4 C:\...\COLORWH

View Slide
DXF In...
WMF In...
WMF In Options...
Make Slide...
DXF Out...
Block Out...
Attributes Out...
PostScript Out...
WMF Out...
BMP Out...

Figure 10.5 Import/Export menu.

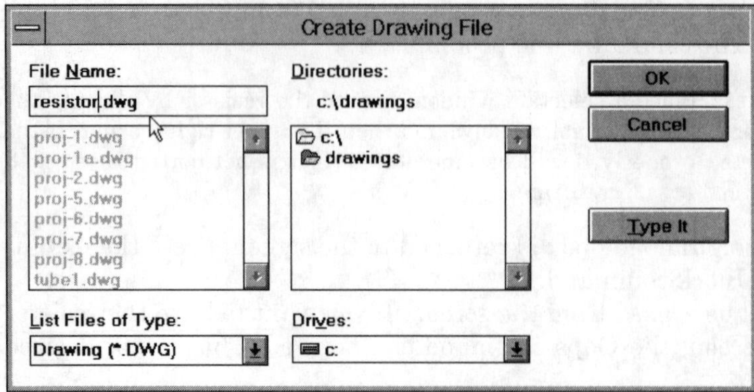

Figure 10.6 Write block to file.

AutoCAD LT now requests at the command line the name of the block to save in the file named Resistor.Dwg. Enter the name of the block—Resistor. In this case since the same name was used for the file as was used for the block, an equal (=) can be entered:

`Block:` **=** <return>

If you want to clean up the drawing, use the Redraw command.

10.4 Draw Potentiometer Block

Use the Insert command to recall the resistor block:

`Draw` <pick> `Insert Block...` <Pick>

The Insert dialogue box (Fig. 10.7) is displayed. The block to be inserted is in the current drawing data base. Press the `Block...` button to display the Blocks list box illustrated in Fig. 10.8. Click on `Resistor` in the list, which moves its name into the Selection box. Then press `OK`. The Insert dialogue box now shows the block name Resistor in the Block name box as shown in Fig. 10.7.

The insertion point, scale, and rotation can be entered in the X, Y, and Z edit boxes in the Options section of the dialogue box. Alternatively, the Specify Parameters on Screen check box can be clicked on and the values entered on screen. When it is on, there is an X in the box as shown, and the X, Y, and Z edit boxes are grayed. Turn it on now. Press OK to exit the dialogue box, and continue the insertion of the Resistor block at the command line:

`Insertion point:` **1,1** <return> `X scale factor <1>/Corner/XYZ:` Use the default value of 1. <return> `Y scale factor (default=X):` <return> `Rotation angle <0>:` <return>

The values entered above could have been specified in the Insert dialogue box, since they were not selected off the screen. They were done this way to

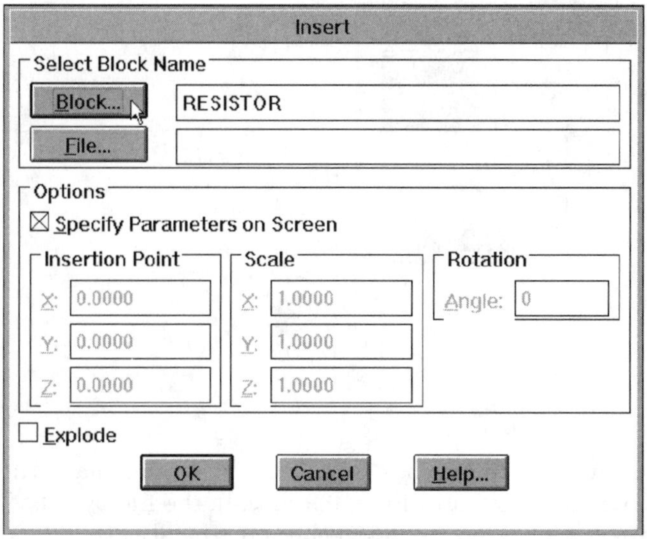

Insert
Select Block Name
Block... RESISTOR
File...
Options
☒ Specify Parameters on Screen
Insertion Point | Scale | Rotation
X: 0.0000 | X: 1.0000 | Angle: 0
Y: 0.0000 | Y: 1.0000
Z: 0.0000 | Z: 1.0000
☐ Explode
OK Cancel Help...

Figure 10.7 Insert dialogue box.

illustrate the procedure. The resistor block now appears on the screen with its insertion point (the left end) at coordinates 1,1. This is now a single entity, taking up less space in the data base than the previous resistor which is composed of a number of lines.

Inserting blocks from a drawing file. If the resistor block to be inserted was not part of the current drawings data base, it would not be listed in the Blocks list box shown in Fig. 10.8. This would happen, for instance, if you wanted to insert the resistor in a different drawing. In that case, the file is located by pressing

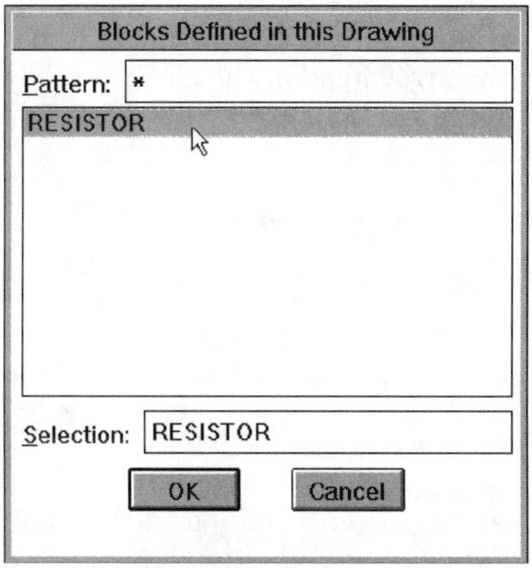

Blocks Defined in this Drawing
Pattern: *
RESISTOR
Selection: RESISTOR
OK Cancel

Figure 10.8 Selecting the block.

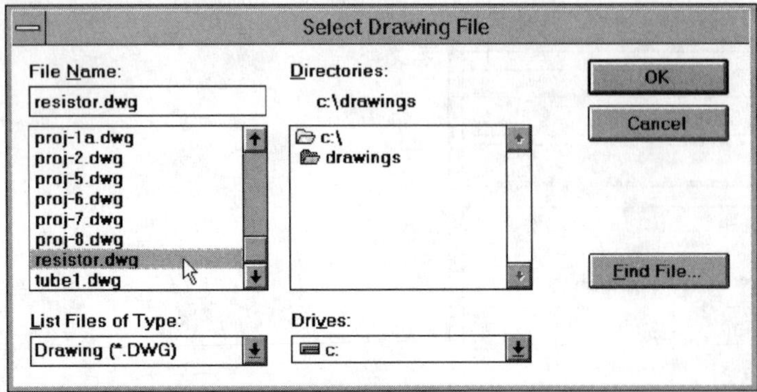

Figure 10.9 Selecting the block drawing file.

the File . . . button in the Insert dialogue box (Fig. 10.7), which displays the Select Drawing File dialogue box shown in Fig. 10.9. Locate the file by choosing the directory in the directory list box and then choosing the drawing file in the file name list box. Then press OK. After the block is inserted in the current drawing it becomes part of that drawing's data base and can be later inserted using the Blocks list box.

Create a variable resistor (potentiometer) by adding an arrow to the resistor using the Dimension and Leader commands. After the initial line of the leader is drawn, press Ctrl-C to cancel the remainder of the leader. If AutoCAD LT does not place an arrowhead on the leader, the leader line is too short. Use the Undo command to delete the leader and then draw a slightly longer one. The Break command can be used to later shorten the leader.

Save the block using the name Var-res. Write the block out to a drawing file using the name c:\drawings\var-res.dwg.

10.5 Draw LED Block

The LED will be drawn, as illustrated in Fig. 10.10, with the grid shown. The Solid command is used to fill in the arrowhead in the block as follows:

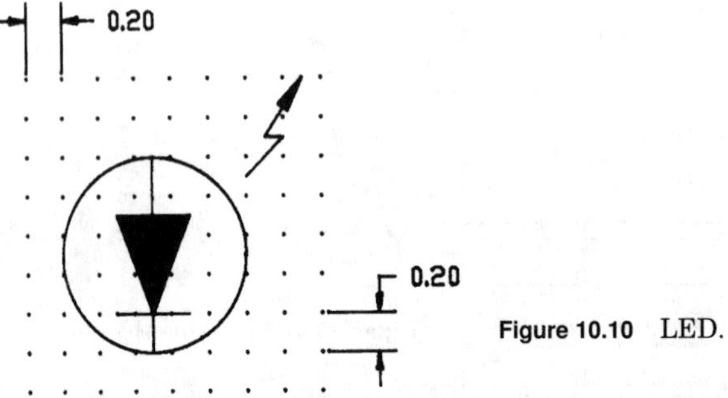

Figure 10.10 LED.

Draw <pick> Solid <Pick> First point: Place the cursor on the tip of the arrowhead in the LED. <pick> Second point: Place the cursor on a corner of the arrowhead. <pick> Third point: Place the cursor on the next corner. <pick> Fourth point: <return> Third point: <return>

Since a triangular solid is being drawn, there was no fourth point to enter. AutoCAD LT then requests a third point, assuming you want to continue with another adjoining solid using the previous second and third points as its first and second point. When drawing a rectangular Solid, the third and fourth points must cross (like a bow tie) so the third point is on the same side as the first, and the fourth on the same side as the second.

Save the LED as a block and then write it to file. The insertion point is the intersection of the line and circle at the top of the circle.

Draw the remaining blocks and write each one to file. The insertion point for each block should be a point on the block where the component connects to the electronic circuit line.

10.6 Block Modifications

Regardless of a block's complexity it is treated as a single entity in a drawing. As such, components in the block cannot be altered. To transcribe a block and retain its separate entities, click on the Explode check box in the Insert dialogue box (Fig. 10.7). The Explode box is on when it contains an X. Normally it should be off.

If the block is already inserted into the drawing it can be exploded using the Explode command in the Modify menu (see App. E, Fig. E.7).

If you try to make a block out of a block that has not been exploded and using the block's original name, AutoCAD LT will not allow you to do it and adds the message "Error this block references itself" to the bottom of the Block Definition dialogue box.

If a block has been exploded it can be modified and reblocked using the same name. In that case AutoCAD LT displays the following Warning box (Fig. 10.11):

If you wish to proceed with replacing the existing block with a new one, then press the redefine button. If not, press the Cancel button and change the name of the block to be created.

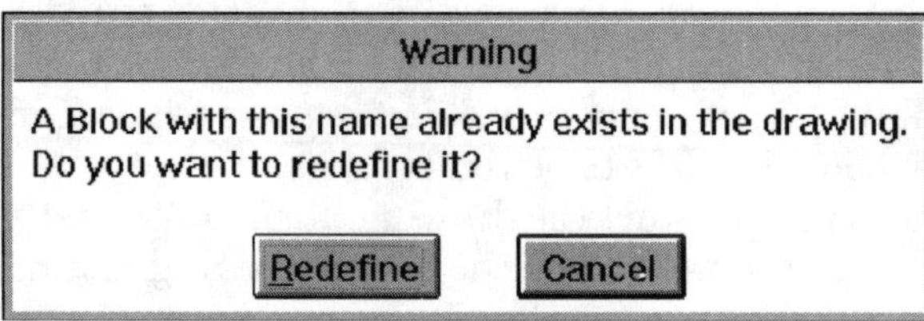

Figure 10.11 Block exists warning box.

10.7 Circuit Drawing

Use the Zoom and All commands to zoom to the full screen limits of 0,0 and 12,9.

Prior to starting the drawing, familiarize yourself with the block command using the following:

- *Insertion point.* The insertion point can be entered as a coordinate, as a relative coordinate (@), or by digitizing a point.
- *X scale factor <1>/Corner/XYZ.* To use the default value 1, press the Enter key. Any value entered will be a multiplier of the *x* dimension of the resistor. To visually drag the *x* and *y* dimensions of the resistor, use the cursor to drag the length and height of the resistor to that which is desired. An invalid entry will result if you attempt to drag only one axis of the entity by moving the cursor only horizontally or only vertically, which implies that the orthogonal multiplier is 0, an impossible value.
- *Y scale factor (default = X).* Use the same scale as that for the *x* dimension and press the Enter key. Any value entered will be a multiplier of the *y* dimension of the resistor.
- *Rotation angle <0>.* Press Enter to select the default angle 0. To rotate the resistor, enter the angle desired where 0 degrees is horizontal. The mouse can also be used to drag the resistor to the desired angle on the monitor.

Try the various methods of inserting the Var-res block into the drawing. Use the Erase command to erase the Var-res block and begin the circuit drawing.

Prior to drawing the circuit drawing, use the Donut command to draw a small dot to be used for the circuit connections:

`Draw` <pick> `Donut` <pick> `Inside diameter:` **0** <return> `Outside diameter:` **0.1** <return> `Center of doughnut:` Pick a grid point <pick> `Center of doughnut:` <return>

Save the doughnut as a block named Dot. The insertion point is the grid point at the center of the doughnut.

Complete the circuit drawing, as illustrated in Fig. 10.1. Use the object snaps Intersection and Endpoint as required to make the drawing production easier. Use the Copy command to copy segments of the drawing as required; for instance, the resistor connected to a ground is used twice—insert one and then copy it to the next location. The same procedure should be used for the var-res ground and the capacitor ground. Occasionally it is easier to insert the block close to where it is desired and then use the Move command to move it to the desired position, making use of temporary object snaps such as Endpoint. This is especially useful when a block is to be rotated.

Do not worry about where to start the drawing. Remember that you can use the Move command at any time to move the entire drawing to a new location. If the drawing exceeds the drawing limits, change the limits.

Most items will be inserted using an x and y scale factor of 1. When inserting the QCOMP (quad comparator), use a scale factor of 2 (1.5 might appear OK; however, the points on the comparator would not fall on the snap lines, making it more difficult to connect lines to those points). The ground should be inserted using an x and y scale factor of .25. If you insert an object and want to reinsert it at a different scale, use the Undo command and then reinsert the item.

Chapter

11

Custom Menu

Objective. Write a custom menu to simplify drawing construction; use a line editor (Notepad); pull-down menu; buttons menu; create new Windows program item; modify the Toolbar and Toolbox.

11.1 Menu Files

Menu customization allows you to create new AutoCAD LT menus or modify AutoCAD LT's standard menu to meet your specific requirements, increasing your productivity. An AutoCAD LT menu file is a text file with the extension *.mnu.* The customized file is created with any text editor or word processor that does not put extra coding in the text. AutoCAD LT uses two standard menus. If Short menu is set in the Settings menu (Fig. 2.2 and App. E, Fig. E.8) the standard menu is *aclt.mnu.* If Long Menu is set the standard menu is *aclt2.mnu.* Remember, if the Settings menu lists Short menu, Long menu is set, and vice versa. AutoCAD LT shows the option you have, and if Long menu is set the only option is to set Short menu. The Long menu is used in this text.

In order to write menu files you have to be very familiar with the command sequence for AutoCAD LT commands to be used in the menu. The commands and their syntax can be obtained using AutoCAD LT's Help program (see App. A4) and are also outlined in the *AutoCAD LT User's Guide.*

11.2 Section Labels

Menus can be written for AutoCAD LT as pull-down menus, button menus, and icon menus. The screen menu cannot be loaded in AutoCAD LT. Table 11.1 lists types of menus that can be used in AutoCAD LT, and the labels used to define the section in the menu.

This text will only cover pull-down menus and cursor menus. For information on writing other menus refer to your *AutoCAD LT User's Guide.*

TABLE 11.1 Menu Section Labels

Section label	Menu area
***AUXn	System pointing device button menu (where n is a number from 1 to 4)
***POPn	Pull-down/cursor menu (where n is a number from 1 to 4)
***ICON	Image tile menu area

11.3 Writing a Menu

An AutoCAD LT menu file is a text file with the name *aclt* or *aclt2* and the extension *.mnu*. The customized file is created with any text editor or word processor that does not put extra coding in the text. Notepad is a suitable text edit provided with Windows, and is used in this text. Notepad is limited in the size of files it can edit. For editing longer menus, such as AutoCAD LT's standard menu, a different editor such as DOS's Edit may have to be used.

You should currently be in the Windows Program Manager screen (Fig. 1.1). Click on the `Accessories` Window to bring it to the front, and then double click on the `Notepad` icon as shown in Fig. 11.1, to load Notepad (if Notepad is not in the Accessories window, look for it in others).

Write the menu shown in Fig. 11.2 (don't worry about the ACLT2.MNU title for the file). Type in each line exactly as it is shown and press <return> at the end of each line. If you make a mistake move the cursor to the line containing the error and fix it using the Delete and Insert keys.

AutoCAD LT processes each blank space in a menu as though the space bar were pressed. As is normal with AutoCAD, the space bar usually functions as <return>. For instance, in AutoCAD LT when you type Line and press the space bar, the Line command is invoked. This same process happens in the

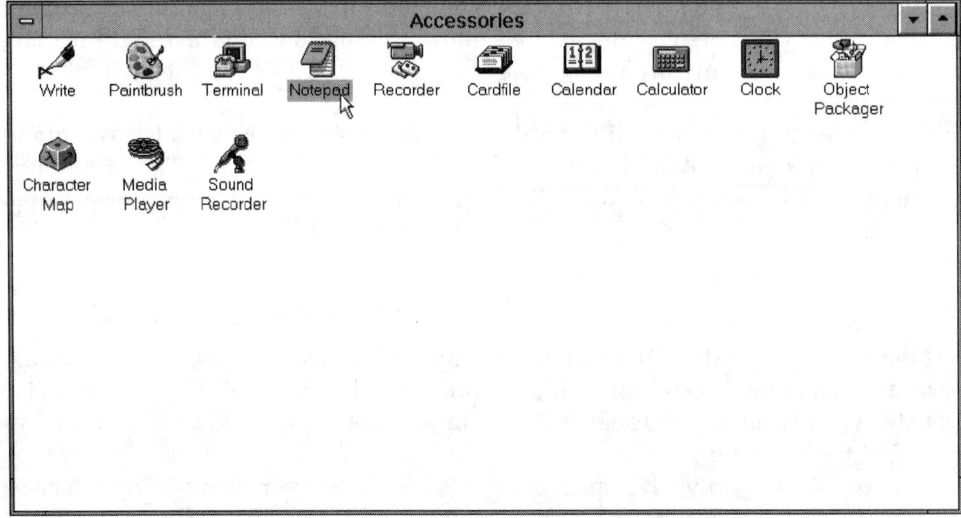

Figure 11.1 Loading Notepad.

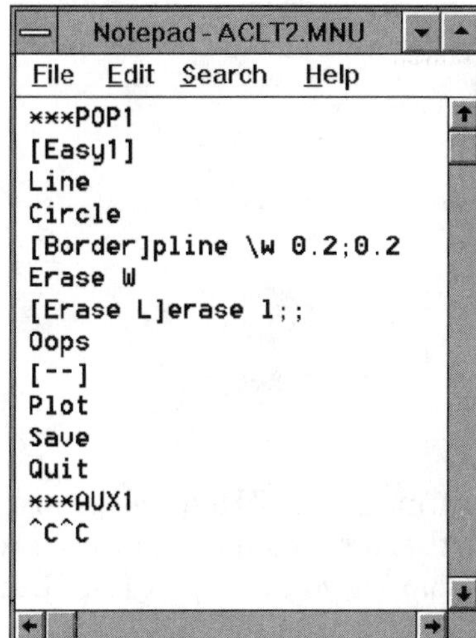
Notepad - ACLT2.MNU
File Edit Search Help
***POP1
[Easy1]
Line
Circle
[Border]pline \w 0.2;0.2
Erase W
[Erase L]erase l;;
Oops
[--]
Plot
Save
Quit
***AUX1
^C^C

Figure 11.2 Writing the menu.

menu, so each space is critical. Adding two spaces is like typing a command and pressing the space bar twice. AutoCAD LT also adds a space at the end of each line, unless it ends with a semicolon which is interpreted as the <return> key by AutoCAD LT. This menu is discussed in detail in the following sections.

11.4 Pull-Down (POPn) Menus

Up to 16 pull-down menus (POP1–POP16) can be defined for AutoCAD LT's Menu Bar (see Fig. I.1). The pull-down menus display as cascading menus. Pull-down menus can contain up to 999 menu items; however, the maximum number of items that can be displayed is governed by the number of rows visible on the display device, and may be as low as 21. The first item in the menu in Fig. 11.2 is the POP1 menu's title, i.e., `Easy1`. Titles in the menu can be up to 14 characters long, but many displays allow only 80 characters, so if all 16 POP positions are to be used, the title is limited to 5 characters. If all menu titles cannot fit on the screen, AutoCAD LT truncates them, often ending up with odd titles.

11.5 POPn Menu Syntax

The item `***POP1` at the top of the menu in Fig. 11.2 is the *section label* for a pull-down menu in the first position (at the left side) of the Menu bar. Immediately below that, enclosed in rectangular braces, is the title `[EASY1]` that will appear in the POP1 position of the menu bar. Fig. 11.3 shows the menu as it will appear in AutoCAD LT.

The Line and Circle commands are standard AutoCAD LT commands. When chosen in the Easy1 menu in AutoCAD LT they behave as they do in AutoCAD LT's standard menu.

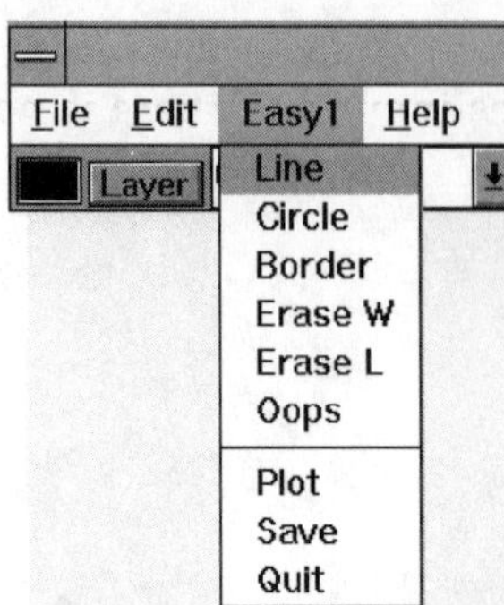

Figure 11.3 Easy1 menu.

Notice that Windows File menu, Edit menu, and Help menu are automatically included in the menu bar, and the new menu headings are inserted between Edit and Help in the buttons bar. If you create a File, Edit, or Help menu, your menu lines will be added to the Windows listings.

11.5.1 Menu item labels

```
[Border]Pline \w 0.2 0.2
```

Rather than have this entire line (see Fig. 11.2) displayed on the screen when the menu is displayed, a *menu item label,* [Border], is used. Menu item labels are enclosed in rectangular braces and appear on the screen when the menu is displayed. The remainder of the menu is invisible to the drafter as shown in Fig. 11.3.

This line in the menu is called a *macro* because it performs a sequence of operations. The operation immediately following the closing brace (]) of the menu item label is invoked when the label is selected in the menu. AutoCAD LT's **Pline** command draws connected lines and arcs of varying width. When Pline is invoked, it asks for the `Start point of line`. This is entered by the user (see the following section). After the start point of the line is input AutoCAD LT requests: `arc/Close/Halfwidth/Length/Undo/Width/<endpoint of line>`. The option **w** (Width) is read from the macro. AutoCAD LT then requests the starting line width which is read from the macro as **0.2,** and the end width which is read from the macro as **0.2.** Consequently when Border is selected in the menu the Pline command is invoked and you are able to draw polylines 0.2 units in width. The syntax of this macro is discussed further in following sections.

11.5.2 Embedding keyboard input

```
[Border]Pline \w 0.2;0.2
```

To allow keyboard input in the menu macro, place a backslash character (\) at the location where the keyboard input is required. In this line, AutoCAD LT pauses at the backslash (\) allowing the user to enter the start point of the polyline. Note there is no blank space following the backslash.

A backslash is not required at the end of a line since control automatically returns to the user if the command requires input and there is no additional data in the menu line.

11.5.3 Embedding enter key

```
[Border]Pline \w 0.2;0.2
Erase W
[Erase L]erase 1;;
```

The <return> key is embedded in a menu line by placing a semicolon (;) or a single blank space (representing the Space bar) at the location where the <return> key is required. AutoCAD LT interprets the Space bar as the enter key, except when text is being entered and the space bar is interpreted as a blank space in the text. There is a single space in the macro immediately following the Pline command. This is interpreted as <return> which enters the command. There is no blank space or semicolon (;) following the backslash (\) which embeds keyboard input in the menu. When keyboard input is required, the user enters the required data and must press the <return> key or the pick button to enter the data.

In the `Erase W` menu line, the Erase command is entered using a single blank space to invoke <return> following the command. The W (Window) option is then read from the menu. The remainder of the operation continues at the command line as follows:

> `Window First corner:` **Pick a corner of the window <pick>** `Other corner:` **Pick the next corner <pick>** `Select objects:`

After the window is defined, the Erase command continues to request entities to be erased. In order to exit the command, the user must press <return>.

In the next line an item label, `[Erase L]`, is used. The text within the rectangular braces only appears as a label in the menu when it is displayed on the monitor. The item label text itself is meaningless to AutoCAD LT. When this item is selected in the menu, the Erase command *immediately* following the right brace of the item label (`[Erase L]erase`) is invoked. AutoCAD LT then reads the 1 (Last) and the <return> key is invoked by the semicolon immediately following 1. As is normal with AutoCAD LT, the last entity drawn becomes dotted and AutoCAD LT request `Select objects.` In this case, however, the next semicolon enters <return> and the command is exited. Consequently, the last entity drawn is immediately erased.

11.5.4 Menu separator

```
[--]
```

A menu item with two hyphens in rectangular braces creates a separator the width of the pull-down menu. Menu items can also be grayed out by placing a tilde (~) at the start of the menu item, so the following would create a grayed-out separator: [~--].

11.5.5 POPn menu syntax reference

Table 11.2 lists some of the special characters used in pull-down/cursor menu files.

11.6 AUXn Menu Syntax

The AUXn menu controls the buttons on your system pointing device. You cannot reassign the pick button on your pointing device. Consequently, on a two-button system pointing device, there is only one button left to program. You can, however, use a key/button sequence to invoke other AUX menus. This is used in AutoCAD LT's standard menu where holding down the Shift key and pressing the second button on the mouse displays the floating object snap cursor menu. Table 11.3 shows the Button menus accessed with key/button sequences:

11.6.1 Adding a buttons (AUXn) menu

Complete the EASY1 menu exactly as shown in Fig. 11.4. To add the POP0 menu section, move the cursor to the top left corner of the existing menu using

TABLE 11.2 Menu Characters

Character	Description
[]	Encloses a label
;	Issues <return>
	Single blank space is equivalent to Space bar
\	Pauses for user input
[--]	Item label to create a separator line in the menu
->	Label prefix for a cascading menu
<-	Label prefix indicates last item in cascading menu
+	Continues menu line on the next line
$	Loads a menu
=*	Displays the current pull-down or cursor menu
*^C^C	Prefix for a repeating item
^B	Toggles Snap on/off
^C	Cancel command
^D	Toggles coordinates
^E	Toggles isometric planes
^G	Toggles Grid on/off
^O	Toggles Ortho mode on/off
^P	Toggles menu echoing on/off
^V	Changes current viewport

TABLE 11.3 Button Menus

Button menu	Key/button sequence
AUX1	Simple button pick
AUX2	Shift + button
AUX3	Ctrl + button
AUX4	Ctrl + Shift + button

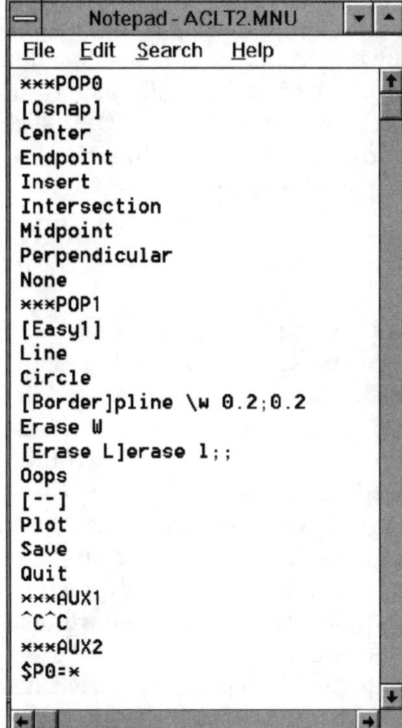
Notepad - ACLT2.MNU
File Edit Search Help
***POP0
[Osnap]
Center
Endpoint
Insert
Intersection
Midpoint
Perpendicular
None
***POP1
[Easy1]
Line
Circle
[Border]pline \w 0.2;0.2
Erase W
[Erase L]erase l;;
Oops
[--]
Plot
Save
Quit
***AUX1
^C^C
***AUX2
$P0=*

Figure 11.4 Completing the menu.

the mouse and press <return>. This pushes the current top line down one line. Move the cursor up to the blank line and begin entering the new lines. Press <return> at the end of line to make space below it for the next line. If you want to delete a blank line, move the cursor to the blank line and press Delete. The new entries are discussed in the following.

`***AUX1` is the section label for the first programmable button on the pointing device. On a two-button mouse this is the second button. The first button is reserved as the <pick> button. In this menu, the second button invokes two cancel commands, ^C^C. If you have a three or more button pointing device, you can add more lines of commands (operations) in this section.

11.7 Floating Cursor Menu

```
***AUX2
$P0=*
```

AUX2 is the section label for the menu section invoked by holding down the Shift key and clicking the second button on the pointing device. The line immediately following the section label is invoked. In this case, `$P0` is interpreted by AutoCAD LT as load menu POP0, and =* is interpreted as display the current loaded menu, which in this case is POP0. Consequently, menu POP0 is displayed at the current location of the cursor on the monitor.

`***POPO` is the section label for the cursor menu. The first line of the menu must be the menu title. In this case, the menu title [Osnap] is used. The title has a specific application for pull-down menu since it is displayed in the menu bar. It is meaningless for the cursor menu since it is not displayed, but it is a syntax requirement by AutoCAD LT. The lines in the POP0 section of this menu object snaps. This menu could include macros like those used in the POP1 menu. It is not limited to being an object snap menu.

11.8 Saving the Menu

Click on Notepad's Control menu box, i.e., the dash (-) in the top left corner of the Notepad Window (see Fig. 11.4), to display the Control menu. Choose `Save As` from the Control menu. The Save As dialogue box illustrated in Fig. 11.5 is displayed. Set the directory to `c:\drawings` as shown. Then enter the File Name as **aclt2.mnu.** Be sure the file extension is entered as .mnu.

The file name used, Aclt2, is based on the assumption you have set Long Menu in AutoCAD LT's Settings menu. If you have set Short Menu, you must use the file name Aclt. All menu files must have the extension .mnu. Each custom menu created for AutoCAD LT must be saved in a new directory, since they all must use the same name. Do *not* erase the standard aclt.mnu and aclt2.mnu menu files provided with AutoCAD LT.

The first time a menu is loaded, AutoCAD LT compiles it creating a compiled menu named aclt2.mnx. This is done automatically. If the file is revised, AutoCAD LT compares the dates and times of the mnu and mnx file. If the mnu file has a later date/time, it is recompiled, and a new mnx file is created. The file loaded into AutoCAD LT is the compiled version.

Press `OK` to exit the Save As dialogue box. Then redisplay the Control menu and choose `Close`.

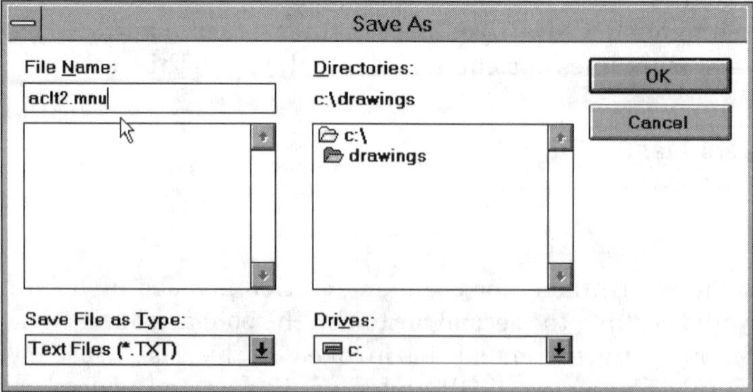

Figure 11.5 Saving a menu file.

11.9 Loading a Menu

A menu cannot be loaded into AutoCAD LT when you are in the drawing editor. The menu is loaded when AutoCAD LT is booted, and must be named Aclt.mnu or Aclt2.mnu (see Sec. 11.8). The menu must also be located in the Working directory defined in the AutoCAD LT program item. This means you must create an new AutoCAD LT program item in Windows. In Windows bring the `Applications Window` to the front (see Fig. 1.1). (If your AutoCAD LT icon is in another Window then bring that one to the front instead.) Click *once* (note only once) on the AutoCAD LT icon to highlight it.

Click on Program Manager's `File` menu to display the menu illustrated in Fig. 11.6. Click on `Copy...` to display the Copy Program Item dialogue box illustrated in Fig. 11.7. The To Group box is where you specify the window in which this program item is to be placed. Click the down arrow beside the To Group edit box to display the drop-down box as illustrated in Fig. 11.7. Then choose `Applications` in the drop-down list (or whatever Window group you want this new AutoCAD icon to be in). Press **OK** to complete the dialogue.

A second AutoCAD LT icon is now displayed in the Applications Window. Click on it once to highlight it. Click on Program Manager's `File` menu (see Fig. 11.6), and then click on `Properties...` to display the Program Items Properties dialogue box shown in Fig. 11.8. Set the `Working Directory` to `C:\DRAWINGS`. (This is the directory where the modified aclt2.mnu file is located.) Next click the `Change Icon` button and select a different icon from the one you currently use for AutoCAD LT. Change the `Description` to **ACADLT PROTO1.** Press `OK` to exit. The copied AutoCAD LT icon is changed in the Applications Window using the icon selected and the name ACADLT PROTO1. When you want to use the standard AutoCAD LT menu, choose the original AutoCAD LT icon. When you want to use the Easy1 menu, choose the `ACADLT PROTO1` icon. Do that now.

11.10 Using the Aclt2 Menu

Try your Easy1 menu. Invoke the line command and draw a triangle using your floating cursor menu (holding down Shift and pressing the second button on your mouse) to snap the last line onto the start of the first.

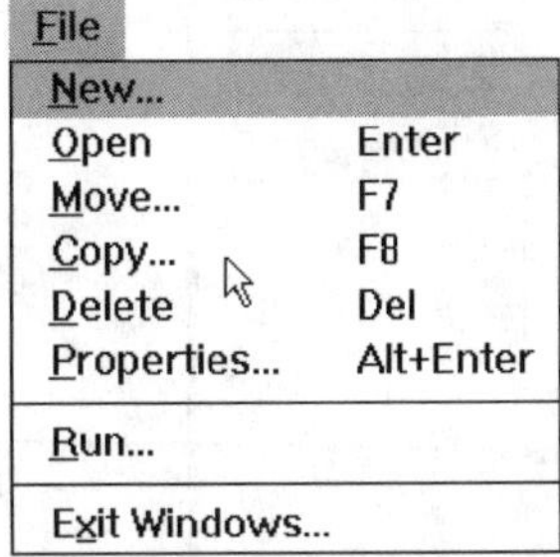

Figure 11.6 Program Manager File menu.

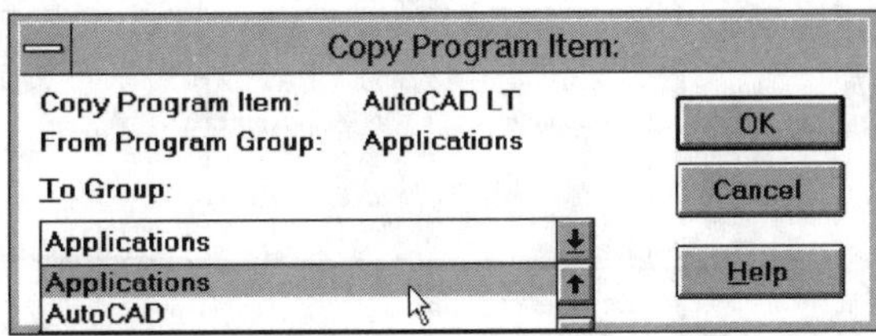

Figure 11.7 Copying a program item.

Program Item Properties

Description: ACADLT PROTO1
Command Line: C:\ACLTWIN\aclt.exe
Working Directory: C:\DRAWINGS
Shortcut Key: None
Run Minimized
OK
Cancel
Browse...
Change Icon...
Help

Figure 11.8 Changing program item, properties.

If your menu does not work correctly, you will have to correct it in Notepad. You will have a chance to do that in the following section.

11.11 Cascading Menu

Exit AutoCAD LT. There is no need to save the drawing.

Load Notepad as outlined in Sec. 11.3. Click on `File` in Notepad's menu bar (see Fig. 11.2), and then click `Open...` to display the Open file dialogue box shown in Fig. 11.9. Set the Directories to `c:\drawings`. Then move the cursor into the File Name edit box and change *.txt to ***.mnu,** and press <return>. The menu files in directory c:\drawings are listed in the file list box. Double click `aclt2.mnu` to load it.

Insert the POP2 menu section to your menu, shown in Fig. 11.10 between Quit and ***AUX1 (the other sections of the menu completed earlier are not shown).

The POP2 menu section is not complete since no operations follow the menu item labels, [A Size] and [B Size]. The operations (commands) to follow these item labels will be written in Chap. 12. The menu item labels are added here to illustrate the use of cascading menus. The menu is shown in Fig. 11.11 as it will appear in AutoCAD LT when Metric is selected in the Title Blk menu.

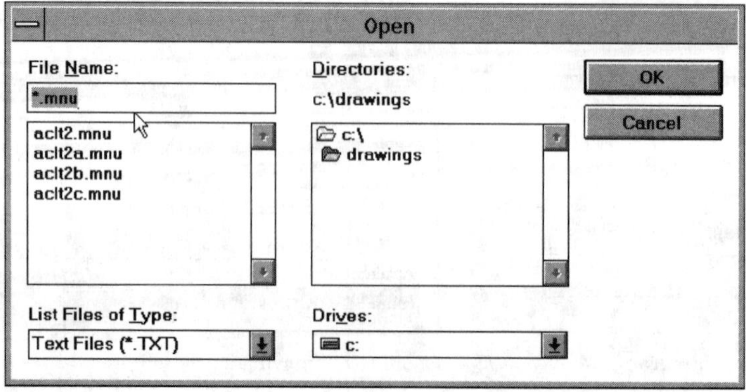

Figure 11.9 Open the menu file for editing.

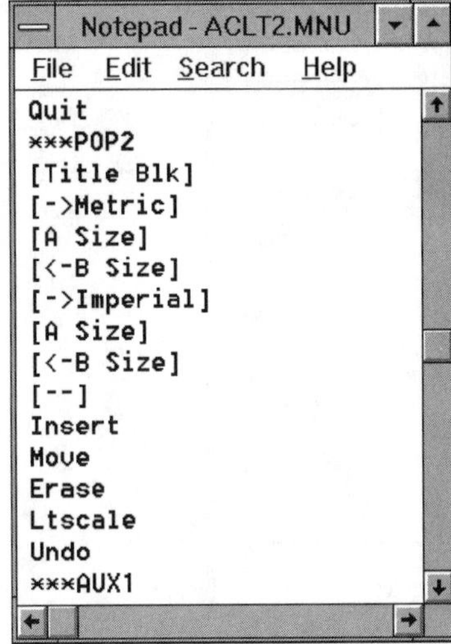

Figure 11.10 Adding POP2.

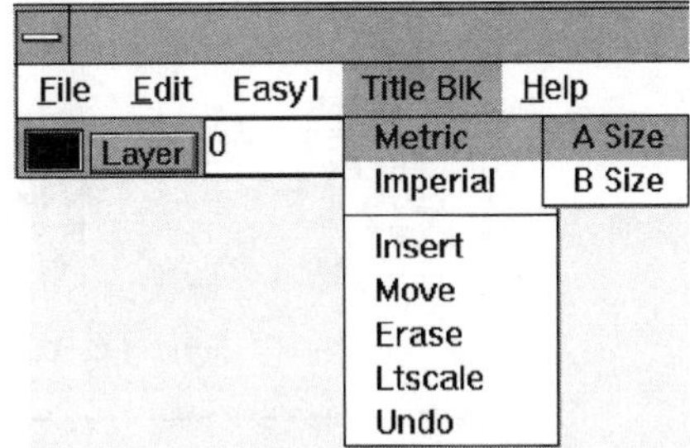

Figure 11.11 Cascading menu.

In the menu (Fig. 11.10), the → in [→Metric] is a label prefix indicating the start of a cascading menu. The cascading menu continues until the label prefix ←, i.e. [←B Size], is encountered indicating the last item in the cascading menu.

Each cascading menu starts with the label prefix →. If more than one menu cascades from a parent menu, the last item in the last cascading menu must have one ← symbol for each cascading menu, that is:

```
[->Metric]
[->Landscape]
[A Size]
[<-<-B Size]
```

Save the menu using the file name `c:\drawings\aclt2.mnu`. Load AutoCAD LT by choosing the `ACADLT PROTO1` icon.

Try the menu. Check that your cascading menus work. (Nothing happens if you select A-Size or B-Size, since we have not put any commands in the menu yet.) If you still have errors, edit the menu and fix them.

11.12 Customizing the Toolbar

If there are any blank buttons on your toolbar (see App. E, Fig. E.11) they can be customized to invoke an AutoCAD LT command, mode, or string of commands. You can also change any of the standard button settings in the toolbar. A button in the toolbar is customized as follows:

1. Using the right button on the mouse, choose the toolbar button to be customized (pick a blank one if possible).

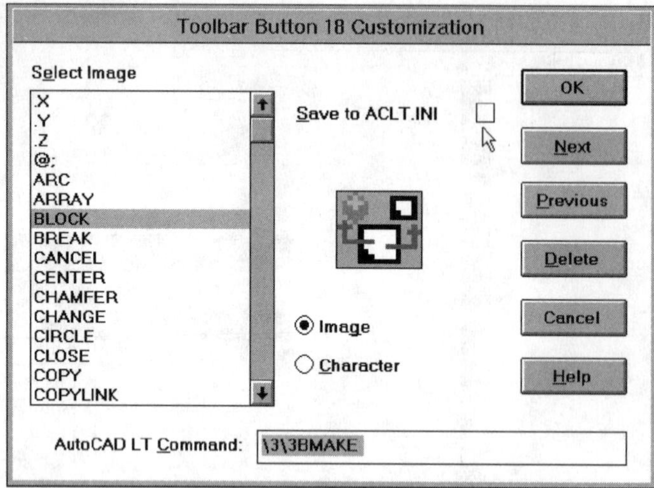

Figure 11.12 Customizing the toolbar.

2. A Toolbar Customization box similar to that shown in Fig. 11.12 is displayed. As an example, the Block command will be added to the toolbar using an image. Click the `Image` radio button. Then locate `BLOCK` in the Select Image list box (on the left side of the dialogue box) and click on it once. In the AutoCAD LT Command box, enter **\3\3BMAKE** as shown. This operation invokes two cancel commands (see the table at the end of this section), and then the BMake command which displays the Block Definition dialogue box (Fig. 10.4). If you want this command to be in the toolbar each time AutoCAD LT is booted, turn the Save to ACLT.INI check box on. It is on when there is an X in its box.
3. Click `OK` to exit the dialogue box and create the toolbar item. Try the command by clicking it in the toolbar.

Table 11.4 lists the special characters that can be used in command sequences, such as \3\3 used above.

TABLE 11.4 Toolbar/Toolbox Characters

Character	Meaning
	<return>
;	Suppresses <space> at the end of a command string
\\	Interpreted as \ in a file path name
\n	New line
\2	Toggles snap
\3	Cancel
\4	Toggles coordinates
\5	Toggles isoplanes
\7	Toggles grid

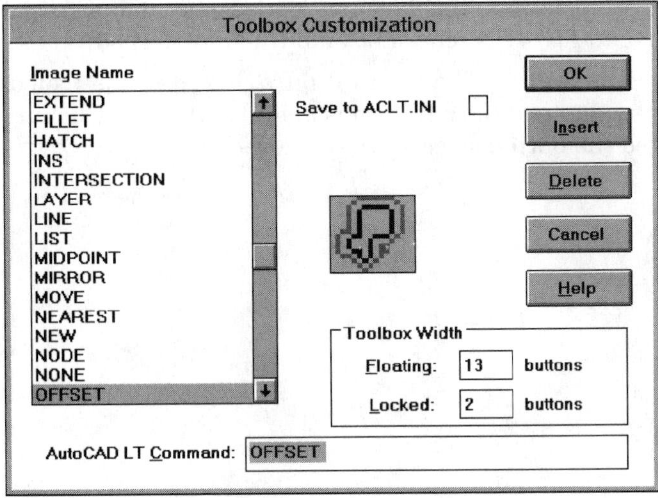

Figure 11.13 Customizing the toolbox.

Pressing the `Character` button (see Fig. 11.12) allows you to use an alphabetic character rather than an image on the button. There are not images available for all commands.

Pressing `Next` (Fig. 11.12) moves you to the next button to the right on the toolbar. `Previous` moves you one button to the left. `Delete` allows you to delete the current button.

If you have spare buttons in the buttons bar, set up some commands/operations you use often.

11.13 Customizing the Toolbox

The process to customize the toolbox is similar to that used for the toolbar. The toolbox, however, does not have any blank buttons at this time. To make space and add the OFFSET command (see Chap. 14, Sec. 14.3) to the toolbox:

1. Using the second button on the mouse, click the button in the bottom-right corner of the toolbox.
2. A Toolbox Customization dialogue box similar to that shown in Fig. 11.13 is displayed.
3. Change the Toolbox Width Floating buttons to **13.** You are adding space for one more column in the toolbox.
4. Locate OFFSET in the Image Name file and click once on it. Its image is placed in the image box as shown.
5. Move the cursor to the AutoCAD LT Command box and enter the command **OFFSET** (or \3\3OFFSET if you prefer).

6. If you want to have this revised toolbox loaded when AutoCAD LT is booted, turn the Save to ACLT.INI check box on. If not, turn it off.
7. Click the `Insert` button. The item initially clicked in the toolbox moves to the right one space and the new icon is placed in its spot. Clicking OK would have changed the button selected to the new one.

Chapter

12

Attributes

Objective. Use blocks with attributes to construct a custom menu to draw borders and title blocks for drawings; insert drawings to scale into a border plot drawing.

12.1 Attributes

Attributes are used to tag information to graphical drawing elements that are stored as blocks. The information can be constants, such as heat loss coefficients tagged with window blocks, or variable information requested from the user by AutoCAD LT as the block is being inserted into the drawing.

Attribute information can be displayed on the drawing with the graphic block, or the information can be collected on a disk for later processing to create, for instance, a bill of material. Such information can be collected from the disk by other software such as dbase IV.

The procedure for using attributes is as follows:

1. Create an Attribute Definition using the Attdef command.
2. Create a block that includes the desired graphic information and the Attribute Definition.

The block, including the Attribute Definition, can be part of the current drawing only or it can be saved as a separate file using the Wblock command and inserted into any other drawing. The block will always retain the attribute information tagged to it.

A block can have more than one attribute associated with it. AutoCAD will prompt the user for the value of each attribute when the block is inserted.

12.2 ATTDEF Command

The Attribute Definition is created with the (Define Attributes) command.

When (Define Attributes) is chosen, the following settings are available:

Invisible. When the invisible mode is turned on, information relevant to that attribute is not displayed on the drawing with the block it is tagged to. For instance, if you wish to tag building window blocks with heat-loss factors, you might not want that information to be displayed on the drawing. The information is stored in the drawing file, however, and can be retrieved from the file by another program which might perform heat-loss calculations. When the invisible mode is off, attribute information tagged to a block is displayed on the drawing with the block.

Constant. When the constant mode is off, the attribute tagged to the block is variable, and data is requested from the user by AutoCAD LT when the block is inserted. If the constant mode is on, the attribute information tagged with the block is inserted when the block is created and cannot be changed when the block is inserted into a drawing.

Verify. If verify is on, any variable information entered by the user when the block is inserted will be redisplayed and the user will be given an opportunity to modify the entry. If verify is off, the information will be accepted immediately as it is entered, and the user will not be given an opportunity to modify it.

Preset. This mode allows you to create attributes that are variable but are not requested during block insertion.

Attribute tag. The attribute tag is any name that you want to use to identify the attribute. This tag name must not include blank spaces and must not be a null value. It is printed on the drawing when the attribute is created and disappears when the block is created. It is not printed on a drawing when the block is inserted. Generally, the attribute tag should be a short identifier name.

Attribute prompt. You can enter a prompt line that is to be displayed in the command line when the block containing this attribute is inserted into a drawing. The prompt is not displayed on the block during the creation of the attribute. The prompt is any text that you want displayed to prompt the user to input the attribute value when the block is inserted into a drawing.

Attribute value. If Constant and Preset are off, this is the default value that will be displayed with the attribute prompt. As with normal AutoCAD LT default values it will be displayed in triangular braces (<>). If Constant or Preset are on, this is a constant that will be inserted with the attribute and the user will not be prompted for input.

Insertion point. The attribute location can be entered directly into the dialogue box or entered from the command line.

Text options. This defines the attribute text that will be inserted when the attribute is invoked. The text Justification and Style can be set from drop-down boxes. Note that only styles that are loaded (see Chap. 5, Sec. 5.13) will be available. The Height and Rotation can be entered in the dialogue box or selected on the screen.

```
Justify/Style/<start point>
Height <default>:
Rotation angle <default>:
```

12.3 Border and Title Block with Attributes

As an example, a standard border and title block will be constructed for an A-size (8.5 by 11 in or 215 by 280 mm) drawing and stored as a block. Attributes will be used to add the text information to the title block when the block is inserted into a drawing.

12.3.1 Border and title block construction

In this example, metric units will be used on an A-size sheet; therefore, the screen limits will be set at 280 by 215 mm. A 20-mm border will be provided on the top long-side of the page, and 15 mm will be provided on the other side. The drawing border line will be started at coordinates 0,15 (for a Hewlett Packard HP 7470A Graphics Plotter), and the sides will then be 250 by 175 mm long.

The border dimensions and the start point are dependent on the plotter you are using. You can determine the proper values for your plotter by drawing the border as outlined in Sec. 12.3.2, but use the Line command rather than the Polyline command. Then plot the display. If any of the border lines are not plotted, use the plot sheet to estimate where the line should be, and move the line on the screen using the Move command. Plot the display again, and relocate lines if necessary. You also might have to move the entire border so that it fits properly on the sheet. When your border is plotting properly, use the Id Point command and the Intersec object snap to locate the start point and the List command to specify the border line lengths. Then erase the lines. Replace the values in the following section with those for your plotter.

12.3.2 Draw the border

Boot AutoCAD LT. This drawing will not be saved following normal procedures so we will not use the New command to name it. Set the drawing units to decimal with two digits to the right of the decimal. Set the drawing limits at –5, –5 and 280,215. Use the Zoom and All commands to zoom the screen to the limits set.

The border is to be drawn on a new layer named Border. That layer name should be reserved for the border and not used on any other entities on your drawing. Choose the following:

Settings <pick> **Layer Control . . .** <pick>

The Layer Control dialogue box similar to that shown in Fig. 6.5 is displayed. Following the procedures discussed in Chap. 6, Sec. 6.2.2 create a new layer named **Border** by entering it in the layer name edit box and pressing the `New` button. Then choose Border in the layer list box and press the `Current` button to make border the current working layer. Press OK to exit the dialogue box. Border should appear in the Current Layer name box in the buttons bar.

The border lines are to be drawn using the Polyline command with a 0.2 unit (millimeters) wide polyline:

`Draw` <pick> `Polyline` <pick> `From point:` **0,15** <return> `Current line width is 0.00. Arc/Close/Halfwidth/Length/Undo/Width/<Endpoint of line>:` **w** (Width) <return> `Starting width <0.00>:` **0.2** <return> `Ending width <0.20>:` <return> `Arc/Close/Halfwidth/Length/Undo/Width/<Endpoint of line>:` **@250<0** <return> `Arc/Close/Halfwidth/Length/Undo/Width/<Endpoint of line>:` **@175<90** <return> `Arc/Close/Halfwidth/Length/Undo/Width/<Endpoint of line>:` **@250<180** <return> `Arc/Close/Halfwidth/Length/Undo/Width/<Endpoint of line>:` **c** (Close) <return>

Use the Polyline command to draw the 125- by 30-mm title block shown in Fig. 12.1. Use 0.2 unit wide lines. Start at coordinate 125,50 as shown.

12.3.3 Title block headings

When entering headings in the title block, we must be very specific where the text is located. AutoCAD LT use the Dtext (dynamic text) command for text. Dtext is useful for most text since it allows you to enter text dynamically on the screen. When you press <return> after typing in the text, the cursor drops down to the next line so you can continue the text directly below the previous text. That is what we want in the title block, but we want the spacing between

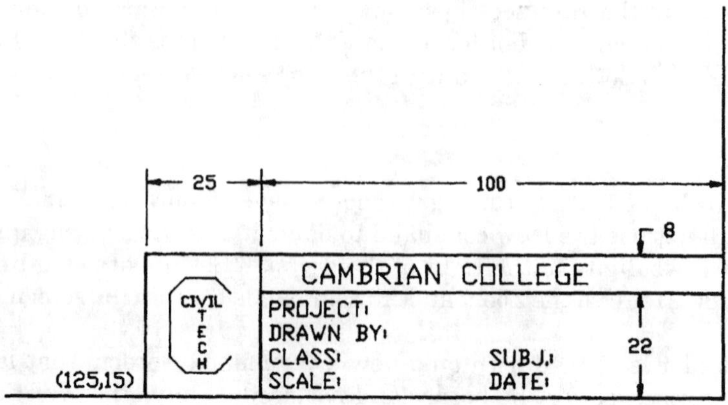

Figure 12.1 Title block dimensions and headings.

the text to meet our requirements. It also assumes you want the same text height and justification. Consequently, we will use the Text command instead. This is a good command to put in your toolbar following the procedure outlined in Chap. 11, Sec. 11.13. Use the character T and the command TEXT. The title block headings are entered as follows:

> **Text** (Type at command line) <return> `Justify/Style/<Start point>:` **J** (Justify) <return> `Align/Fit/Center/Middle/Right:` **c** (Center) <return> `Center point:` **200,39** Use the cursor to verify this on the monitor. <return> `Height <0.20>:` **4** <return> `Rotation angle <0>:` <return> `Text:` **Cambrian College** <return> <return> `Text Justify/Style/<Start point>:` **152,32** <return> `Height <4>:` **3** <return> `Rotation angle <0>:` <return> `Text:` **Project** <return>

Add the remaining text using a space of 2 units between the text and a text height of 3 units.

The logo was drawn as a block and saved with Block Out. It was then inserted into the drawing. If you want to draw the logo using a different color pen, draw it onto a new layer.

12.3.4 Create attributes

Attributes are to be used to put variable text into the title block. As they are created AutoCAD LT puts the attribute tag in the location where the text is to go. When the attributes are invoked later, you will be requested for the actual text to go into each title block. Create the attributes as follows:

> `Construct` <pick> `Define Attributes...` <pick>

The Attribute Definition dialogue box (Fig. 12.2) is displayed. The options are discussed at the beginning of this chapter. Enter the Tag and prompt as shown. The text height is entered as 3 units (mm). The Insertion point of the text is its start point in the title block. Enter X as 175 and Y as 32. If you wanted to select the points on the screen you would press the Pick Point< button. Click the Verify check box on (it is on when it has X in it). Press OK to exit the dialogue box.

AutoCAD LT enters the attribute tag PROJECT beside the heading PROJECT: in the title block as shown in Fig. 12.3. This is where the attribute text (the project name) will go when the attributes are invoked. If the tag is not in the correct location, use the Move command to move it.

Before entering the remaining attributes, zoom on the title block and determine the start point for each attribute tag. Use the cursor to estimate the location reading the coordinates from the coordinate display window in the button bar (press F6 or Ctrl-D if the coordinates are not calculated as the cursor is moved). Then calculate the value using a text height of 3 and the spacing between text lines as 2 units.

Display the Attribute Definition dialogue box and enter the next attribute. There are six attributes to enter. When entering the attribute for the Scale, use a default scale of NTS (not to scale). Default values are entered in the Value edit box (see Fig. 12.1). Fig. 12.3 shows the title block with the attribute tags used by the author.

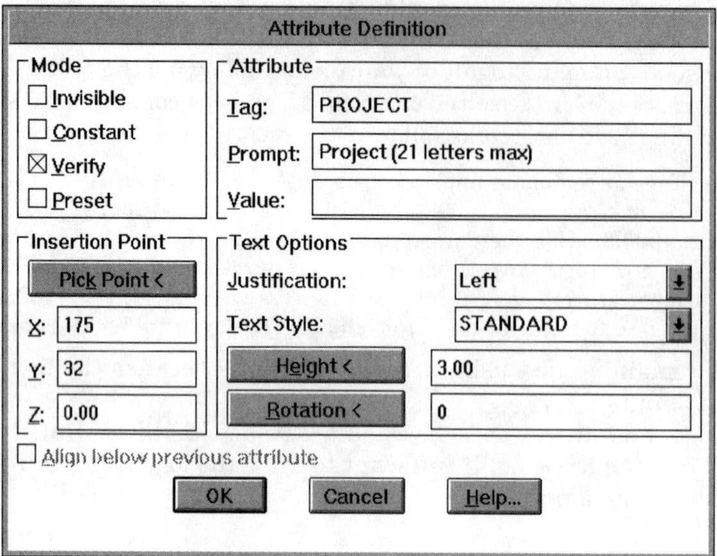

Figure 12.2 Attributes definition dialogue box.

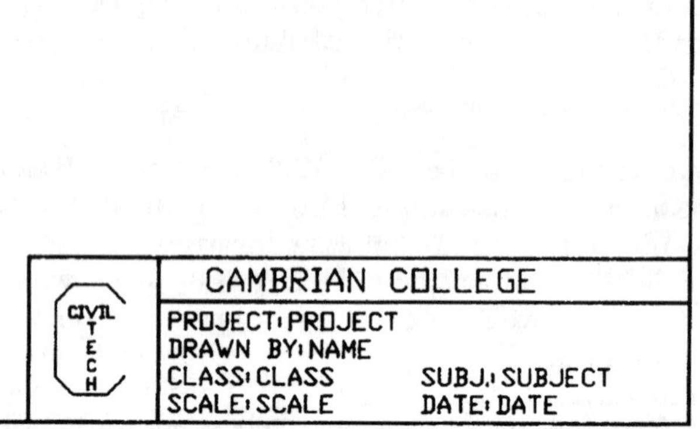

Figure 12.3 Title block attribute tags.

12.3.5 Editing attribute definitions

The attribute definition can be edited as follows:

> `Modify` <pick> `Edit Text` <pick> `<Select a TEXT or ATTDEF object>/Undo:` Click on the attribute tag `PROJECT.` <pick> The Edit Attribute Definition edit box in Fig. 12.4 is displayed. Move the cursor into the Prompt edit box and insert **Name** as shown. Press `OK.` `<Select a TEXT or ATTDEF object>/Undo:` <return>

If you want to change the location of the attribute, it can be moved with the Move command. You can also change the location, height, layer, etc. by choosing Modify <pick> Change properties . . . <pick>.

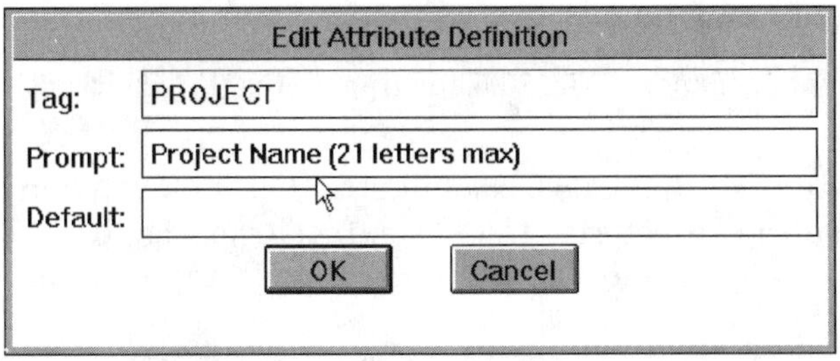

Figure 12.4 Editing an attribute definition.

12.3.6 Create the block

The entire drawing is to be saved as a block for insertion into other drawings. The block name will be Am-hbdr (A-size drawing, metric, horizontal border):

`Construct` <pick> `Make Block...` <pick>

A Block Definition dialogue box shown in Fig. 12.5 is displayed. Enter the Block Name as **AM-HBDR.** The Base point (insertion point) is `X:` **0** and `Y:` **0.** Click the `Retain Entities` check box to turn it off—there should not be an X in it. When retain entities is off, entities are not removed from the screen when they are blocked. If it is on, entities remain on the screen after they are blocked. Next, press the `Select Objects<` button. The dialogue box is removed from the screen and the border and title block are visible. The command line prompts are:

> `Select objects:` Click the lower left corner of a window to the left and below the border. <pick> `Other corner:` Move the cursor up and to the right enclosing the border in a selection window. <pick> `Select objects:` If the drawing is selected properly it will become dotted. If any lines are not dotted, select them by clicking on them. <Pick> `Select objects:` <return>

The Block Definition dialogue box is returned to the screen. Press the OK button.

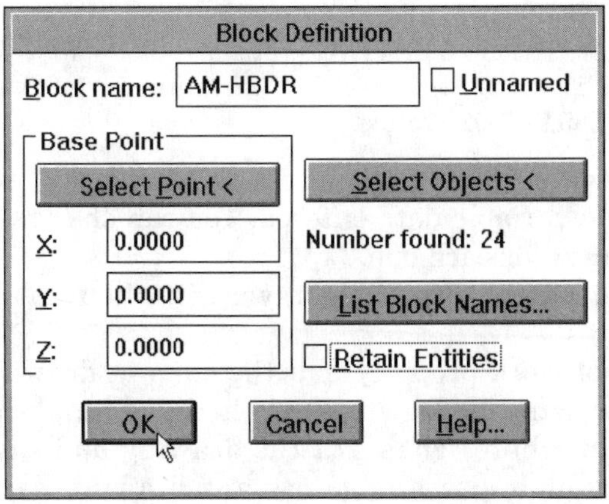

Figure 12.5 Defining the block.

Now, write the block to file:

`File` <pick> `Import/Export` (Fig. 10.5 and App. E, Fig. E.1) <pick> `Block Out...` <pick>

The Create Drawing File dialogue box similar to that illustrated in Fig. 10.6 is displayed. Change the Directories to `c:/drawings` (see Fig. 10.6). Then move the cursor to the `File Name:` edit box and enter the file name as **am-hbdr.dwg.** Press `OK` to open the file.

AutoCAD LT now requests at the command line the name of the block to save in the file named Am-hbdr.Dwg. Enter = indicating the block name is the same as the file name opened (am-hbdr):

`Block name:` **=** <return>

12.3.7 Test Am-hbdr file

The Am-hbdr file will be used to draw a border and title block. Data prompted from the user will be inserted into the title block.

`Draw` <pick> `Insert Block . . .` <pick>

The Insert dialogue box similar to that illustrated in Fig. 10.7 is displayed. The block to be inserted is in the current drawing data base. Press the `Block...` button to display the Blocks list box similar to that shown in Fig. 10.8. Click on `AM-HBDR` in the list, which moves its name into the Selection box. Then press `OK`. The Insert dialogue box now shows the block name Resistor in the Block name box as shown in Fig. 10.7.

Click the Specify Parameters on Screen box to off (there should not be an X in it). Then enter the insertion point values of `X:` **0,** `Y:` **0.** Enter an X and Y Scale of **1.0,** and a scale and rotation angle of 0. Press OK to exit the dialogue box.

AutoCAD LT will prompt the user, using the prompts entered with the attribute, to enter data for each variable attribute (the order of the requests may be different):

`Proj. name (21 letters max):` **TESTING** <return> `Your name:` **J. D. Smith** <return> `Class:` **CVTY 11** <return> `Scale <NTS>:` <return> `Subject #:` **CAD 1000-3** <return> `Date:` **1994-03-02** <return>

Because the verify mode was turned on when setting Attdef, the prompts will be redisplayed showing the variable data entered. You can change the data if desired or simply press Enter for each one.

The drawing border and title block will be drawn with the text information inserted into the title block.

If your attributes did not work properly, exit the current drawing without saving it. Then edit the drawing c:\drawings\am-hbdr, and make the appropriate corrections to the attribute. Then exit the drawing and save it using the name c:\drawings\am-hbdr. Start another blank drawing, set the limits to –5,–5 and 280,215, and zoom all. Then try inserting the c:\drawings\am-hbdr block.

Do not exit the current drawing with the inserted block am-hbdr, and the attributes. It will be used to demonstrate editing attributes.

12.4 Editing Attributes

After attributes have been invoked (i.e., after the block containing the attributes is inserted) they can be edited as follows:

```
Modify <pick> Edit Attributes . . . <pick>
```

The Edit Attributes dialogue box in Fig. 12.6 is displayed. Change the scale from NTS to ½ as shown. Select OK to exit. Then exit AutoCAD LT without saving the current drawing, which was a test of the border.

12.5 Create a Special Border Menu

When you tested the Am-hbdr.dwg file, you were required to set limits and use the Insert command. A special menu will now be created to draw borders and title blocks automatically.

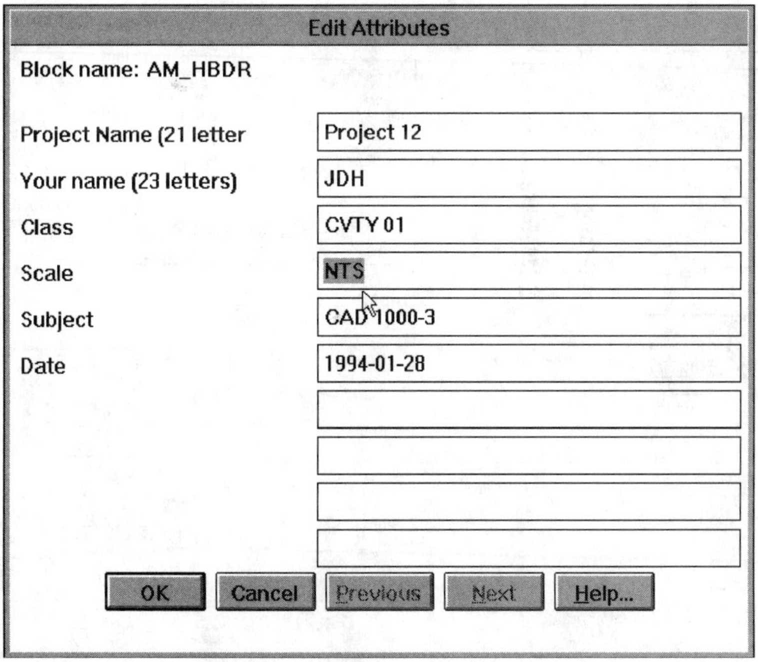

Edit Attributes
Block name: AM_HBDR
Project Name (21 letter — Project 12
Your name (23 letters) — JDH
Class — CVTY 01
Scale — NTS
Subject — CAD 1000-3
Date — 1994-01-28
OK | Cancel | Previous | Next | Help...

Figure 12.6 Editing attributes.

The aclt2 menu will be used to set up a plot drawing. A plot drawing has its limits set to the size of the sheet on which the drawing is to be plotted. Amhbdr.dwg is inserted into the plot drawing and drawings to be plotted are then inserted to scale as blocks into the plot drawing. A number of drawing files can be inserted onto the plot drawings, each at a different scale.

The procedure is illustrated in Fig. 12.7 where the Aclt2.mnu is loaded. Amhbdr is then inserted into the plot drawing, providing a border and title block. Next, a drawing named Proj-5 is inserted into the plot drawing, using a ¾ scale. The plot drawing is then saved with the drawing name of Plot-5. Plot-5 can now be plotted using a 1:1 scale to provide a hard copy drawing.

12.5.1 Creating the menu

The Aclt2.mnu file created in Chap. 11 is to be modified and used to insert the border and title block. Windows should currently be displayed on your screen. Follow the procedures outlined in Chap. 11, Sec. 11.3 to load Notepad. When Notepad is loaded choose `File` and then `Open`. The Open dialogue box in Fig. 11.9 is displayed. Set the Directories to `c:\drawings`. Then move the cursor to the file name box and change `*.txt` to ***.mnu** and press <return>. The menu files in c:\drawings are displayed in the files list box. Click on `aclt2.mnu` and then press `OK`.

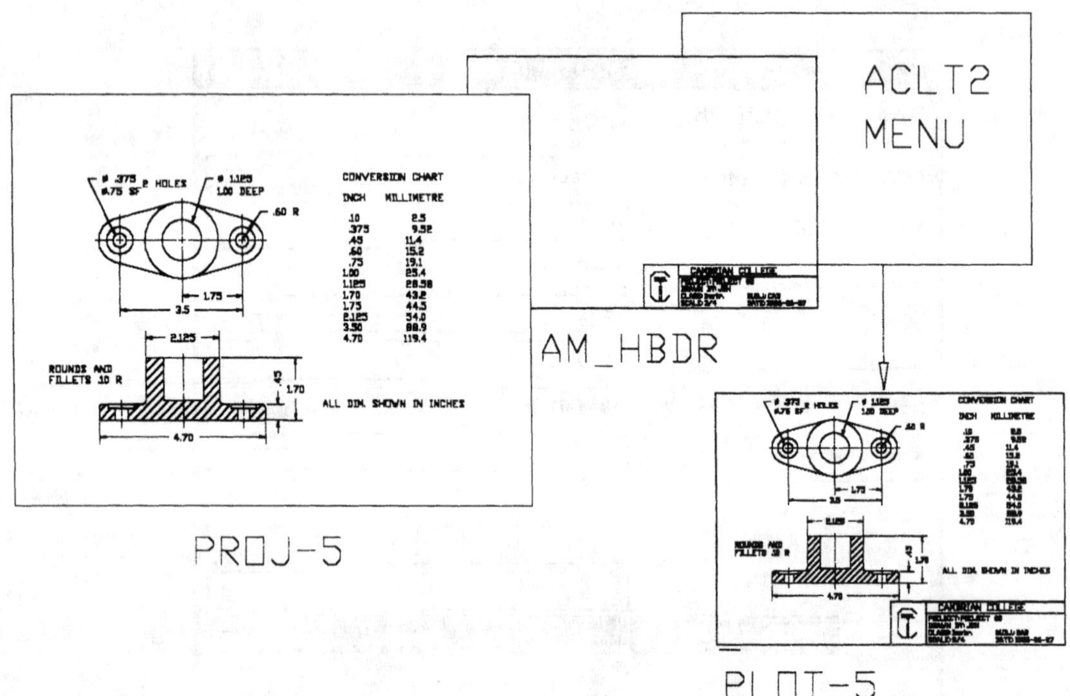

Figure 12.7 Plot drawing construction sequence.

Edit the aclt2.mnu file adding the commands shown in Fig. 12.8 to the POP2 section of the menu. Commands in other sections of the menu are not changed.

When your aclt2 menu is exactly the same as the author's, choose `Save` in the File menu to save the file and then choose `Exit`.

The macro added to the menu is:

[A-Size]limits -5,-5 280,215 zoom a +
insert c:/drawings/am-hbdr;0,0 1 1 0

When aclt2.mnu is loaded into AutoCAD LT the pulled-down menu appears as shown in Fig. 11.11. If `A-Size` is chosen from the menu, the following sequence of operations is invoked:

- The limits command is loaded and entered by the single blank space following it.
- The lower-left corner limits are read from the menu as –5,–5 and entered by the space following the coordinates.
- The upper-right corner limits are read as 280,215 and entered.
- The Zoom command is entered and the All option is entered.
- The plus sign indicates to AutoCAD LT the line continues onto the next line, where the Insert command is read and entered.
- Insert requests the block to insert and reads c:/drawings/am-hbdr from the menu, which is entered with the semicolon (;) following it. Note that file paths are indicated by a forward slash in a menu file. The backslash is reserved for user input (see Chap. 11, Sec. 11.5.2).
- Insert requests the insertion point for the block and reads coordinates 0,0 from the menu. The blank space enters the coordinates.

Notepad - ACLT2.MNU

File Edit Search Help

```
***POP2
[Title Blk]
[->Metric]
[A Size]limits -5,-5 280,215 zoom a +
insert c:/drawings/am-hbdr;0,0 1 1 0
[<-B Size]
[->Imperial]
[A Size]
[<-B Size]
[--]
Insert
Move
Erase
Ltscale
Undo
```

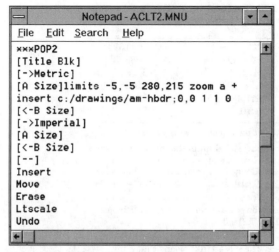

Figure 12.8 Adding POP3.

- Insert next requests the X scale factor for the block being inserted, and reads 1 followed by the blank space to enter the 1. The remaining entries are the Y scale of 1, and the rotation angle of 0.

The line [A-Size] then sets the screen to a 280 by 215 sheet of paper, and inserts the block c:\drawings\am-hbdr. When the block is inserted, the attributes are invoked and you are able to enter the title block variables.

Other useful commands in the menu (see Figs. 11.4, 12.8, and App. G) are Insert, which is used to Insert other drawings into the border drawing, and Move, which is used to move entities that have been inserted. The completed drawing is then plotted using the Plot command.

The menu currently is only developed for drawings limits set to 280 by 215, which is a sheet of A-size paper (11 by 8.5) in millimeters. When drawings are inserted, you will be required to enter the insertion point. Enter 0,0 and then use Move to relocate the entity if necessary. Next, you will be asked to enter an X-scale factor. If you had both an Imperial unit border and a metric border, the scale factors you would enter are listed in Table 12.1 and App. B. Imperial unit borders are to be drawn later.

12.6 Plot Drawing Example

Boot AutoCAD LT using the `ACADLT PROTO1` icon created in Chap. 11. This loads the customized aclt2.mnu file from the c:\drawings directory.

Click on `Title Blk` in the toolbar (Fig. 11.11). Then click on `Metric` and `A Size`. AutoCAD LT inserts am-hbdr.dwg, and invokes the attributes. Enter the requested data. When the scale is asked for, enter ¾, assuming proj-5 is being plotted on an A-size (11- by 8.5-in) sheet.

TABLE 12.1 Plot-Drawing Scale Factors*

Dwg. units	Scale	X scale factor
Feet (architect)	⅛″ = 1′0″	.0104167†
Feet (architect)	¼″ = 1′0″	.0208333†
Inches (decimal)	¾″	.75
Feet (engineer)	1″ = 50′0″	.0016667‡
Meters (decimal)	1:100	10§
Millimeters (decimal)	1:100	.01

*See Table B.1 for a complete listing of plot-drawing scale factor.

†When using AutoCAD LT's architectural units, the drawing units are always inches even though the coordinates are displayed on the monitor in feet and inches. The scale factor is then 1/(N*12). For ⅛ in = 1 ft the scale factor is 1/(8*12) = 0.0104167.

‡AutoCAD LT's engineering units are in inches even though the monitor displays feet and inches. The scale factor is then 1/(N*12). For 1 in = 50 ft the scale factor is 1/(50*12) = 0.0016667.

§The units used to draw the border are millimeters, and the units used for the drawing are meters. The scale 1:100 means that 1 mm = 100 mm or 1 mm = 0.1 m. The scale factor is then 1/0.1 = 10.

When inserting the Proj-5.dwg drawing into the plot-5.dwg drawing, you must take into account that plot-5.dwg was drawn using millimeter units; therefore, the scale becomes ¾ * 25.4 = 19.05. Select INSERT from the menu:

Insert <pick> Block name: **c:\drawings\proj-5** <return> Insertion point: **0,0** <return> X-Scale factor <1>: **19.05** <return> Y-Scale factor <19.05>: <return> Rotation angle: **0** <return> <return>

You can call the File dialogue box when AutoCAD LT requests the block name by entering a tilde (~) as follows:

Insert: <pick> Block name: ~ <return>

Use the Move command in the Modify menu or Toolbox to put the entity into a better location on the drawing. The entire Proj-5 drawing is now a single entity because it was inserted as a block. To move it using the Move command, use the following:

Move <pick> Select objects: Assist <pick> Select <pick> Last <pick> Select objects: <return> Base point or displacement: Digitize a convenient point on the Proj-5 entity to act as a first point during the move. <pick> Second point: Digitize a point on the monitor where you would like the first point to be moved to. <pick>

The entire Proj-5 entity will now be moved from the first to the second point. You can move the entity as often as desired.

12.7 Plotting a Plot Drawing

Use the Plot command to plot the drawing. The scale to be selected is 1:1 because the drawing was scaled when it was inserted into the plot drawing on the monitor. The plot sequence is as follows:

File <pick> Print/Plot <pick>

A Plot configuration dialogue box similar to that in Fig. 7.1 is displayed. Set the appropriate plotter/printer as outlined in Chap. 7, Sec. 7.3. Set the pens as outlined in Chap. 7, Sec. 7.5. The paper size is set at 280 by 215 which is an A-size sheet converted to millimeters. The scale is 1=1. Complete the other settings and preview the plot. If the preview is proper, press OK to complete the plot.

Use the Save command in the Easy1 menu to save the drawing using the file name c:\drawings\plot-5. Do *not* save the drawing as Proj-5 or you will write the block over your original drawing, thereby loosing both. If you get a warning the drawing already exists, look carefully at the file name. Use the Quit command to exit.

The drawing cannot be modified on the plot drawing because it was inserted onto that drawing as a block. If the drawing is to be modified, it is changed on the original drawing and the block definition is updated, following the procedure illustrated in Chap. 10, Sec. 10.6.

12.7.1 Plot Proj-6.dwg

Use a similar procedure to plot the Proj-6.dwg drawing. That drawing was done in meter units and will be inserted into a plot drawing using a scale of 1 mm = 300 mm. The x and y insertion scale factor will be $\frac{1}{300} * 1000 = 3.33$ (because the drawing was in meters and the border is in millimeters, the 1000 multiplier converts the drawing units from meters to millimeters).

12.7.2 Linetype scale

When a block is inserted into a drawing, it uses the line-type scale (Ltscale) of the current drawing. This is because there is only one Ltscale setting for a drawing. After Proj-6 is inserted into the border drawing, the linetype scale is set using the Ltscale command in our menu because different line types were used for layers in the drawing. The Ltscale used in Chap. 6, Sec. 6.7 was 5.7. This value must be multiplied by the *x,y* insertion scale factor of 3.33, giving an Ltscale of 19:

```
Ltscale <pick> New scale factor <1>: 19 <return>
```

The drawing will be regenerated with the new linetype scale.

Use the Plot command to plot the drawing. The size units for the plotted drawing are millimeters. The plot origin is 0,0 and the plot size is 280 by 215. Plot the drawing using a scale of 1 = 1.

12.7.3 Assignment

Boot AutoCAD LT and open the c:\drawings\am-hbdr drawing. Then invoke the Block command (see Chap. 10, Sec. 10.3.1) and make a block of the title block. The Base point (insertion point) of the block is selected from the screen at the lower-right corner of the border. Use an Intersection object snap. Select the block using a selection Window enclosing only the title block. Although the selection window crosses the two borderlines, they are not included in the block. Name the block Title, and then write it to file (Block Out), using the file name c:\drawings\title.dwg. Exit the drawing without saving the changes.

You are to create an Imperial A-size (11- by 8.5-in) border, an Imperial B-size (17- by 11-in) border, and a metric B-size (430 mm by 280 mm) border, each with a title block, following the procedures outlined in this chapter. Each is to be saved in the c:\drawings directory using an original name. The actual border frame size is to be less than the sheet sizes, and may be governed by your plotter's limitations.

The procedure to draw each of the borders is as follows:

- Draw the borders using lines instead of polylines. Do not draw a title block.
- Plot the border to see how it fits the sheet. Edit the border as required.
- Use the Polyline command to draw a solid polyline over the border lines, snapping onto the intersections. Use a polyline width of 0.2 mm with the metric border and width of .01″ for the Imperial borders.

- Insert (read Chap. 10, Sec. 10.4) the title block created above and written to a file named c:\drawings\title.dwg. The insertion point is picked from the screen as the lower-right corner of the border. Use the Intersection object snap to select the insertion point. The X and Y scale factors are 1 when inserting title block into a metric drawing (since title was drawn in millimeters). When inserting into an Imperial, units drawing the X and Y scale factors are **0.0394** (1/25.4) to convert the title block from millimeters to inches. Click the `Explode` check box on (see Fig. 10.7) so the attributes are not invoked when the title.dwg block is inserted.
- Save the border to a file in c:\drawings using an original name.

When all of the blocks have been written to disk, edit the customized c:\drawings\aclt2.mnu menu and add the appropriate macros to the lines in the POP2 section following the same procedures used for the metric A-Size item.

Chapter

13

Working Spaces and External References

Objectives. Use paper space for creating borders and title blocks; viewports; external references; stretching associative dimensions.

Drawing. Drawing Proj-6 will be edited.

13.1 Working Space

AutoCAD LT has two working space areas—models space and paper space. Model space is where you do most of your drafting; e.g., all of the drawings in previous chapters were done in model space. Paper space is where you create the image, usually within a border, that will be sent to the printer/plotter to be transferred onto paper. The application of paper space is similar to that of the border drawing introduced in Chap. 12, where you arrange and scale views to plot. In Chap. 12, however, the border was also done in model space.

Boot AutoCAD LT and Open drawing Proj-6, completed in Chap. 6.

The coordinate system icon illustrated in Fig. 13.1 is displayed in the lower-left corner of the screen when you are working in model space. If the icon is not displayed, choose the following commands to display the icon at the origin (coordinates 0,0,0):

Assist <pick> UCS icon <pick> ON/OFF/ALL/Noorgin/ORigin <OFF>: On <return> <return> ON/OFF/All/Noorgin/ORigin <ON>: **OR** (Origin) <return>

The model space icon is turned on and set to appear at the origin point (0,0,0) of the current viewport.

Paper space will be used to place a border around drawing Proj-6 and to plot the drawing using a scale of 1:300. To turn paper space on, the Tilemode system variable must be turned off by setting it to 0. Tilemode is discussed more in later chapters. Choose the following commands:

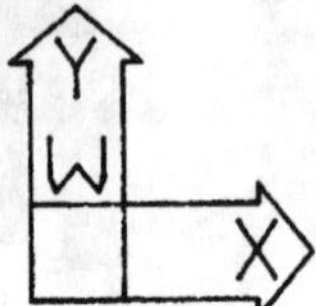

Figure 13.1 Model space icon.

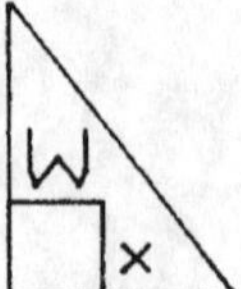

Figure 13.2 Paper space icon.

View <pick> Paper Space <pick> A check mark in added in front of Paper Space indicating paper space is on (Tilemode is off).

AutoCAD LT shows the following at the command line:

```
New value for TILEMODE <1>: 0 Entering Paper Space. Use MVIEW to insert
Model space viewports.
```

The working mode is now paper space. The model space icon in the bottom-left corner is replaced by the paper space icon (Fig. 13.2). If there is no paper space icon on your screen, follow the commands at the start of this chapter to turn the UCS (coordinate system) icon on. When paper space is on, the paper space button "P" (see App. E, Fig. E.11) in the buttons bar is pressed, and appears white.

Your Proj-6 drawing has also disappeared. Actually it is not gone, it is in model space. To see it, you have to open a viewport in paper space or return to model space.

Move the cursor around the screen noting that drawing limits have changed to 0,0 and about 12,9. These are the default limits of paper space in the English measurement setting.

13.1.1 Adding a border in paper space

Now that paper space is enabled, the menu file (aclt2.mnu, created in Chaps. 11 and 12) is to be used to draw a border and title block:

File <pick> Exit... <pick>

An options box shown in Fig. 1.20 is displayed. Press the Save Changes... button and save the drawing in its origin file c:\drawings\proj-6.dwg. Proj-6 is now saved in the paper space mode. It will retain that mode when reopened.

Boot AutoCAD LT choosing the ACADLT PROTO1 icon. AutoCAD LT is reloaded with the customized aclt2.mnu menu file. Choose Open... in the File menu and open drawing Proj-6 again. Proj-6 is displayed on the screen in paper space. The paper space icon should be visible in the lower-left corner of the screen.

The customized menu is now loaded into AutoCAD LT, and Proj-6 is open for editing. Click on Title Blk in the toolbar (Fig. 11.11). Then click on Metric and A-Size. The macro sets the screen limits to –5,–5 and 280,215, and invokes Zoom and All. The c:\drawings\am-hbdr.dwg drawing is then inserted and the attributes are invoked. Enter the requested data. When the scale is asked for, enter 1:300.

When the border and title block are completed, the customized menu is no longer required. AutoCAD LT is exited and reloaded with its standard menu as follows:

File <pick> Exit... <pick>

An options box shown in Fig. 1.20 is displayed. Press the Save Changes... button and save the drawing in its origin file c:\drawings\proj-6.dwg.

Boot AutoCAD LT choosing the AutoCAD LT (standard) icon. AutoCAD LT is reloaded with the standard aclt2.mnu menu file. Choose Open... in the File menu and open drawing Proj-6 again. The current working space is paper space, indicated by the paper space icon in the lower-left corner of the screen.

13.1.2 Opening a viewport

Prior to opening a viewport to see the Proj-6 drawing, a layer is to be created for the viewport to reside on. Create a new layer name VIEWLYR1 (View-layer 1) and set its color to green. Make Viewlyr1 the current layer. The current layer should be Viewlyr1.

In order to view the model (object) drawn in model space, a viewport must be opened in paper space:

View <pick> Viewports <pick> Make Viewport <pick>

The Viewports menu is shown in Fig. 13.3. These are the paper space menus. Some items in the menu are grayed indicating they are not accessible in paper space (see App. E, Fig. E.4.2 for a listing of the options that can be invoked in paper space or model space).

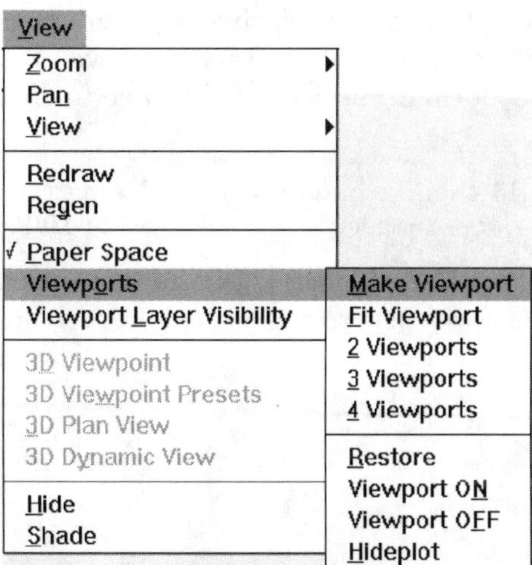

Figure 13.3 Opening a viewport.

The command continues at the command line:

> ON/OFF/Hideplot/Fit/2/3/4/Restore/<First point>: Press the Shift and second button on the mouse [Shift->2B] Intersection <pick> of Place the intersection target on the lower left corner of the border. <pick> Second point: [Shift->2B] Intersection <pick> of Place the intersection target on the upper-right corner. <pick>

The two points selected open a viewport the size of the border. Alternatively, you could have used the Fit option to open a viewport the size of the graphics screen. The other options are discussed in later chapters.

Proj-6 is now visible on the screen and a green line bounds the border. The green line is the viewport boundary opened with make Viewports. It is green because it resides on layer Viewlyr1, which was the current layer when the viewport was created.

Proj-6 was scaled by AutoCAD LT to fit the viewport opened with Make Viewports. As specified in Chap. 6, the drawing scale is to be 1:300. Because the border limits are in millimeters and Proj-6 is drawn in meters, the scale should be 1/0.3 or 3.33 as discussed in Chap. 12, Sec. 12.7.1. The XP option to the Zoom command allows you to scale the model space "times paper space." Because the Proj-6 lot plan drawing resides in model space, you must first return to model space before you can zoom the lot plan:

> Press the P button in the buttons bar <pick>

When Tilemode is set to 1 and a viewport has been opened, you can toggle between paper and model space using the P button in the buttons bar.

When the Mspace command is invoked, the paper space icon disappears and the model space icon appears in the bottom-left corner of the screen. The letter P in the buttons bar appears off (grayed). Move the cursor on the screen noting the cursor coordinates reported are those for model space. When the cursor is moved outside of the viewport (around the border), the cursor is changed to an arrow.

The model space view can now be zoomed relative to paper space using the Zoom and Xp commands as follows (the scale is 1/0.3; however, AutoCAD LT might not accept the 0.3 in that format and you might have to enter the division as 10/3 or as 3.333.):

> Press the Zoom button (Fig. 13.4) in the buttons bar. <pick> Zoom All/Center/Dynamic/Extents/Left/Previous/Window/<Scale> (X/XP): **10/3xp** <return>

The model is now scaled by 3.33 in the viewport. Use the Pan command in the View menu to pan the object in the viewport so it is located properly in the border.

Figure 13.4 Zoom button.

The green line around the perimeter of the screen is the viewport boundary. The List command can be used to list its data; however, the viewport boundary line resides in paper space so you will have to return to paper space before you can select it:

Press the P button in the buttons bar <pick>

The List command is now used to obtain information about the viewport boundary:

Assist <pick> List <pick> Select object: Click on the border <pick> Select objects: <return>

AutoCAD LT reports:

```
VIEWPORT Layer: VIEWLYR1
         Space: Paper space
         Status: On and Active
         Scale relative to Paper space: 3.3333 x p
  center point, X = 125.000 Y = 102.500 Z = 0.000
  width 249.800
  height 174.800
```

Press F2 to exit the text screen. Noting the viewport green boundary line is on layer Viewlyr 1, use the Layer Control dialogue box to set layer Text as current and freeze layer Viewlyr1. The green boundary line will disappear.

If at any time your drawing disappears, use the Regen command to regenerate the screen.

Use the Zoom and Window commands to zoom on a small area of the drawing. Try erasing something in the Proj-6 lot plan drawing. It can't be done because the current working space is paper space.

You cannot edit items that are in model space when you are in paper space. Use the Zoom and Previous commands to return to the previous zoom view.

Change to model space using the Mspace command. Now use the Zoom and Window commands. What happened?

In model space, items in paper space are not accessible with any commands so the border in paper space did not zoom. Use the Zoom and Previous commands to return to the original zoom, or reenter the Zoom and 10/3Xp commands. If you set Tilemode to 1, the working space is changed to model space and anything drawn in paper space is deleted from the screen. Resetting Tilemode to 0 returns the paper space entities to the screen.

Notice that because you are working in the Proj-6.Dwg, you did not have to reset the Ltscale as you did when you inserted Proj-6.Dwg into the Border.Dwg in Chap. 12.

13.1.3 Plotting paper space drawings

Set the working space to paper space before continuing.

Because the border is drawn to suit a sheet of paper 280 by 215 mm, which is the size of the paper you are to plot on, the plot scale is 1=1. Plot the drawing following the procedures outlined in Chap. 7, Sec. 7.3.

After the plot is complete, set the working space to model space and try plotting again using a scale of 1=1. Notice how small the plot is. That is because in model space the screen limits are those set for Proj-6 which are 0,0 an 70,50 (see Chap. 6), and the drawing units are meters. If you plot using a scale of 1=1 then 1 mm of the plot = 1 meter of the drawing, and the drawing fits in an area of about 70 by 50 mm. If you plot from model space, you have to consider the 1:300 scale of the drawing which for plotting is interpreted as 1 mm of the plot = 0.3 meters of the drawing, giving a plot scale of 1=0.3. Also notice that the border, which is in paper space, is not plotted when you plot from model space.

You should usually plot from paper space using a scale of 1=1. Change the drawing back to paper space so it is ready if you want to plot it again. Save the drawing and Exit AutoCAD LT.

13.2 External References

AutoCAD LT's external reference (xref) is similar to the concept used in Chap. 12 to insert drawings as blocks into a plot drawing. Although the concept is similar, attaching an external reference, Xref, is different from inserting a block file into a drawing in a number of ways.

Unlike a block, an Xrefs definition is not saved with the drawing. It is reloaded each time the drawing is edited so that if the referenced drawing is updated, its latest version will be read into the parent drawing the next time it is edited. Because the referenced drawing data is not read into the drawing file, using Xrefs also reduces the size of drawing files. The only reference to the referenced drawing in the master drawing file is the referenced drawing's name, path, and insertion scale and location.

Any drawing or Block written to file can be attached to a master drawing as an external reference.

Xrefs can be nested so that one Xref loads another which loads another, etc. A change in the lower-level Xref would then cause a change in all of the Xrefs above it.

13.2.1 The drawing

A border will be drawn using the aclt2.mnu (ACADLT PROTO1 icon) menu from Chap. 12 and the lot drawn in Chap. 6 will be linked to the border drawing as an external reference.

Boot AutoCAD LT using the `ACADLT PROTO1` icon to load AutoCAD LT with the customized aclt2 menu.

Use the `New...` option in the `File` menu to start a new drawing named `Proj-6X` in the directory `c:\drawings`.

Tilemode is to be set to 0 to enable paper space; however, there is no command in this menu, so it is entered from the command line:

```
Command: Tilemode <return> New value for Tilemode <1>: 0 <return>
New value for TILEMODE <1>: 0 Entering Paper Space.
Use MVIEW to insert Model space viewports.
```

The working mode is now paper space. The model space icon in the bottom-left corner is replaced by the paper space icon (Fig. 13.2), and the paper space button, marked P in the toolbar, is displayed pressed on (white). If there is no paper space icon on your screen enter the following at the command prompt to turn the UCS (coordinate system) icon on:

```
Command: ucsicon <return> ON/OFF/All/Noorigin/ORigin <OFF>: on <return>
```

Use your menu to draw a metric A-size border. Use the name Proj-6X in the border and enter the scale as 1:300. Once the border is complete, AutoCAD LT's standard menu is to be loaded. Save the drawing and then Exit AutoCAD LT. Reboot the original version of AutoCAD LT. Use the Open . . . command in the File menu to open drawing Proj-6X again.

The standard AutoCAD LT menu is loaded and you are working in a drawing name Proj-6X. The drawing currently displays a border and title block.

13.2.2 XREF command

External references are added to a drawing using the Xref command. The Proj-6.Dwg file is to be attached to this drawing with a scale of 3.33. See Chap. 12, Sec. 12.7.1. This can be entered as 10/3, as follows:

```
Draw <pick> External Reference (see App. E, Fig. E.3.2) <pick> Attach... <pick>
```

A Select File to Attach dialogue box similar to the dialogue box shown in Fig. 10.9 is displayed. Set the Directories edit box to `c:\drawings` and choose the file `proj-6.dwg` in the file selection box. Press `OK` to continue the command at the command line:

```
PROJ-6 loaded
Insertion point: 0,0 <return>
X Scale factor <1>/Corner/XYZ: 10/3 <return>
Y Scale factor <default = x>: <return>
Rotation angle <0>: <return>
```

The Proj-6 drawing is now attached and displayed. Notice that the border that was added to the Proj-6 drawing in Chap. 13, Sec. 13.1 and drawn in paper space is not displayed. When reading entities from the attached drawing, AutoCAD LT copies only entities created in model space. This is useful as you would not want the border copied into the current drawing.

Use the Move command to relocate the lot plan better within the border. Note how the entire lot plan is treated as a single entity when being moved.

The property boundary center linetype appears to be a continuous line rather than a center line as on Proj-6.Dwg. When a referenced drawing is loaded it uses the linetype scale of the master drawing. This is because Auto-

CAD LT allows only one Linetype Scale for a drawing. Change the Linetype Scale setting to 19 as calculated in Chap. 12, Sec. 12.7.2.

13.2.3 Reporting XRef partnerships

The List? option to the XRef command lists a report of the external references. Enter the following:

Draw <pick> External Reference (see App. E, Fig. E.3.2) <pick> List? <pick>

AutoCAD LT reports:

```
Xref Name                Path
PROJ-6                   C:\DRAWINGS\PROJ-6.DWG
TOTAL Xref(s): 1
```

Press F2 to return to the graphics window.

XRefs are also reported in response to the ? option to the Block command. The Make Block . . . command in the Construct menu loads a dialogue box. In order to display the Block command at the command prompt and get the desired option, type Block and press <return>. AutoCAD LT continues with:

Block name (or ?): **?** <return> Block(s) to list <*>: <return>

A report similar to the following is displayed:

```
 Defined blocks.
   A
   AM_HBDR
   LOGO
   PROJ-6                        Xref: resolved
   PROJ-6|A                      Xdep: PROJ-6
   PROJ-6|AM_HBDR                Xdep: PROJ-6
   PROJ-6|LOGO                   Xdep: PROJ-6

 User       External      Dependent      Unnamed
Blocks     References      Blocks        Blocks
   3            1             3             12
```

The Xref: resolved statement beside PROJ-6 indicates that AutoCAD LT had no problem attaching the Xref, and that object name conflicts were successfully managed (see Chap. 13, Sec. 13.2.4). The Xdep: PROJ-6 statements in the next three lines indicate that those blocks are named object in the referenced drawing Proj-6. Press F2 to return to the graphics window.

13.2.4 External references and named objects

Certain objects associated with a drawing are referred to as named objects: blocks, dimension styles, layers, linetypes, text styles; and items to be discussed in later chapters such as named user coordinate systems, named views, and named viewport configurations.

Named objects can be renamed with the Rename command and purged from the drawing using the Purge command. When prompted for a named object by AutoCAD LT, you can also utilize wildcard characters such as * and ?. Refer to your *AutoCAD LT User's Guide* or the Help routine (APP.A4) for more information on named objects.

When a drawing is attached to another as an external reference, its definition is reloaded from the reference file each time the master drawing is loaded. The named objects in the attached drawing are referred to as dependent symbols and are temporarily renamed by AutoCAD LT so they do not conflict with similarly named objects in the master drawing. Dependent symbol names are formed as a combination of the referenced drawings name and the named objects name separated by a vertical bar (|). For example, the report by the ? option to the Block command in the previous chapter shows blocks A, AM_HBDR and LOGO from the referenced drawing, Proj-6, to be temporarily renamed as PROJ-6 | A, PROJ-6 | AM_HBDR, and PROJ-6 | LOGO respectively.

Layer name objects are also temporarily renamed and may be displayed in the Layer Control dialogue box using the pull-down menu:

`Settings` <pick> `Layer Control...`<pick>

The layers in the Proj-6 drawing have been temporarily renamed as illustrated in Fig. 13.5. For example, layer Center, which has a Center linetype (see Chap. 6, Sec. 6.2) has been temporarily renamed to layer PROJ-6 | CENTER and its linetype renamed to PROJ-6 | CENTER. This allows you to have a layer named Center with a color red on the master drawing, and a layer named Center on the referenced drawing with a color blue, because the referenced drawing layer is temporarily renamed PROJ-6 | CENTER.

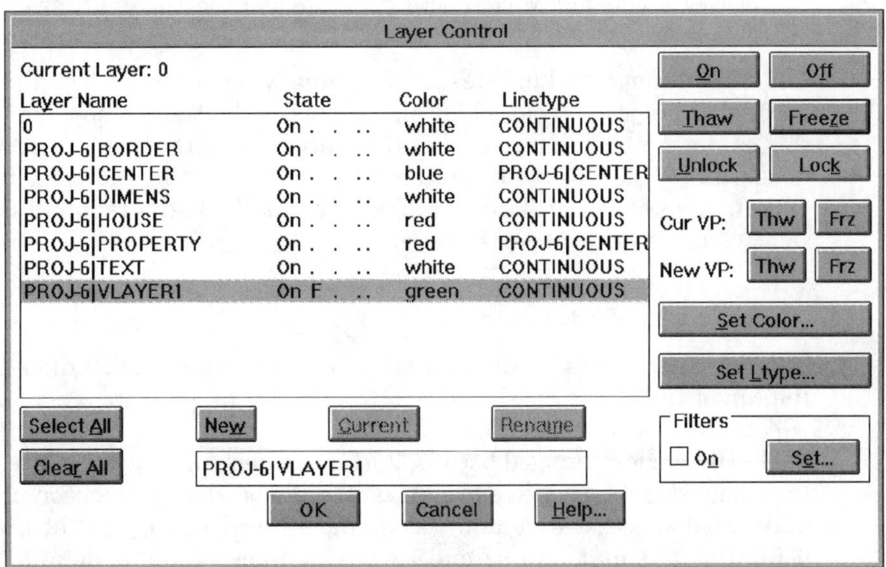

Figure 13.5 Dependent symbols.

Layers 0 and DEFPOINTS (see Chap. 13, Sec. 13.2.5) and the linetype CONTINUOUS are not renamed when the referenced drawing is loaded. The drawing overrides those named objects so that if layer 0 is red on the master drawing and green on the referenced drawing, objects on layer 0 in the referenced drawing will appear as red. Because layer DEFPOINTS resides on the master drawing, Proj-6X, and also on the referenced drawing, Proj-6, AutoCAD LT reports that the duplicate DEFPOINTS layer definition is ignored, when this drawing is reloaded (see Chap. 13, Sec. 13.2.6).

You are able to change the color and linetype of dependent layers on the master drawing; however, the changes are temporary because the reference file is not saved with the master drawing. Each time the master drawing is loaded, AutoCAD LT reloads the reference file and only changes made to that file are displayed.

Use the *Save*... command to save drawing Proj-6X. Do not exit AutoCAD.

Drawing Proj-6 will be edited and Proj-6X reloaded to see the effects of the editing.

13.2.5 Stretching associative dimensions

Open an existing drawing c:\drawings\proj-6.

If the drawing is in paper space (if the "P" button in the button menu is pressed) click on the P button turning it off to change to model space. Then stretch the house width from 7.200 meters to 8.000 meters as follows:

> `Modify` <pick> `Stretch` <pick>
> `Select objects to stretch by window or polygon...`
> `Select objects: C`
> `First corner:` Select point A in Fig. 13.6 <pick> `Other corner:` Select point B placing a crossing window through or around the house, driveway, and house dimension to be stretched. <pick> `Select objects:`

The Stretch command invokes the Crossing window option. The Crossing window selects objects enclosed within or crossed by the window boundaries. In this case you must ensure that entities affected by the change in width of the house from 7.200 to 8.000 are crossed or enclosed in the crossing window. Objects missed can still be selected individually. If the required entities are selected press return to exit the selection:

> `Select objects:` <return> `Base point:` Select any point as a reference. <pick>
> `New point:` **@0.8<0** <return>

Notice that the house width increased by 0.8 meters and the dimension along the top of the house also increased from 7.200 to 8.000 meters (the hatching will not have stretched).

The dimension changed because, prior to dimensioning the house, you made the dimensions associative by setting the Associative Dimension on, in Chap. 6, Sec. 6.9.4. Associative dimensions have a definition point at the selection points for the first and second extension lines. When a definition point is moved, for instance by the Stretch command, AutoCAD LT automatically modifies the dimension to suit the relocation of the definition point.

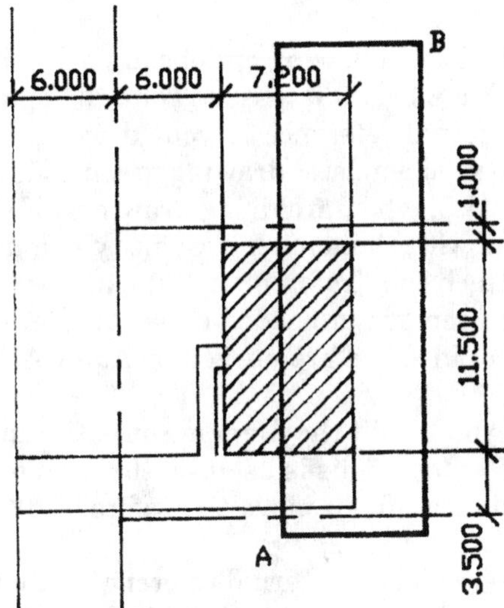

Figure 13.6 Stretch crossing window.

The associative dimension definition points might occasionally be visible on the screen; however, they will not be visible on the plot because AutoCAD LT puts them on a layer named Defpoints which is not plotted by AutoCAD LT.

Because the house hatching did not stretch, erase it and redo it on layer House (refer to Chap. 6, Sec. 6.6).

Set the working space to paper space and then use the Save command to save drawing Proj-6. Do not exit AutoCAD LT.

13.2.6 Reloading the master drawing

Open an existing drawing c:\drawings\proj-6X. AutoCAD LT will load Proj-6X, and if it has no problems attaching the Proj-6 Xref, it will report the following:

```
Resolved Xref PROJ-6: c:\drawings\proj-6
duplicate DEFPOINTS layer entry ignored
PROJ-6 loaded
Loaded menu c:\ACLTWIN\ACLT2.MNX
```

If AutoCAD LT is unable to locate the Xref file (Proj-6.dwg) on the diskette in drive A: (or in the original path used when you attached it to Proj-6), it reports the following error:

```
"c:\drawings\proj-6.dwg". Can't open file
error resolving Xref PROJ-6.
```

If this happens, check that the Proj-6.dwg file is where it should be and invoke the Reload or Path option to the Xref command (see Sec. 13.2.7).

Notice that the latest version of the reference file with the house width modified from 7.200 to 8.000 is loaded.

13.2.7 Other Xref commands

When the Xref command is invoked the following options are available:

The Attach and List? options have been discussed. The Bind option allows you to permanently attach an external reference to your drawing. This command might be used if you wish to send a master drawing to someone but do not wish to send the Xref drawings. Also, when archiving drawings, if you do not wish to archive the Xref drawings with the master drawing you must use the bind command to permanently attach the Xreferences to the master drawing.

The Detach option allows you to remove unneeded external references from your drawing. Xrefs loaded but not inserted are purged by AutoCAD LT when the master drawing is exited.

The Change Path option allows you to edit the filename or path AutoCAD LT uses when loading an external reference. This is useful if the path to an external reference is changed, for instance, if you move the referenced file from a floppy diskette to the hard drive.

The Reload option allows you to reload an external reference without exiting and reentering the master drawing. This might be useful if, for instance, a colleague has modified the referenced drawing and you wish to reload the new edition.

The Bind Symbols command lets you add a selected subset of an external reference's dependent symbols to your master drawing permanently. For instance, PROJ-6|CENTER linetype cannot be accessed. Try it. Pull down the layer Control dialogue box and try to change the linetype for layer House to PROJ-6|CENTER. AutoCAD LT will report that you cannot make an externally referenced linetype current.

Use the Bind Symbols command to load the PROJ-6|CENTER linetype into the master drawing as follows:

Draw <pick> External Reference <pick> Bind Symbols <pick> Linetype <pick>
Dependent Linetype name(s): **proj-6|center** (Note the bar (|) separator)
<return> 1 Linetype(s) found

Now pull down the Layer Control dialogue box. Notice that the PROJ-6|CENTER linetype has been renamed to PROJ-6$0$CEN>. The bar (|) is replaced with 0. The name is really PROJ-6$0$CENTER, but there is not enough room to show the entire name. To see the remainder of the name pick the symbol > at the end of the linetype name.

Change the linetype for layer House to PROJ-6$0$CENTER.

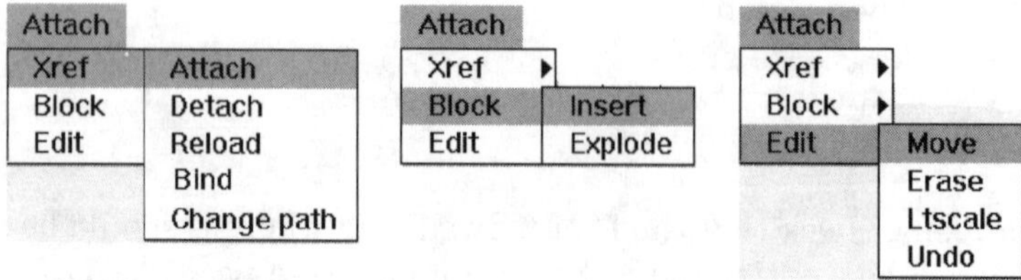

Figure 13.7 POP3 attach menu.

Plot the drawing on a A-size sheet using millimeter units and a scale of 1=1.

Notice that the layer House linetype is plotted as a continuous linetype. The House layer linetype was changed to PROJ-6$0$CENTER in the master drawing; however, it was only temporary. AutoCAD LT reloads the reference drawing file each time the master drawing is loaded.

Assignment. Using Notepad modify the customized menu file c:\drawings\aclt2.mnu file adding the POP3 Attach menu section illustrated in Fig. 13.7. Attach is to have three options: Xref, Block, and Edit, each with cascading menus as shown.

Chapter

14

Multiscale Drawings

Objective. Create a "protodrawing" to be used as a preliminary drawing border; plot a building floor plan to one scale and, on the same sheet, plot different scale details maintaining uniform text and dimension variable sizes.

Drawing. The final plotted drawing is illustrated in Fig. 14.1. The steps required to complete that drawing are outlined in the following text.

14.1 Scaling Drawings

When drawing with AutoCAD LT, items are drawn full scale using the drawing editor. The scaling takes place during the plotting of the drawing or on a plot drawing as outlined in Chap. 12.

To create a multiscale drawing, the items for each scale will have to be drawn full size on a separate drawing and later inserted into a final plot drawing using the scale desired for that item.

The procedure is illustrated in Fig. 14.1, where the Plan View and the Wall Elevation are to reside on the same final drawing, but each is to be drawn using a different scale. The Plan View and Wall Elevation are first drawn full-scale as separate drawing files. In the final hard copy drawing, the Plan View is to be drawn at a scale of ¼ in = 1 ft 0 in and the Wall Elevation is to be drawn at a scale of ½ in = 1 ft 0 in. This is done by loading the customized aclt2.mnu file created in Chap. 12, and inserting the Plan View using an x and y factor of 0.020833 [1/(4 × 12)] and the Wall Elevation using an x and y factor of 0.0416667 [1/(2 × 12)] into a plot drawing. The drawing is then plotted using a scale of 1:1. The insertion scale factors are illustrated in Table 12.1 and Table B in App. B.

You also have to ensure that the text height, dimension variables, and hatch scale factors are set for each entity drawing to provide a consistent size on the composite drawing. If the text height desired on the plotted drawing is ³⁄₃₂ in, the text height on drawing Plan View, which is to be plotted at a scale of ¼ in = 1 ft 0 in, will have to be 4.5 in [1/(4 × 12) × H = ³⁄₃₂]. The text height on the Wall Elevation drawing, which is to be plotted at a scale of ½ in = 1 ft 0 in, will have

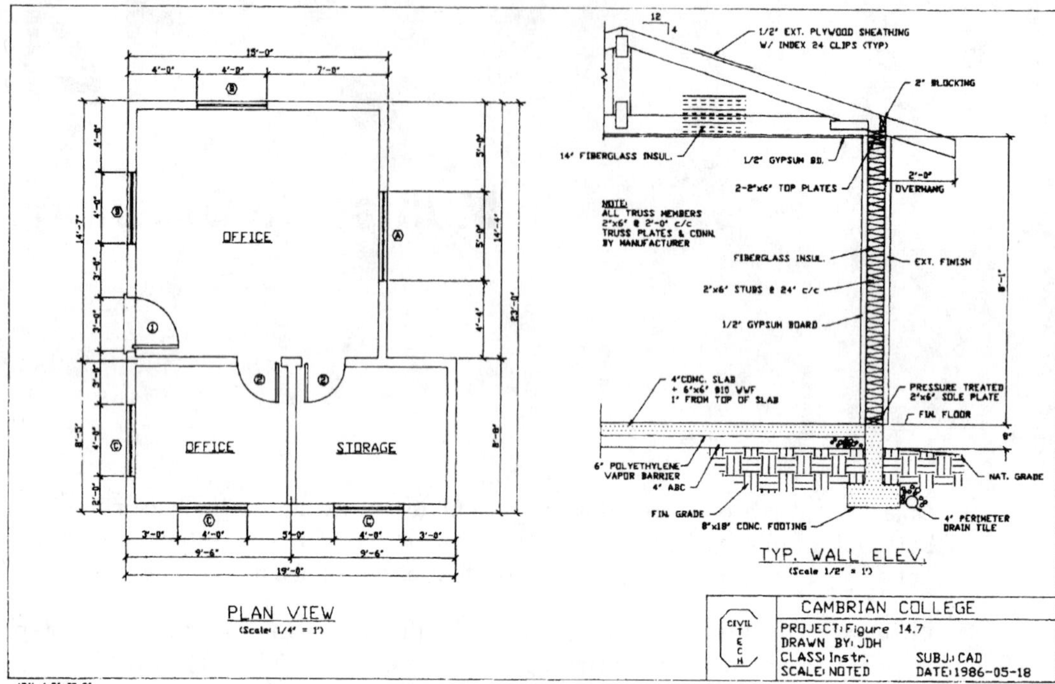

Figure 14.1 Project 8 office plan.

to be 2.25 in [1/(2 × 12) × H = 3/32]. This same ratio must be used for the dimension variables and the hatch scale. (Also see App. C, Table C.1 item B).

14.2 Creating a Protodrawing

The purpose of the protodrawing is to provide a preliminary drawing sheet on which to develop drawings that will later be inserted into a plot drawing. The protodrawing dimensions are the reverse of the plot drawing; i.e., the limits are based on the full-scale size of the object. The title block and border is inserted into the drawing, providing a real-size drawing area for the object.

This project will be drawn on a B-size sheet (17 by 11 in) with a drawing area assumed to be 15 by 9.5 in, allowing for borders. For the drawing to be plotted using an architectural scale of ¼ in = 1 ft 0 in, the limits will have to be set at 0,0 and 720,456 (15 × 4/1 × 12 and 9.5 × 4/1 × 12).

A menu will be created to set the drawing size, draw the border, and insert the title block.

14.2.1 Create the title.dwg block

The title block will be adopted from the title block created in Chap. 12. Boot AutoCAD LT and open an existing drawing named c:\drawings\am-hbdr.dwg (which you drew in Chap. 12).

Create a new layer named Border1. Then use the Change command as follows to transfer the title block to Border1:

`Settings` <pick> `Layer Control...` <pick>

The layer Control dialogue box (Fig. 6.5) is displayed. Create a New layer named `Border1`, and then press OK.

`Modify` <pick> `Change Properties` <pick> `Select objects:` Digitize the lower-left corner of a window to enclose the title block. <pick> `Second point:` Digitize the other corner of the window enclosing the title block. <pick> `Select objects:`

The title block and text in it should be dotted indicating they are in the selection set. The drawing borders should not be dotted. If parts of the title block are not dotted, digitize them. If parts of the border are dotted, use the Remove command (see App. E, Fig. E.5). Press <return> when selection is complete.

The Change Properties dialogue box (Fig. 9.7) is displayed. Click on `Layer...` to display a Layer selection dialogue box. Click layer `Border1` and press `OK`. Border1 appears beside the Layer . . . box in the Change Properties dialogue box. Press `OK` to change the selected entities (the title block) to layer Border1.

Use the `Make Block...` in the Construct menu to create a block named **Title.** The procedure is outlined in Chap. 12, Sec. 12.3.6. Use the lower-right corner of the border as the insertion point (base point), selecting it using the Intersection object snap.

Next, use the `Block Out...` in the Import/Export directory of the File menu to write the block named `Title` to the file `c:\drawings\title.dwg`. Follow the procedure outlined in Chap. 12, Sec. 12.3.6.

Use the `Exit...` command in the File menu to exit AutoCAD LT. Do *not* save the changes to the drawing. This drawing was used only to write a copy of the title block to file, and the original drawing am-hbdr is not to be changed.

14.2.2 Additional menu operations

From Windows load Notepad and open the file c:\drawings\aclt2.mnu created in Chap. 12 (refer to Chap. 12, Sec. 12.5.1). Sections of the menu are shown in Figs. 11.4, 11.10, and 12.8. The completed menu is listed in App. G. Edit the menu inserting the POP4 section shown in Fig. 14.2. POP4 is completed for only Imperial units with a B-size sheet, and AutoCAD LT's architectural units. Other sections are to be completed later.

The POP4 section of the menu has the heading Full Size and is used to draw a border and title block on a sheet scaled up so the drawing can be drawn full-scale, such as the Plan View or the Wall Elevation in Fig. 14.1. When the menu is pulled down in AutoCAD LT, and Imperial clicked, it appears as shown in Fig. 14.3.

When `B-Size` is chosen the following sequence of commands is initiated:

`layer` The Layer command is read and entered with the single blank space following it.

Notepad - ACLT2.MNU

File Edit Search Help

```
***POP4
[Full Size]
[->Metric]
[A Size]
[<-B size]
[->Imperial]
[A-Size]
[<-B-Size]layer make border1;;limits 0,0 15,9.5 zoom a +
line 0,0 15,0 15,9.5 0,9.5 c insert c:/drawings/title;15,0 +
0.039 0.039 0 \\\\\\\\\\\\block b2;0,0 c 0,0 15,9.5;;$p4=ib $p4=*
**ib
[Scale]
[->Archit.]
[1/8"=1'-0"]limits 0,0 1440,912 insert b2;0,0 96 96 0 zoom a +
layer set 0;;$p4=POP4
[1/4"=1'-0"]limits 0,0 720,456 insert b2;0,0 48 48 0 zoom a +
layer set 0;;$p4=POP4
[1/2"=1'-0"]limits 0,0 360,228 insert b2;0,0 24 24 0 zoom a +
layer set 0;;$p4=POP4
[3/4"=1'-0"]limits 0,0 240,152 insert b2;0,0 16 16 0 zoom a +
layer set 0;;$p4=POP4
[1"=1'-0"  ]limits 0,0 180,114 insert b2;0,0 12 12 0 zoom a +
layer set 0;;$p4=POP4
[<-1:N     ]limits 0,0 \insert b2;0,0 \\0 zoom a +
layer set 0;;$p4=POP4
***AUX1
```

Figure 14.2 Adding POP4.

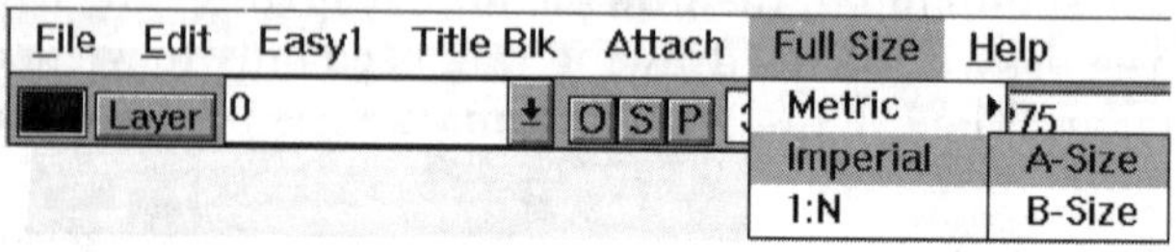

Figure 14.3 POP4 menu.

`make` The Make option to Layer creates a new layer and makes it the current working layer. AutoCAD LT's response is to request the new layer's name.

`border1;;` The new layer's name is read as Border1. It is entered with the first semicolon. The layer command is still in effect. The next semicolon invokes <return> to exit Layer.

`limits 0,0 15,9.5` The Limits command is entered and the limits of 0,0 and 15,9.5 are read and entered from the menu.

`zoom a` Zoom and All are entered to zoom on the new limits.

`+` Tells AutoCAD LT this macro continues on the next line.

`line 0,0 15,0 15,9.5 0,9.5 c` Draws a border around the drawing with its lower-left corner at 0,0 and the upper-right at 15,9.5.

`insert c:/drawings/title;15,0 +` The Insert command is invoked and the drawing to be inserted is c:\drawing\title. Note that the usual path symbol, a backslash (\), must be entered as a forward slash (/) in a menu. The semicolon enters the drawing name. The insertion point is read from the menu as 15,0. The plus sign (+) indicates the menu macro continues onto the next line.

`0.039 0.039 0` Continuing the Insert command, AutoCAD LT requests the X scale factor which is read as 0.039. Since the title block was drawn in millimeter units and this border is to be inch units, the scale factor is 1/25.4 = 0.039. The next value is the Y scale factor of 0.039 and the insertion angle of 0 degrees.

`\\\\\\\\\\\\` The 12 backslashes are necessary to cause AutoCAD LT to pause for six attribute entries by the user in the title block plus six verifications of those entries. There is no space following the last backslash.

`block b2;0,0 c 0,0 15,9.5;;` The Block command is invoked and the name of the block is read as b2 from the menu, and entered with the semicolon. A blank space cannot be used for enter following text data. AutoCAD LT requests the block's insertion point which is read as 0,0. AutoCAD LT then expects the object to be selected. C enters the crossing window option, so that entities crossing or enclosed by the window are included in the selection set. The corners of the crossing window are read as 0,0 and 15,9.5, so the entire border and title block are included in the selection set. AutoCAD LT is still expecting the selection of objects. The last semicolon invokes <return> to exit the command. The entire drawing is blocked with the name B2 and removed from the screen.

`$p4=ib` This loads the submenu named ib into the POP4 position.

`$p4=*` This displays the loaded menu in the POP4 position.

14.2.3 Submenu **ib

A submenu label item begins with two asterisks (**) followed by the submenu name. The submenu items follow the submenu label up to the next section label (***AUX) or another submenu label. When $p4=ib $p4=* is invoked, the submenu ib is loaded in the POP4 position and then displayed. The submenu with its Archit. menu cascaded is shown in Fig. 14.4. Refer to Fig. 14.2 for the menu listing.

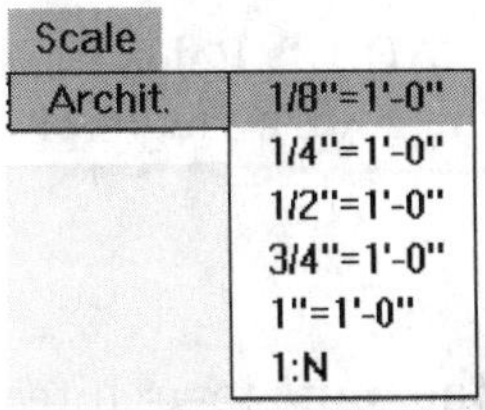

Scale
Archit. 1/8"=1'-0"
1/4"=1'-0"
1/2"=1'-0"
3/4"=1'-0"
1"=1'-0"
1:N

Figure 14.4 Archit. submenu.

The lines in the menu are interpreted as follows:

`[1/4"=1'-0"]limits 0,0 720,456` When 1/4″=1′0″ is selected in the menu, the Limits command is entered and the limits are read from the menu as 0,0 and 720,456. In AutoCAD LT's architectural units the scale 1/4″=1′0″ is interpreted as 1/4 = 12 or 1/48. Consequently the drawing is to be enlarged by 48/1 in order to draw full-size on the sheet. The limits are based on a B-size sheet with a drawing area of 15 in by 9.5 in, each multiplied by 48 giving 720 in by 456 in.

`insert b2;0,0 48 48 0` The block B2 created earlier in the menu is the border and title block. It is inserted at coordinates 0,0 with an x=scale of 48, a y-scale of 48, and a rotation angle of 0.

`zoom a +` Invokes Zooms All to zoom on the new limits, and continues the macro onto the next line.

`layer set 0;;` Sets layer 0 as the current layer. The first semicolon enters the layer name of 0, and the next semicolon exits the layer command.

`$p4=POP4` Loads the POP4 menu back in the POP4 position, in place of the **ib submenu loaded earlier. The POP4 menu is not displayed since there is no $p4=* command.

Complete the POP4 menu and ib submenu exactly as shown. When completed use the `Save...` command in the Notepad File menu to save the file using its original name c:\drawings\aclt2.mnu. Exit Notepad.

14.2.4 Creating the full-size border drawing

Boot AutoCAD LT using the `ACADLT PROTO1` icon. This will load AutoCAD LT with the customized c:\drawings\aclt2.mnu menu.

Use the `New...` command in the File menu to open a new drawing named `c:\drawings\proj-14a.dwg.`

Choose `Full Size` in the pull-down menu to display the menu shown in Fig. 14.3. Choose `Imperial` and then `B-Size`. The macro in the menu is invoked drawing the border, and inserting the title block. Enter the data requested by the attributes. When the attributes are complete the block b2 is created removing the border and title block from the screen. The Scale menu is pulled down. Choose `1/4"=1'-0"`. The block b2 is inserted into the drawing at a scale of 48, and the layer is set to 0. You can now draw full-size on the screen and plot the drawing on a B-Size sheet using a scale of 1/4″=1′–0″.

Save the current drawing and then exit AutoCAD LT. Reload the standard version of AutoCAD LT and then open the drawing c:\drawings\proj-14a.dwg.

14.3 Floor-Plan Drawing

Display the Units Control dialogue box and set the units to architectural with no fractional units as shown in Fig. 14.5.

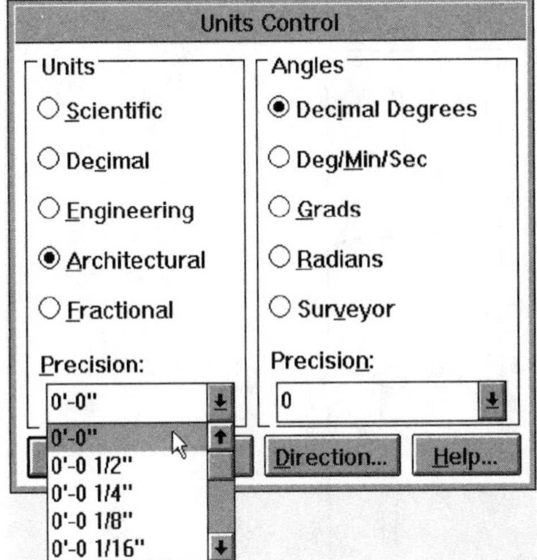

Figure 14.5 Architectural units.

Use the Drawing Aids dialogue box to set a grid of 12 (in) by 12 (in) and set snap to 2 (in). Turn Snap and Grid on. Exit the dialogue box and then press Ctrl-D or F6 to turn the coordinate display on. Refer to App. E, Fig. E.10 for functions to toggle snap and grid on/off.

Use the Layer Control dialogue box to Create the following layers, and set the current layer as Plan:

Item	Name	Color	Linetype
Object lines	Plan	White (7)	Continuous
Dimensions	Dim	Red (1)	Continuous
Text	Text	Red (1)	Continuous
Doors and windows	Details	Blue (5)	Continuous

Layer 0 is created automatically and layer Border1 was created when the border and title block were inserted.

Draw the outside walls of the house, as illustrated in Fig. 14.6 (the current layer should be Plan). Use the grid and the cursor snap and also observe the line lengths and angles in the coordinate display at the top of the screen.

Notice that when using the architectural or engineering mode, dimensions can be entered in inches with no units symbol displayed, i.e., 228, or in feet with the foot symbol displayed, i.e., 19′6 (the inch symbol is optional).

> `LINE` <pick> `Line from point: Digitize the location of the front left corner of the building.` <return> `To point:` **@19′<0** <return> `To point:` **@8′8<90** <return>, etc.

To draw the inside wall of the house, the Offset command will be used to offset the outside wall inward by 6 in. The corners are then trimmed by selecting Fillet 0 command:

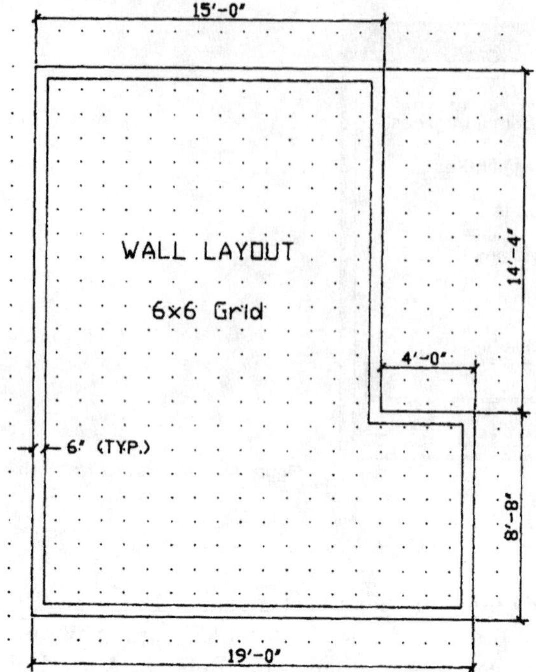

Figure 14.6 Office building wall layout.

`Construct` <pick> `Offset` <pick> `Offset distance or Through <0>:` **6** <return> `Select object to offset:` **Digitize one of the outside walls.** <pick> `Side to offset:` **Digitize a point on the inside of the wall selected.** <pick> `Select object to offset:` **Repeat the selection for each wall.**

`Construct` <pick> `Fillet` <pick> `Polyline/Radius/<Select first object>:` **r** (Radius) <return> `Enter fillet radius <default>:` **0** <return> <return> `Polyline/Radius/<Select first object>:`

Digitize two of the inside corners of the wall. The radius 0 fillet will join the two lines with a 0-radius fillet. Recall the fillet command and repeat for each inside wall.

14.3.1 Text and dimension scales

The floor plan is to be plotted using a scale of $\frac{1}{4}$ = 1 ft 0 in. For the plotted text to be about $\frac{3}{32}$ in high, the text height on the monitor is calculated as follows:

$$1/(4 \times 12) \times H = \tfrac{3}{32} \text{ in}$$
$$H = 4.5$$

The text height is made relatively small because the mechanically made letters will be quite legible and the smaller-dimension text will fit more easily into the space between the extension lines.

Dimscale is calculated using Eq. (4.2):

$$Dimscale \times 0.18 = \text{text height}$$
$$Dimscale \times 0.18 = 4.5 \text{ gives Dimscale} = 25$$

Review the procedures for setting dimensions styles introduced in Chaps. 4 and 5. Choose `Dimension Styles...` in the Settings menu to display the Dimension Style and Settings dialogue box (see Fig. 3.5). Make the following settings:

- Set the `Feature Scaling` (Dimscale) to 25. This is done in the Scale and Colors dialogue box (Fig. 4.3).
- Set the `Text Locations` shown in Fig. 14.7. All dimension text will fall within dimension lines, will be located above the dimension lines, and will be aligned with the dimension lines. The dimension text height is set to 3/16″ (0.18 converted to a fraction). Even though you enter a text height of 3/16″, AutoCAD LT may change it to 0 and indicate an error. If this happens, cancel the dimension settings dialogue boxes. Display the Units Control dialogue box, set the smallest unit to 0′-1/32″, and then retry the dimension style settings. Also, although we are not using tolerance text, the smallest unit is set to 0″ (see Sec. 14.3) and AutoCAD LT reads a 0 unit value and may indicate there is an error. Consequently, you may be required to enter a tolerance value greater than 0, i.e., 3/16″.
- Set the `Text Format` as shown in Fig. 14.8. Settings made here are in the Zero Suppression check box. Boxes without an X are off:

  0 feet suppression is off so that 6″ will appear as 0′-6″.

  0 inches suppression is off so 1′ will appear as 1′-0″.

  The other settings are not required. In decimal drawings turning Leading zero suppression off means .500 becomes 0.500. Trailing zero suppression off means 12.5 becomes 12.500—depending on the units settings.
- Set the `Arrows` to `Tick` with an Arrow Size of **3/32″** (refer to Fig. 6.19).

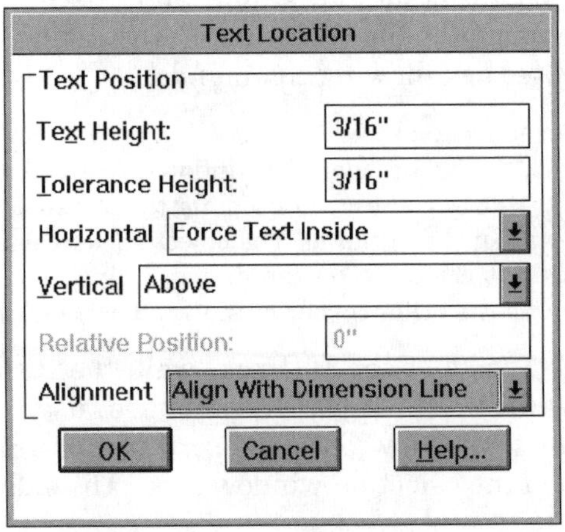

Figure 14.7 Dimension text location settings.

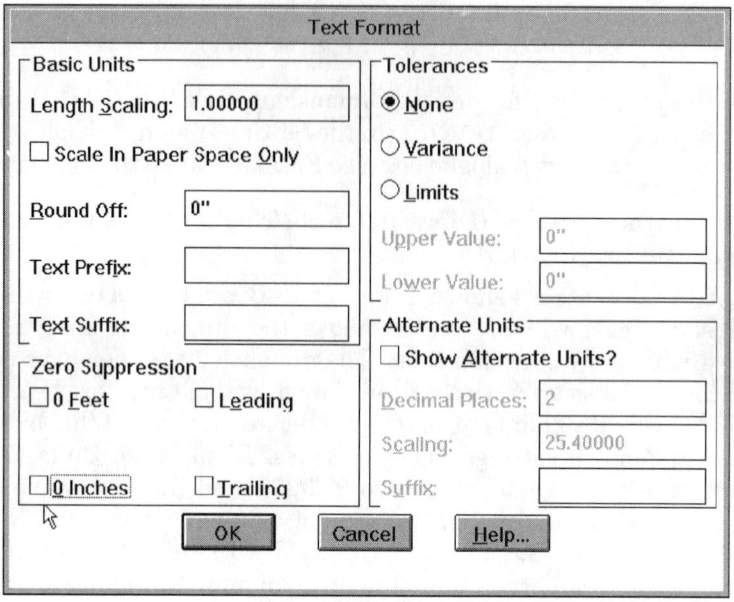

Text Format

Basic Units
Length Scaling: 1.00000
Scale In Paper Space Only
Round Off: 0"
Text Prefix:
Text Suffix:

Zero Suppression
0 Feet
Leading
0 Inches
Trailing

Tolerances
None
Variance
Limits
Upper Value: 0"
Lower Value: 0"

Alternate Units
Show Alternate Units?
Decimal Places: 2
Scaling: 25.40000
Suffix:

OK Cancel Help...

Figure 14.8 Dimension text format settings.

Make sure Associative dimensioning is on. In AutoCAD LT it has a check mark beside Associative Dimensions in the settings menu when it is on. When *all* the dimension style settings are complete, if you had to set the units to 0′-3/32″, change the units back to 0′-0″ now.

14.3.2 Naming Views

Set the current layer to `Dim`. When doing a large drawing, you often have to view specific sections a number of times throughout the drawing construction. The View command allows you to name views and later recall those views quickly. The front wall will be named F, the back wall, B, the right-side wall, R, and the left-side wall, L. Choose the following commands:

> `View` <Pick> `View` <pick> `Window` <pick> `View name to save:` **F** (Front wall) <return> `First corner:` Pick the first corner of a window selection box to enclose the front wall of the building, allowing sufficient room for the dimensions that will be required along the front wall of the building. The objective is to obtain a larger view of the front wall making it easier to do the dimensioning along that wall. <pick> `Other corner:` Digitize the other corner of the window. <pick>

Repeat the process naming a view of the B (Back) wall, the R (Right-side) wall, and the L (Left-side) wall. When all walls are named, use the `Restore` option to restore the F (Front wall) view onto the screen. The front wall is enlarged on the screen based on the selection window used. The side walls will also be visible.

14.3.3 Dimensioning the drawing

Dimensions will be added to the building before drawing doors and windows. This way those items are located by the dimensions and may be easily inserted as blocks. It will be easier to do the dimensioning if snap is set as large as possible. The smallest dimensional unit along the front wall is 6 in. Using the Drawing Aides dialogue box set Snap to 6, and turn Snap on. The dimensions are entered as follows (choose the object snaps from the toolbox):

> `Draw` <pick> `Linear Dimensions` <pick> `Horizontal` <pick> `First extension line origin or RETURN to select:` `Intersection` <pick> `of` Place the target on the lower-left corner of the building. <pick> `Second extension line origin:` Digitize a 3 ft 0 in distance on the grid using the 6″ snap (see Fig. 14.9). <pick> `Dimension line location:` Digitize a point-3 snaps (1 ft 6 in) in front of the wall. <pick> `Dimension text <3′-0″>:` <return> etc.

When all dimensions are added to the front wall, use the View command to restore the left-side wall (view name is L) for dimensioning.

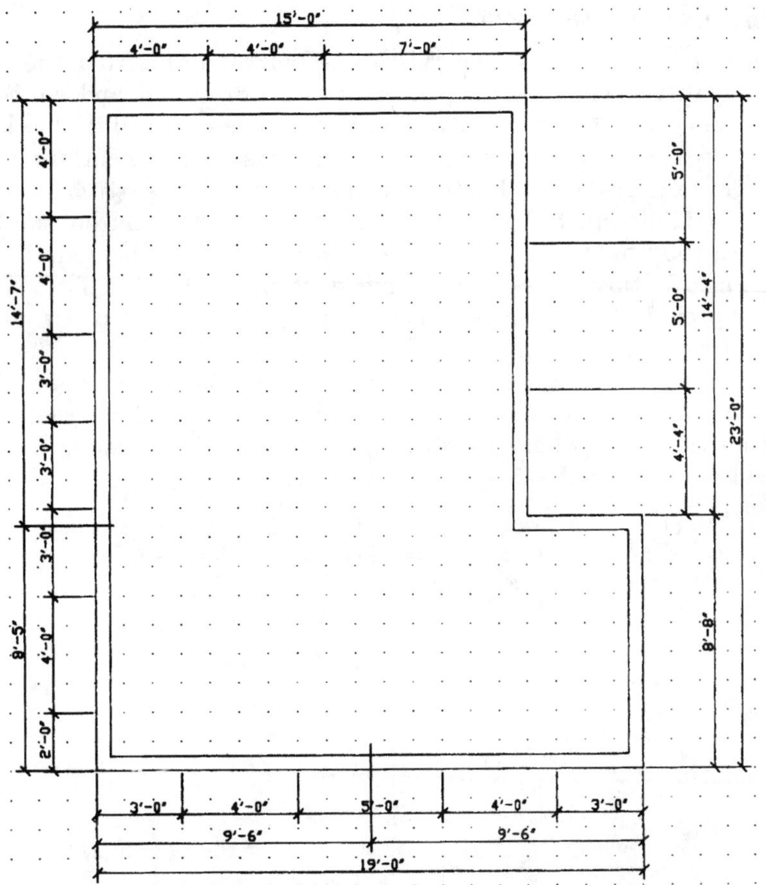

Figure 14.9 Exterior wall dimensions.

Complete the dimensions illustrated in Fig. 14.9. Remember to adjust Snap as required to make it easier to locate points. Also use the Intersection object snap and the Aerial View window Locate command where necessary.

14.3.4 Window and door blocks

Set the current drawing layer to `Details`. Use the Zoom command to enlarge an area about 6 ft 0 in by 6 ft 0 in, and draw the windows and doors illustrated in Fig. 14.10. As each is drawn, use the Block command to save it as a block and, if desired, use Block Out (see App. E, Fig. E.1) to save the block to file for use in other drawings. Use the block names illustrated in Fig. 14.12. Insertion points are marked x. Attributes will not be used to tag information to the windows and doors; however, consider the possibilities—a program could be written to read the door files and then create a door schedule, etc.

When drawing the doors and windows, use appropriate snap settings to alternate snap as required to facilitate the drawing.

14.3.5 Inserting the windows and doors

Set the current layer as `Plan`. When the blocks are inserted, they will retain their identity on layer Details (which they were drawn on) and will not reside on layer Plan even though that is the current drawing layer. If the blocks had been drawn on layer 0, when inserted, they would reside on the current layer (Plan).

Prior to inserting the blocks, draw the internal 6-in partition walls. Use the dimension lines and Snap to locate the walls. Press O in the buttons bar to turn on the orthogonal mode to facilitate the drawing of the horizontal and vertical wall lines. To turn the orthogonal mode off, press O in the buttons bar again. Do not provide door openings yet. Experiment with the Double Line command in the Draw pull-down menu.

Restore the F (Front) view. Then Zoom on the section of the front wall where the window on the left side of the wall is to be located, or use the Aerial View window to zoom on the area where the window is to be located. An opening for the window is made and the window is inserted using the following sequence of commands:

`BREAK` (Toolbox) <pick> `Select objects:` Digitize the outside wall selecting a point clear of any dimension extension lines. <pick> `Enter second point (or F for first point):` **F** <return> `First point:` Digitize the left side of the win-

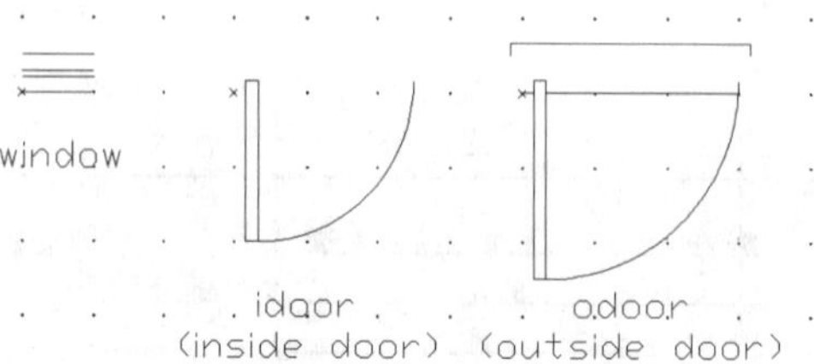

Figure 14.10 Windows and door blocks.

dow—in line with the dimension line—on the outside face of the wall. <pick> Second point: **@48<0** <return> <return> Break Select objects: **@6<90** <return> Enter second point (or F for first point): **@48<180** <return>

LINE (Toolbox) <pick> From point: **@** <return> To point: **@6<270** <return> To point: <return> <return> Line From point: **@48<0** <return> To point: **@6<90** <return> To point: <return>

Draw <pick> Insert Block... <pick>

An Insert dialogue box similar to that shown in Fig. 10.7 is displayed. The name of the Block to be inserted is Window. Click the Specify Parameters on Screen box on, and enter the parameters as follows:

Insertion point: INTERSECTION (Toolbox) <pick> of Place the target over the lower-left corner of the window's opening. <pick> X scale factor <1>/Corner/XYZ: **4** <return> Y scale factor (default=X): **1** <return> Rotation angle <0>: <return>

Notice that the initial object selection to break the opening was made clear of any dimension extension lines. The reason is that AutoCAD LT puts control point for associative dimensions at the selection points of the dimension extension lines, which in this case is on the wall line. When an entity selection is made, such as for the Break command, and two entities overlap, AutoCAD LT selects the more recent one which is the associative dimension point in this case. To prevent this, the wall is selected in an uncluttered location.

Restore the F (Front) view. Add the window to the right side of the front wall. Use a similar procedure to insert all of the windows and doors. To insert a "mirror" image of the door block (see doors referenced as 2 in Fig. 14.1), use a negative value for the x scale factor when inserting the block.

Door and window reference symbol blocks. The door reference symbol is inserted by creating a block drawing of a hexagon, with the reference symbol tagged to the block as a variable visible attribute. This information is drawn on the text layer. Set the current layer as Text.

Zoom on an area 4 ft 0 in by 4 ft 0 in and draw the block using the following commands:

Draw <pick> Polygon <pick> Number of sides <4>: **6** <return> Edge/<Center of polygon>: **e** (Edge) <return> First endpoint of edge: Pick a point on the screen. <pick> Second point of edge: **@4<0** <return>

Following the procedures outlined in Chap. 12, Sec. 12.3.4, and referring to Fig. 12.2 create one visible attribute using the tag A, and the prompt "Enter the letter." For the Insertion point pick the bottom-left corner for the letter A inside the polygon. The Height of the attribute text is 4 units, and the rotation angle is 0 degrees.

Create a block named Hex made up of the polygon (hexagon) and the attribute. The insertion point of the block is the midpoint of the bottom line of the hexagon.

Following the same procedures create the door reference symbol using a circle 5 units in diameter, with an attribute in it. Save it as a block.

Insert the window and door reference blocks into the drawing.

Set the current layer to `Text` and add the text to the drawing.

14.3.6 Test plot drawing and save file

Check that the floor plan is located on the drawing where you would like it located on the final plot. If not, use the Move command to relocate the floor.

Plot the drawing to visually ensure that the floor plan is complete. The drawing was done on the "full size" border for a B-size sheet (17 by 11 in, giving a plot area of 15 by 9.5 in), and is plotted using a scale of ¼ in = 1 ft 0 in. The plot scale will be 1 = 48 (or 1 = 4′).

When the drawing is complete set the current layer to Plan and turn the Border1 layer off. Use the Save command to save the file menu.

14.4 Wall Detail Drawing

Before continuing ensure the floor plan drawing has been saved using the file name c:\drawings\proj-14a.dwg.

Choose `Exit...` in the File menu. Then reboot AutoCAD LT using the `ACADLT PROTO1` icon. This will load AutoCAD LT with the customized c:\drawings\aclt2.mnu menu. Use the `New...` command in the File menu to open a new drawing named `c:\drawings\proj-14b.dwg`.

Choose `Full Size` in the pull-down menu to display the menu shown in Fig. 14.5. Choose `Imperial` and then `B-Size`. The macro in the menu is invoked drawing the border, and inserting the title block. Enter the data requested by the attributes. When the attributes are complete, the block B2 is created removing the border and title block from the screen. The Scale menu is pulled down. Choose `1/2″=1′-0″`. The border returns with the drawing limits set for a full size drawing.

Save the current drawing and then exit AutoCAD LT. Reload the standard version of AutoCAD LT and then open the drawing c:\drawings\proj-14b.dwg.

The standard AutoCAD LT aclt2 menu will now be loaded. Use the Layer Control dialogue box to create the following layers:

Object	**Name**	**Color**	**Linetype**
Wall	Elev1	White (7)	Continuous
Text	Text	Red (1)	Continuous
Dimensions	Dim	Red (1)	Continuous
Details	Details	Blue (5)	Continuous
Hatch border	Hatcho	White (7)	Continuous
Hatching	Hatch	Yellow (2)	Continuous
Construction lines	Const	White (7)	Continuous

Set `Elev1` as the current drawing layer. Select architectural units with 1 as the smallest fraction. Set Grid to 12 and Snap to 6.

14.4.1 Text and dimension scale

The floor plan previously drawn is to be plotted using a scale of ¼ in = 1 ft 0 in. In Sec. 14.3.1 the text height was calculated as 4 in. Because the wall detail is to be plotted using a scale of ½ in = 1 ft 0 in and because the two plots are to reside on the same drawing, the text height for the detail drawing is calculated as follows:

$$\tfrac{1}{2} \times H = \tfrac{1}{4} \times 4$$
$$H = 4 \times (\tfrac{1}{4})/(\tfrac{1}{2}) \text{ giving } H = 2$$

Dimscale was set as 25 for the floor plan. For the wall Dimscale is calculated as follows:

$$Dimscale = 25 \times (\tfrac{1}{4})/(\tfrac{1}{2}) \text{ giving } Dimscale = 12.5$$

Set the dimension variable exactly as outlined in Sec. 14.3.1—except for the Feature Scaling (Dimscale) setting which is to be 12.5.

14.4.2 Wall

The current layer should be `Elev1`. Draw the wall footing on the right side of the drawing area using the grid. The footing wall was drawn 18 in high. This is unsatisfactory in northern climates; but remember, this is a CAD, not a building design, exercise. Use break lines in the footing if you want.

Set the current layer to `Const`. Draw construction lines representing the face of the wall, the 2-ft 0-in roof overhang, and the bottom of the roof beam:

> `LINE` (Toolbox) <pick> `From point:` `INTERSECTION` <pick> `of` Place the target on the top-right corner of the footing wall. <pick> `To point:` **@8′1<90** <return> `To point:` <return> <return> `Line From point:` **@2′<0** <return> `To point:` **@1′<270** <return> `To point:` <return>

The roof slope is 4/12 which means a 4-in rise for every 12-in (1 ft 0 in) run. For the 15-ft 0-in width section of the building the rise will be 4 × 15/2 = 30 in (2 ft 6 in). The construction line for the bottom of the roof is drawn as follows (see Fig. 14.11).

> `POINT` (Toolbox) <pick> `Point:` `ENDPOINT` <pick> `of` Place the target on the top of the wall construction line, point a. <pick> `LINE` <pick> `From point:` **@–7′6,2′6** (7′6″ to the left of a and 2′-6″ above a) <return> `To point:` `ENDPOINT` <pick> `of` Place the target on the top of the wall construction line, point *a*. <pick> `To point:` <return> `Modify` <pick> `Extend` <pick> `Select boundary edge(s)...Select objects:` Digitize the vertical line 2 ft from the wall that defines the roof edge. <pick> <return> `Select object to extend:` Pick the roof line. <pick> <return>

The grid will now be rotated (by rotating snap) so that it aligns with the roof slope, and snap will be set to the roof thickness of 6 in. Normally snap is

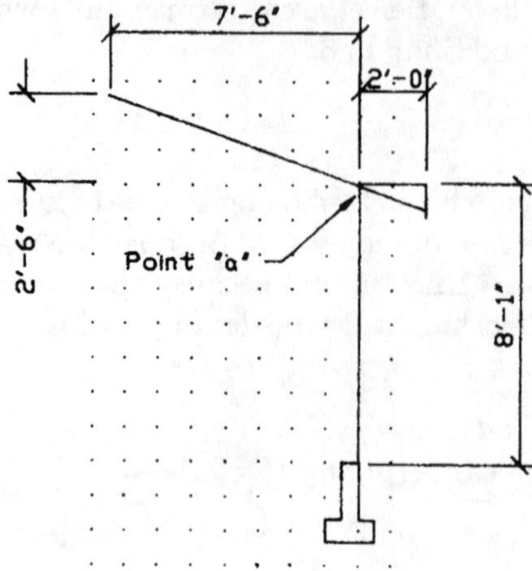

Figure 14.11 Wall elevation.

set using the Drawing Aids dialogue box (Fig. 9.2); however, in this case the Snap command will be entered from the keyboard. When grid is located we will want to enter the rotation angle by selecting points on the screen. The dialogue box does not allow for that. Enter the following at the command line:

> **Snap** <return> `Snap spacing or ON/OFF/Aspect/Rotate/Style:` **r** (rotate) <return> `Base point: INTERSECTION` (Toolbox) <pick> `of` Place the aperture on the intersection point of the roof and wall. <pick> `Rotation angle: ENDPOINT` <pick> `of` Place the target on the left end of the roof line. <pick> <return> `Snap spacing or ON/OFF/Aspect/Rotate/Style:` **6** <return>

Now press O in the buttons bar to turn the orthogonal mode on. Draw a copy of the previous line 6 in above it:

> `COPY` (Toolbox) <pick> `Select objects:` Digitize the current roof line <pick> <return> `Base point or displacement:` Digitize a point on the current roof line. <pick> `Second point of displacement:` Digitize a point one snap step above the previous roof line. <pick>

Press O in the buttons bar to turn the orthogonal mode off. Return grid to original snap plane, and set Snap to 2 in:

> **Snap** <return> `Snap spacing or ON/OFF/Aspect/Rotate/Style:` **r** (Rotate) <return> `Base point:` **0.0** <return> `Rotation angle:` **0** <return> <return> `Snap spacing or ON/OFF/Aspect/Rotate/style:` **2** <return>

If the vertical construction line at the 2-ft 0-in overhang does not cross the line just completed use the Extend command to extend it so the lines meet. Then move the roof to align with the 2-ft 0-in overhang:

> `MOVE` (Toolbox) <pick> `Select objects: Assist` <pick> `Select` <pick> `Last` <pick> `Select objects:` <return> `Base point or displacement: ENDPOINT` (Toolbox) `of` Place the aperture on the right side of the top roof line. <pick> `Second point: INTERSECTION` <pick> `of` Place the aperture on the intersection of the top roof line and the vertical (2′-0″) construction line. <pick>

Use the Trim command to trim the vertical line to form the end of the roof joist. Use the Change command (see Chap. 9, Sec. 9.3.3) to transfer the roof beam and wall line to the Elev1 layer.

Now turn the Const layer off and set Elev1 as the current layer.

Draw the remaining roof lines. Do not draw the 2- by 6-in members individually—draw one as a block and then use the Insert command to insert the others where required.

The insulation is first drawn as a 1-ft 0-in block, see Fig. 14.12 (or see Chap. 18, Sec. 18.3 and file c:\symbols\architec\framing\insl-6.wmf). One block is inserted at the base of the wall. The Array command is then used to repeat the entity seven times. To make up the missing piece at the top, the last insulation unit is inserted as a block with the Explode box on (see Fig. 10.7), i.e., an x in it, to retain its entities so that the parts running into other members may be erased.

14.4.3 Hatching

The hatch scale is calculated using Eq. (6.1):

$$\text{Plot scale} \times \text{Hatch} = 1 \text{ in} \times \text{conversion}$$
$$\tfrac{1}{2} \times \text{Hatch} = 1 \times 12$$
$$\text{Hatch} = 24$$

Set the current layer to `Hatch`. Hatch the wall and floor separately using the dots hatch style. Select the boundaries by digitizing each boundary line.

The earth hatch requires a boundary line. Set the current layer to `Hatcho` and draw a lower boundary for the earth hatching and a boundary for the fiberglass hatching. When using AutoCAD LT hatch styles, you might have to try different hatch scales to get the desired hatching effect.

Set the current layer to `Hatch` and use the earth hatch style for the earth, and the insul hatch style for the insulation. When the hatching is complete, turn layer `Hatcho` off.

14.4.4 Text and dimensions

Set the current layer to `Dim` and add the dimensions. Set the current layer to `Text` and add the text to the drawing.

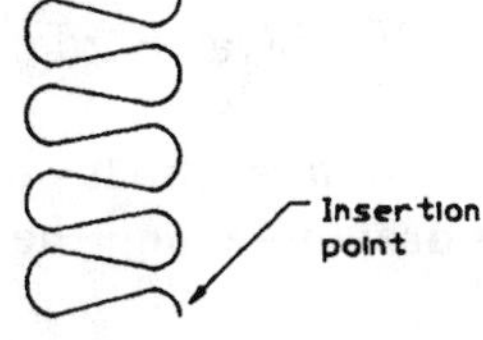

Figure 14.12 Insulation block.

14.4.5 Test plot and save file

Test plot the drawing on a B-size sheet using a scale of ½ in = 1 ft 0 in. The plot units are inches. The scale is 1 = 24.

Make necessary corrections to the drawing and then turn layer `Border1` off and Freeze it.

Use the Save command to save the file.

14.5 Creating the Plot Drawing

Before continuing, ensure the wall elevation drawing has been saved using the file name **c:\drawings\proj-14b.dwg.**

Choose `Exit...` in the File menu. Then reboot AutoCAD LT using the `ACADLT PROTO1` icon. This will load AutoCAD LT with the customized c:\drawings\aclt2.mnu menu. Use the `New...` command in the File menu to open a new drawing named **c:\drawings\plot-14.dwg.**

Choose `Title Blk` in the pull-down menu to display the menu shown in Fig. 11.11. Choose `Imperial` and then `B-Size.` The macro in the menu is invoked by inserting your B-size border created in Chap. 12, Sec. 12.7.3. Enter the data requested by the attributes. The border remains on the screen and the limits are based on a B-size sheet of paper.

Use the Xref command (added to the Border menu from the assignment at the end of Chap. 13) to Attach the Proj-14a drawing to the current drawing (if you did not do that assignment, type the command):

`XREF` <pick> `?/Bind/Detach/Path/Reload<Attach>:` **A** (Attach) <return> `Xref to attach:` **c:\drawings\proj-14a** (or enter <TILDE>~ to display the file dialogue box). <return>
`PROJ_14A loaded`

`Insertion point:` **0.0** <return> `X-Scale factor (1):`
0.0208 [1/(4 × 12)] <return>
`Y-scale factor (default=x):` <return> `Rotation angle <0>:` <return>

Repeat the procedure to attach your Proj-14b drawing to the current drawing. The insertion point is 0,0 and the scale is 0.0417 [1/(2 × +12)].

If modifications to the views are necessary, edit the original Proj-14a and Proj-14b drawings. Since the drawings were attached to the multiview drawing as external references, the revised files will be loaded when the master drawing is reloaded.

Prior to plotting, list the layers to ensure that layer Border1 is off and the layer colors are as desired.

Use the Move command to move entities as required to lay out the drawing.

When the drawing is completed plot the drawing using the following data, and then save the drawing.

- Units = inches
- Width = 17 in

- Height = 11 in
- Scale is 1 = 1

Save the file and then use the Quit command to exit AutoCAD LT.

14.6 Multiscale Drawings Using Paper Space

You could have created the entire drawing for this chapter in one file using paper space for the border and model space for the multiscale views. The paper space drawing would be composed of two viewports: one viewport opened to display only the floor plan and another to display only the wall elevation. Both views would be drawn full-size in model space and zoomed times paper space in their viewport to the appropriate scale. Refer to Chap. 17 for a more thorough discussion of viewports and paper/working space drawings.

Paper space and model space are very applicable to creating a drawing composed of multiview/multiscale views of a single three-dimensional object, as outlined in Chap. 17. When a drawing is composed of entities not created from a single three-dimensional object, such as the floor plan and wall elevation drawing, the procedures outlined in this chapter are more applicable and less complicated.

Chapter

15

3-D Drawing

Objective. To introduce the concepts of three-dimensional drafting, elevation and thickness, viewing objects in 3-D; Polylines; hatching on a 3-D plane; dynamic 3-D views; perspective views; clipping views; user coordinate system.

15.1 Elevation and Thickness

To construct three-dimensional (3-D) objects, you must define entity positions using three-dimensional (X,Y,Z) coordinates. The Elev command lets you set a default Z value and extrusion thickness for subsequent entities that you draw. Two-dimensional objects can be converted to 3-D by changing their elevation and thickness.

15.2 Convert Proj-4 Drawing to 3-D

Boot up AutoCAD LT and Open an existing Drawing: Proj-4.

When Proj-4 was drawn, all of the entities were on layer 0. Because the objective of this exercise is to create a three-dimensional view of the object, the Change command will be used to change the layer on which the object resides. The dimensions and text will be left on layer 0, which will be turned off. Also, because layer 0 will not be used for this drawing, you should Freeze it. When a layer is frozen, it is turned off and the items on that layer are ignored by AutoCAD LT when the drawing is regenerated. If the layer is quite complex and it is not to be displayed, freezing it speeds up the regeneration process considerably. In this case the layer is not complex and there is little regeneration speed gained by freezing the layer. It is done to demonstrate the command. To turn a frozen layer on, the Thaw command is used.

Using the Layer Control dialogue box, make a new layer named **Object** and set it as the current layer. Then using the Change Properties dialogue box (see Fig. 14.3), change the object on the Proj-4 drawing to the Object layer. When asked to Select objects, digitize each of the object lines in the drawing including the circle. Do not digitize any of the text or dimension lines.

Now the object has been changed to layer Object. Using the Layer Control dialogue box, Freeze layer 0.

15.2.1 Adding 3-D to 2-D entities

Two-dimensional objects are drawn on a flat plane using an x,y axis. For an entity to be a three-dimensional extruded plane, it must have thickness along the z axis. If an object was initially drawn with two-dimensional entities, the Change command can be used to specify the depth in the z axis, making the entity three-dimensional. For this project, the base of the object will be set as elevation 0 (any value can be used, even a negative elevation). The thickness of the object will be assumed to be 6 units.

The circle (hole) in the object will be given a base elevation of 3 units and a thickness of 3 units. This will place the top of the hole at the top of the object (i.e., at elevation 6) and it will extend 3 units into the object. A similar effect could be obtained by setting the elevation of the object and circle as 0 and then defining the thickness of the object as –6 and the thickness of the circle as –3:

> Modify <pick> Change Properties <pick> Select objects: Digitize each of the lines forming the object—do not digitize the circle. <pick> Select objects: <return>

The Change Properties dialogue box illustrated in Fig. 15.1 is displayed. Move the cursor into the Thickness edit box and enter the thickness as **6.** Press OK to exit the dialogue box.

Recall the thickness and set the circle thickness to 3 units.

Now use the Move command to move the circle to a z-elevation of 3-units:

> Modify <pick> Move <pick> Select objects: Digitize the circle. <pick><return> Base point or displacement: **0,0,3** <return> Second point of displacement: <return>

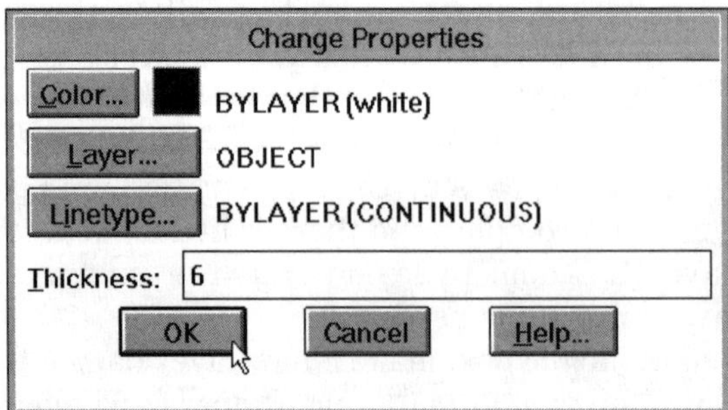

Figure 15.1 Changing the thickness.

15.2.2 Drawing a new 3-D extruded entity

Prior to drawing a new three-dimensional extruded entity, the elevation and thickness for the entity are to be set. This is done by using the Entity Modes dialogue box. The elevation is to be set to 0 (the current default value) and the thickness to 6 units. A new "hole" is then drawn in the object as follows:

```
Settings <pick> Entity Modes... <pick>
```

The Entity Creation Modes dialogue box illustrated in Fig. 15.2 is displayed. Set the Elevation to **0.00** and the Thickness to **6.00.** Press OK to exit. Now draw a circle with its center point at coordinates 10,5, and with a 1.5-unit radius. When the object is viewed from a 3-D viewpoint it will be seen that the circle has a base elevation of 0 and a thickness of 6 units.

The Entity Creation Modes dialogue box can be used to set the layer, linetype and text style. The color can also be changed to By Entity, By Block, or By Layer. *By Block* means that entities will be colored in white until collected into a block. When the block is inserted entities adopt the current color setting. *By Layer* is what is used throughout this text. Colors set *By Entity* means that an entity can be on a blue layer but have its color set to red, which is often confusing.

If other entities are to be drawn with the same current elevation and thickness, they are drawn without resetting the Elevation. If a different elevation or thickness is desired for an entity, the Entity Creation Modes dialogue box must be used to modify the current elevation and thickness prior to drawing the entity (unless the Move and Change commands are used later to modify the elevation and/or thickness of an entity).

15.3 Viewing the *z* Plane of 3-D Objects

The Viewpoint (3-D Viewpoint) menu is used to view the *z* axis of the screen. However, you cannot view one object on the screen in three dimensions and

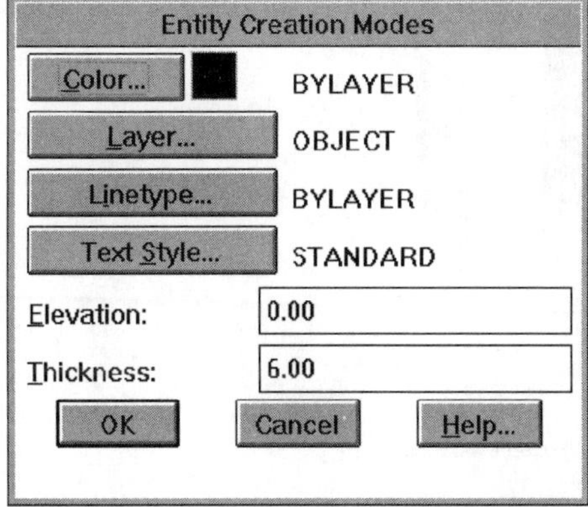

Figure 15.2 Entity Creation Modes dialogue box.

leave other objects on the same screen in two dimensions. To plot an *x,y,z* view of an object within a border and title block in the *x,y* axis, you have to plot the border and title block separately from the three-dimensional view, on the same sheet. Multiview drawings can also be made by defining user coordinate system (UCS) views which are Blocked Out to file and inserted into the drawing or displayed in paper space through viewports (see Chap. 16).

Prior to discussing the 3D Viewpoint options, the command will be used to view the *z* axis of the object:

```
View <pick> 3D Viewpoint <pick> Vector <pick> Vpoint Rotate/<View
point>: -1,-3,3.5 <return>
```

You should now have on your monitor a wire-frame model 3-D view of the object similar to that illustrated in Fig. 15.3.

When the 3D Viewpoint vector (Vpoint) command is executed, the current viewpoint is displayed in angle brackets. If you enter a new *x,y,z* viewpoint (as in the preceding commands), AutoCAD regenerates the drawing and displays the new view. If you select the 3-D Viewpoint Axes command, a compass and tripod will be displayed, as illustrated in Fig. 15.4.

```
View <pick> 3D Viewpoint <pick> Axes <pick>
```

The upper-right corner of the monitor should now display a two-dimensional representation of globe. AutoCAD LT refers to the center point of the globe as the north pole (0,0,1), the inner ring as the equator (n,n,0), and the outer ring as the south pole (0,0,–1). A small cross hair indicates the viewpoint looking toward the coordinate origin (0,0,0).

An axis tripod in the center of the monitor illustrates the view position. As the cursor is moved, the cross hair moves in the globe, and the axis tripod

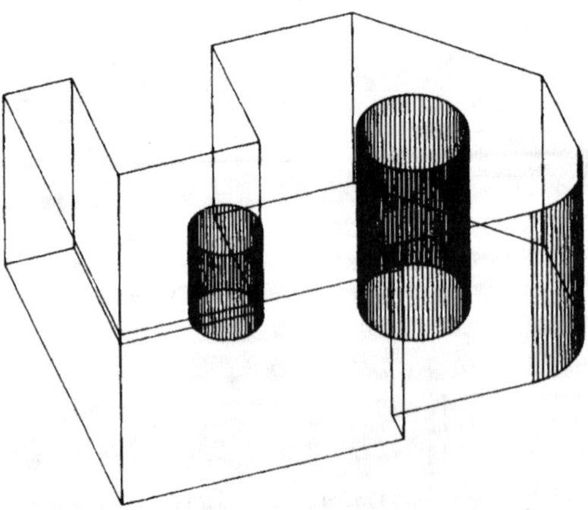

Figure 15.3 Three-dimensional view of project 4.

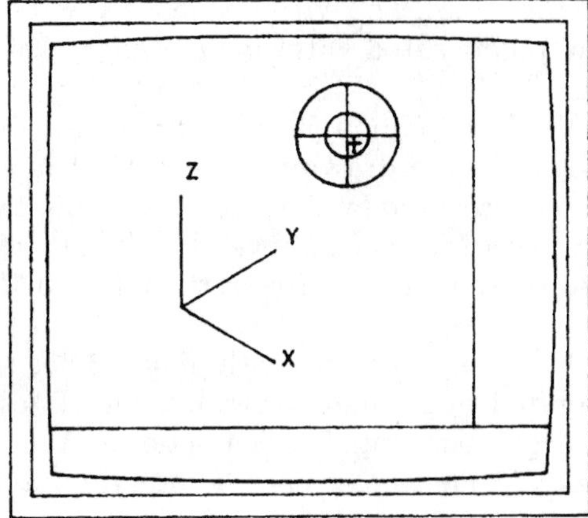

Figure 15.4 Z-plane view selection screen.

rotates indicating the view obtained if that position is selected by pressing the <pick> button. In either case you are only specifying the view direction. It is not possible to specify a view distance: Also try the 3D Viewpoint Presets in the View menu. The following table illustrates the 3D Viewpoint Vectors and Presets to enter to obtain standard views:

Vector	**View**	**Presets**
x,y,z		
0,0,1	Plan view	Top
0,0,–1	Plan view from south pole	—
1,0,0	Right side view	Right
0,–1,0	Front view	Front
0,1,0	View from back	Back

Try a number of viewpoints using 3-D Viewpoint-Axes, Rotate, Vector and the 3D Viewpoint Presets.

15.4 Suppressing Hidden Lines

The Vpoint command draws a wire-frame display of the object. In a wire-frame display all of the lines are present, including those that would be hidden by other parts of the object. The hidden lines can be eliminated by using the Hide command:

```
View <pick> Hide <pick>
```

The screen will go blank for a period of time (depending on the drawing's complexity) as AutoCAD LT proceeds to regenerate the drawing with the hidden lines suppressed (see Fig. 15.5). The wire-frame view will be restored the next time the drawing is regenerated with, for instance, Zoom, Regen, Pan, etc.

As illustrated in Fig. 15.5, the Hide command does not necessarily generate the desired hidden line removal. In the drawing the sides of the circle have been removed only where they are covered by the sides of the object. AutoCAD LT sees the object as a room with the roof removed because the lines were extruded along the z axis and there is no surface on the top or bottom of the object.

To plot a three-dimensional view of the object with hidden lines removed, a view does not have to be generated on the monitor with hidden lines removed. In the Plot Configuration dialogue box (Fig. 7-1) an option in the Additional Parameters box is Hide Lines. If Hide Lines is on the program processes the vectors with hidden lines removed and plots the drawing.

Generate a three-dimensional view of the object and then plot the view with hidden lines removed—a scale of 1 = 3 should fit an 11- by 8.5-in sheet.

15.5 Topographic Map Drawing

A topographic map shows, by contour lines, the spatial configuration of the earth's surface. A contour line is an imaginary line of constant elevation on the ground surface. An example of a contour line is the shore line of a still lake.

In this project a topographic map of a 40- × 40-meter lot is drawn. The ground elevations have been determined by a field survey and are illustrated at grid points in Fig. 15.6. The grid spacings are 10 m c/c vertically and horizontally.

To draw the topographical map, points of equal elevation on the drawing will be located. A line joining those points is called a "contour line." Successive con-

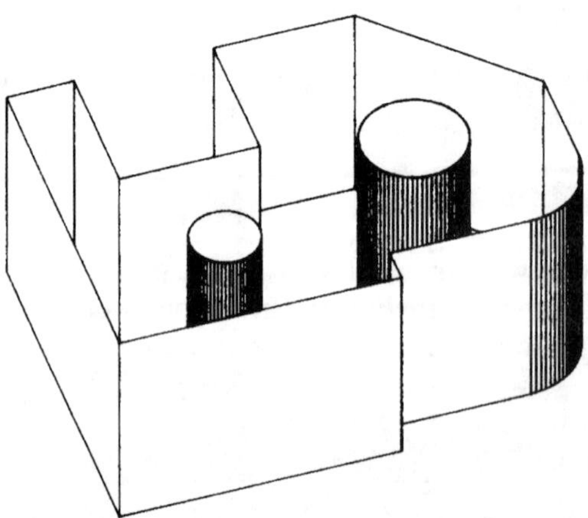

Figure 15.5 Three-dimensional view with hidden lines suppressed.

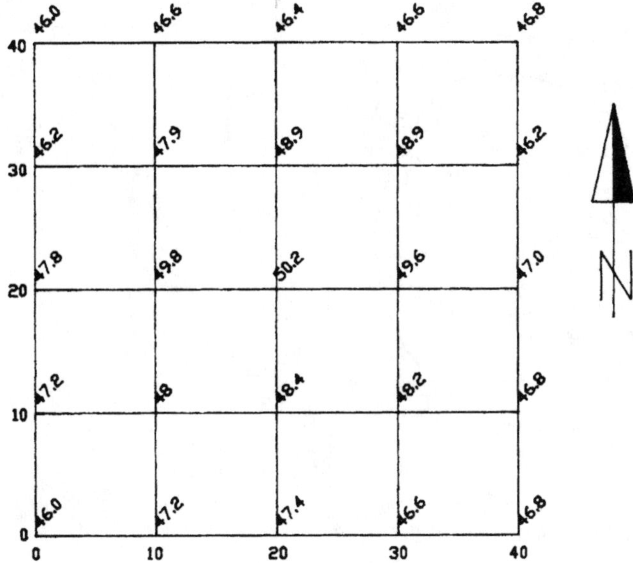

Figure 15.6 Topographic map grid elevations.

tour lines will be drawn at a fixed contour interval of 1 meter. The drawing will then illustrate the spatial "flow of the land." Where contour lines are closely spaced, the change in elevation is steep. Where contour lines are spaced far apart, the change in elevation is gradual. The final topographical map is illustrated in Fig. 15.7.

15.5.1 Calculation of even-contour elevations

Even-contour elevation locations are determined by interpolating elevations between the grid lines. A sample calculation is illustrated below, where the 47-m elevation location is interpolated between the 0- and 10-m grid point on the horizontal (x axis in Fig. 15.6):

$$\begin{aligned}\text{Distance} &= (47.0 - 46.0)/(47.2 - 46.0) \times 10 \text{ m} \\ &= 8.33 \text{ m}\end{aligned}$$

Notice that the only 46-m elevation points are at the lower-left and upper-right corners of the plan. The even elevations required, therefore, fall in the range of 47 to 50 m. The locations where each of those elevations cross the vertical and horizontal grid lines must then be calculated.

To simplify drawing of the contour lines, the lower-left corner of the grid is assumed to be located at coordinate 0,0 on the monitor. As each contour location is calculated, its total distance from point 0,0 is then determined. Those

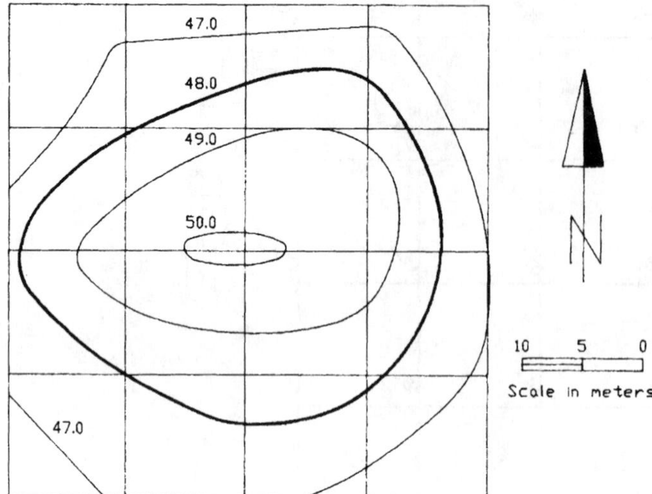

Figure 15.7 Topographic map contours.

coordinates are then used to locate the points on the drawing. The coordinates of the 47-m elevation calculated then become 8.33,0.

The contour line locations illustrated in Table 15.1 were calculated by using the BASIC program in App. D. If you are familiar with programming in BASIC, you might want to enter the program and generate the data. If you are not familiar with BASIC, manually check a few of the values from Table 15.1 to ensure that you understand the concept used to calculate the values. Do not worry too much if you do not understand the process of calculating the data—this text is not intended to teach surveying. You will still be able to complete this project and learn more about AutoCAD LT's 3-D abilities and about polylines. The x and y distances are coordinate distances from point 0,0, which is the lower-left corner of the plan. The distances have been rounded off to two digits to the right of the decimal.

15.5.2 Draw the contour lines

Boot up AutoCAD LT and begin a new drawing named Proj-15. The even-contour distances listed in Table 15.1 are located from the lower-left corner of the grid, which will be given the coordinates of 0,0 to simplify the drawing process. The grid is 40 by 40. Screen limits should allow some space around the grid (5 units) plus additional space on the east side for the north arrow and some text. Set the screen limits as –5,–5 and 65,45.

Set the units as decimal (meters), with two digits to the right of the decimal. Create the following layers (continuous linetype for all):

TABLE 15.1 Contour Locations

Elevation	*x* dist.	*y* dist.	Elevation	*x* dist.	*y* dist.
46	0	0	48	36.15	20
47	8.33	0	49	32.31	20
47	25	0	47	0	25
47	0	8.33	48	10	29.47
48	20	6.00	49	10	24.21
47	30	2.50	49	20	29.33
48	30	8.75	50	20	21.54
48	10	10	49	30	28.57
47	38.57	10	47	4.71	30
48	31.43	10	48	11.00	30
49	10	15.56	47	37.04	30
49	20	13.33	48	33.33	30
50	20	18.89	47	10	36.92
49	30	15.71	47	20	37.60
48	1.00	20	48	20	33.60
49	6.00	20	47	30	38.26
50	15	20	48	30	33.91
50	23.33	20	46	0	40
47	40	20			

Use	**Name**	**Color**
Contour lines	Contour	White
Text	Text	White
Grid lines	Grid	Red
Grid-point elevations	Gridel	Yellow
Elevations	Coord	White

Set `Grid` as the current layer.

Set the elevation. Because the three-dimensional function of AutoCAD LT is to be used, an elevation for each entity will have to be defined. Usually, all text, dimensions, grid lines, etc., are placed on elevation 0 (z coordinate = 0); however, the lowest grid elevation is 47 m (there is no contour for elevation 46), so all text and the grid lines will be placed on elevation 47 (z coordinate = 47). This way, if the text or dimension layers are on when the drawing is viewed in three dimensions, the text and dimensions will appear on the same elevation as the lowest contour in the view. Because each contour line represents a single elevation, the contour lines will have elevation but will have a thickness of 0 units. Using the Entity Creation Modes dialogue box (Fig. 15.2) set the current Elevation to 47, and the Thickness to 0.

Draw the grid. To draw the grid, one grid line will be drawn and the Array command will be used to replicate it:

`Draw` <pick> `Line` <pick> `From point:` **0,0**<return> `To point:` **@40** < **90** <return>
`Construct` <pick> `Array` <pick> `Select objects:` `Assist` <pick> `Select` <pick>

Last <pick> <return> Rectangular or Polar array (R/P): **R** (Rectangular) <return> Number of rows (---) <1>: <return> Number of columns (|||) <1>: **5** <return> Distance between columns (|||): **10** <return>

Use the same procedure to draw the horizontal grid lines.

Add grid elevations and coordinates. The text scale will be based on the drawing being plotted on a 280- by 215-mm (11- by 8.5-in) sheet using a scale of 1:300. The text height on the plotted drawing is to be 3 mm. The drawing text height is then calculated as follows:

$$\frac{1}{300} \times H = 3 \text{ mm}$$
$$H = 900 \text{ mm}$$
$$H = 0.9 \text{ m} \quad \text{(drawing units)}$$

Add the horizontal and vertical coordinates (0, 10, 20, etc.) to the drawing (see Fig. 15.6).

Place the north arrow and the text below it on the drawing. The grid elevations are not to be displayed on the final drawing. They are added to the drawing so that a plot of the grid displaying the grid elevations can be generated, following which, the layer on which they reside is turned off. They are therefore placed on a separate layer named Gridel.

Set Gridel as the current layer. Rather than entering each of the grid point elevations individually, the lower-left corner elevation will be entered, and the Array command will be used to replicate that value across the grid. The Change command will be used to change each of the grid elevations to its proper value. This method is easier than specifying each individual text location, and it also gives a more uniform drawing.

Draw <pick> Text <pick> Justify/Style/<start point>: Digitize the start point for the grid elevation near 0,0. <pick> Height: **0.9** <return> Rotation angle <0>: **45** <return> Text: **46.0** <return>

Construct <pick> Array: <pick> Select objects: Assist <pick> Select <pick> Last <pick> Select objects: <return> Rectangular or Polar array (R/P): **R** (Rectangular) <return> Number of rows (---): **5** <return> Number of columns (|||): **5** <return> Unit cell or distance between rows (---): **10** <return> Distance between columns (|||): **10** <return>

AutoCAD LT will array the 46.0 elevation text to each of the grid points. The grid elevation values at points other than 0,0 are now to be changed to their proper value:

Modify <pick> Edit Text <Pick> <Select a TEXT or ATTDEF object>/Undo: Digitize the second grid elevation from the left along the top of the grid <pick>

The Edit Text dialogue box illustrated in Fig. 15.8 is displayed. Change the text from 46.0 to 46.6 (see Fig. 15.6). Repeat the commands changing each grid elevation to its proper value shown on Fig. 15.6. Compare Fig. 15.8 with Fig. 12.4, noting the different dialogue box displayed depending on whether a text or attribute definition is selected for editing.

15.5.3 Using polylines

Set `Contour` as the current layer and turn layer `Gridel off`. The contour lines will be drawn using the Pline (polyline) command rather than the Line command. Polylines have specific properties that lines do not have (refer to the discussion on polylines in your AutoCAD LT manual). The property to be used in this project is the ability to edit a polyline and create a smooth curve that fits the vertices of the original straight line segments. This creates a better contour line because real contour lines are seldom made up of straight line segments unless the ground elevations have been modified by machinery.

Because the contour drawing will be viewed later in three dimensions, the elevation of each contour line will have to be set; however, the first contour to be drawn is at elevation 47, which was previously set.

The polyline coordinates will be read from Table 15.1. The first coordinate selected for the 47-meter elevation is 8.33,0.

```
Draw <pick> Polyline <pick> From point: 8.33,0 <return>
```

The coordinate 8.33,0 was selected as the first in the list for elevation 47 in Table 15.1 (the second row of the table). Tick this item off in the table so you remember it was used. The next point to be used is 0,8.33 (the fourth row of the table). The reason for this selection will be discussed later. A line is then to be drawn from point 8.33,0 to 0,8.33.

The Pline command causes AutoCAD LT to respond with the following options rather than the familiar "to point" of the Line command. Refer to the AutoCAD LT Help function (App. A, Sec. A.4) for a complete discussion of the options. The entry will be the second coordinate of the line, as follows:

```
Current line-width is 0.00
Arc/Close/Halfwidth/Length/Undo/Width/<Endpoint of line>: 0,8.33
<return>
```

The second coordinate, 0,8.33, was selected by reviewing all of the coordinates for elevation 47 in Table 15.1 and considering the possibilities for the next coordinates. If you look at the previous coordinate entered, 8.33,0, and the grid in Fig. 15.6, you should observe that the next coordinate will be either on the column line where $x = 10$ and y falls between 0 and 10 or the column where $x = 0$ and y falls between 0 and 10 or the row line where x falls between 0 and 10 and $y = 10$. Remember x is horizontal (row) and y is vertical (column). As you use an elevation in Table 15.1, tick it off so you need not consider that one again.

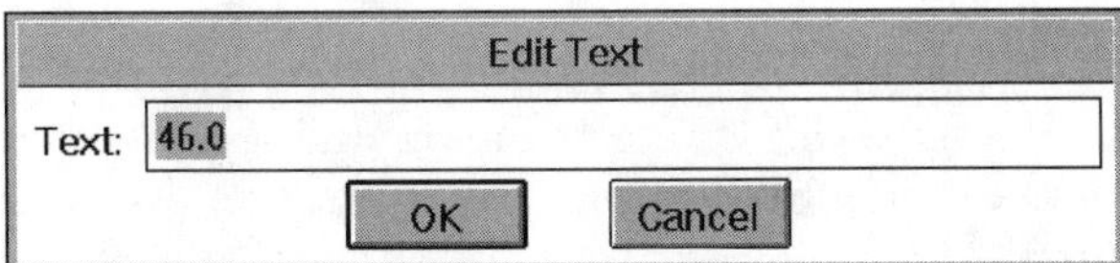

Figure 15.8 Editing text.

AutoCAD LT responds with the list of options again. The next point must fall either on column $x = 10$ with y from 0 to 10 or row $x = 0$ to 10 and $y = 10$. None exist in the list; therefore, this contour is discontinuous (see Fig. 15.9).

Recall the Polyline (Pline) command by pressing <return>. The points entered and the reasoning are listed as follows:

Coordinate	Reasoning
25,0	Next 47 elev. in list
30,2.50	$x = 30$; $y = 0–10$
38.57,10	$x = 30–40$; $y = 0–10$
40,20	$x = 30–40$; $y = 10–20$
37.04,30	$x = 30–40$; $y = 20–30$
30,38.26	$x = 30–40$; $y = 30–40$
20,37.6	$x = 20–30$; $y = 30–40$
10,36.92	$x = 10–20$; $y = 30–40$
4.71,30	$x = 0–10$; $y = 30–40$
0,25	$x = 0–10$; $y = 20–30$

Because there are no more 47 elevations and the contour line is not in the proximity to close on the first point at 25,0, the contour is discontinuous. Press Enter or Ctrl-C to exit the polyline command.

The 48-m elevation contour lines are now to be drawn. Prior to drawing any lines, however, the elevation must be set to 48. Using the Entity Cre-

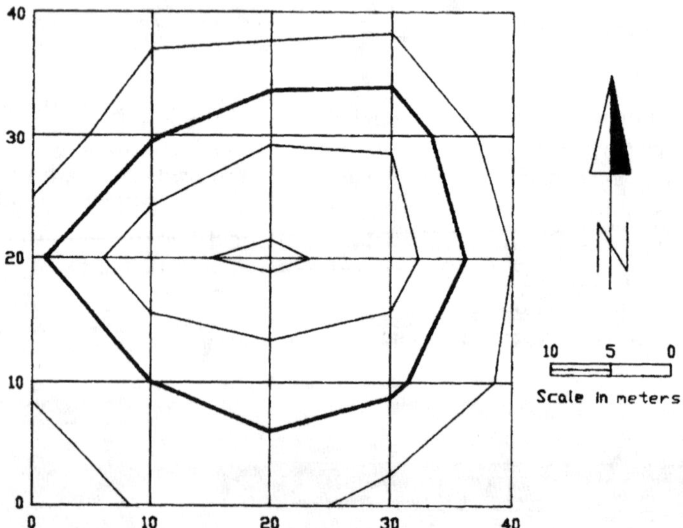

Figure 15.9 Topographic map contour polylines.

ation Modes dialogue box, set the current Elevation to 48, and the Thickness to 0.

When drawing contour lines, it is customary to draw every fifth contour line heavier. For this drawing, the 48-m elevation contour line will be made heavier to demonstrate the procedure to be used with polylines. Assuming that the width of the line on the plotted drawing is to be 0.5 mm and the plot will be done using a scale of 1:300, the width of the polyline in meters (the drawing units) will be:

$$\frac{1}{300} \times W = .5 \text{ mm}$$
$$W = 150 \text{ mm}$$
$$W = 0.15 \text{ m}$$

The polyline will be drawn starting with the first 48 elevation coordinate in the list in Table 15.1. Prior to entering the end point, the Width option for polylines will be selected to enter a polyline width of 0.15 units:

`Draw` <pick> `Polyline` <pick> `From point:` **20,6** <return> `Current line width is 0.00`

`Arc/Close/Halfwidth/length/Undo/Width/<Endpoint of Line>:` **W** (width) <return>

`Starting width <0.00>:` **0.15** <return> `Ending width <0.15>:` <return>

The next `To point:` values entered and the reasoning are as follows:

Coordinate	**Reasoning**
30,8.75	$x = 20–30; y = 0–10$
31.43,10	$x = 30–40; y = 0–10$
36.15,20	$x = 30–40; y = 10–20$
33.33,30	$x = 30–40; y = 20–30$
30,33.91	$x = 30–40; y = 30–40$
20,33.60	$x = 20–30; y = 30–40$
11,30	$x = 10–20; y = 30–40$
10,29.47	$x = 10–20; y = 20–30$
1,20	$x = 0–10; y = 20–30$
10,10	$x = 0–10; y = 10–20$
c	$x = 10–20; y = 0–10$

Notice that the possible coordinates for the last point are the same as those for the first point; therefore, the close command is entered.

Complete the topographical drawing. Remember, begin by setting the contour elevation, then change the polyline width back to 0 because only the 48-m elevation is to be heavier. Figure 15.9 illustrates the plan with all of the contours drawn.

15.5.4 Edit polylines for curve fitting

The Pedit (edit polyline) command allows the user to edit polylines in a number of different ways. Refer to the *AutoCAD LT's User's Guide* for a complete discussion. In this project the "Fit curve" function will be used to create a smooth curve that fits all of the vertices of the polyline for each contour.

`Modify` <Pick> `Edit Polyline` <pick> `Select polyline:` Digitize a point on the 47-m elevation polyline on the east side of the plan <pick>

The edit options similar to the following will now be displayed. The Fit curve option is selected:

`Close/Join/Width/Edit vertex/Fit/Spline/Decurve/Ltype gen/Undo/eXit <x>: Fit` <return>

The 47-m elevation contour will be redrawn by AutoCAD LT as a smooth curve. Repeat the process for each of the contours. The final contour plan is illustrated as Fig. 15.7.

To complete the drawing, set the current layer to Text and the Elevation to 47. Next, add the contour elevation values and save the file. Plot the drawing using a scale of 1:300 on an A-size sheet (280 by 215 mm or 11 by 8.5 in). The scale specified when plotting is 1 = .3 because the drawing is in meter units and the plot sheet size is in millimeters.

15.6 3-D View of Topographical Drawing

If your monitor does not have good resolution, you might want to turn the Grid layer off prior to using the 3D Viewpoint (Axes) command because some views will look quite cluttered. Try the 3D Viewpoint Axes command (see Sec. 15.3) with layer Grid on and also with layer Grid off to see the difference.

Try a number of viewpoints. When you get a good viewpoint (see Fig. 15.10), plot it. If you want to save a view, see the discussion in Sec. 15.7 on naming views prior to creating another viewpoint.

The Hide command does not change the views because none of the entities were given thickness; therefore, no lines are hidden behind any other entity.

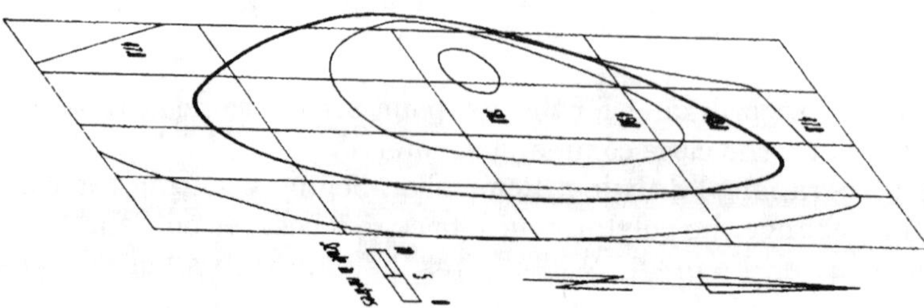

Figure 15.10 Three-dimensional view of contours.

15.7 Naming (Saving) Views

Often the drafter wants to return to a view many times. This is especially true in large drawings where the drafter works with specific zones in a drawing and wants to move quickly from zone (view) to zone (view). In three-dimensional drawings you might also want to save specific viewpoints for later use or reference. The View command is used to name views.

When a view is named, it can be quickly recalled using the View command. Prior to using the View command, use the 3-D Viewpoint commands to get a three-dimensional view of the topographical drawing you want to refer to at a later time. The commands to name the view are:

`View` <pick> `View` <pick> `Save` <pick> `View name to save:` **FIG-1** <return>

If the original plan view had been named it could be restored by following the procedure just completed, but using the Restore option. Since it was not named, the Plan command will be used to get a plan view of the World Coordinate System (see Sec. 15.10):

`View` <pick> `3D Plan View` <pick> `World UCS` <pick>

When plotting, a view may be plotted by pressing the `View` button in the Plot Configuration dialogue box (see Fig. 7.1), which displays the **View Name** list box illustrated in Fig. 15.11. To plot the view `FIG-1`, click on it in the names list and press `OK`. Then press the `View` radio button in the Additional Parameters box of the Plot Configuration dialogue box. Plot the view name FIG-1.

15.8 Lines and Plates in Space

Entities can be drawn in three-dimensional space by entering their x,y,z coordinates when points are requested by AutoCAD LT. The Polyline command,

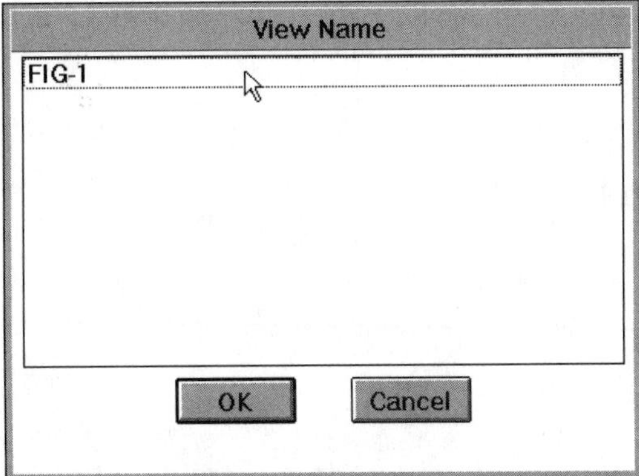

Figure 15.11 View Name list box.

however, is used to draw only two-dimensional polylines. To draw three-dimensional polylines you must use the 3Dpoly command, which creates three-dimensional polylines consisting entirely of straight-line segments. 3D polylines can be edited using the Edit Polyline command.

15.9 3-D Storage Bin

The storage bin illustrated in Fig. 15.12 is to be drawn in three-dimensional space. Begin a new drawing named Bin. Set the drawing units to architectural with the smallest unit to display as ¼ in (0′-0 ¼″). Set the limits to –4′,–4′ and 16′,12′, and use Zoom and All to zoom on the screen limits. Make a new layer named SS (structural steel) and set it as the current layer.

AutoCAD LT does not support the 3Dface command which is available in AutoCAD DOS and AutoCAD Windows, and would be used to draw the sloping side plates of the storage bin. Consequently the sides will be drawn using the Line command, and hatching will be used to "solidify" the plates. The intersection of the top plates and side plates will be used as the current elevation (z = 0).

Using the Entity Creation Modes dialogue box (Fig. 15.2) set the current Elevation as 0 and the Thickness as 1 ft 6 in. Then using the Layer Control dia-

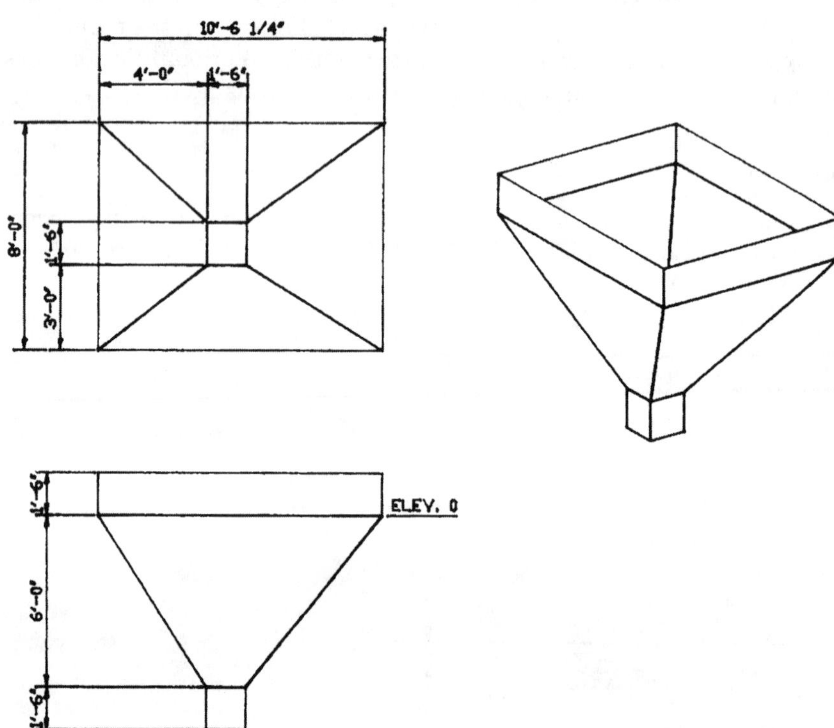

Figure 15.12 Storage bin.

logue box create two new layers named **Hatchl** (hatch left) and **Hatchf** (hatch front). Set layer **0** as the current layer.

As the top section is drawn, the lines will have a thickness of 1 ft 6 in:

> LINE <pick> From point: **0′,0′** <return> To point: **@10′6-1/4 <0** <return> To point: **@8′ <90** <return> To point: **@10′6-1/4 <180** <return> To point: **C** <return>

Draw the bottom opening plates by setting the Elevation to –6′ (negative because it is below elevation zero, in the negative z direction) and the thickness to –1′6 (negative because the thickness is in the negative z direction). The opening is then drawn using the line command, starting at coordinate 4′,3′.

After you have completed the bottom opening, set the Elevation back to 0 and the thickness to 0.

The 3-D Viewpoint Presets will be used to view the storage bin from a point above the right-side corner, which is an isometric view from the southeast:

> View <pick> 3D Viewpoint <pick> Presets <pick> Iso View SE <pick>

If the view is not similar to the isometric view in Fig. 15.13, enter the following:

> View <pick> 3D Viewpoint <pick> Vector <pick> Vpoint Rotate/<Viewpoint>: **10,–10,10** <return>

To get the Iso View SE, AutoCAD LT enters vectors of 1,–1,1. AutoCAD LT interprets the vectors as inches and, due to the proportionately larger dimensions of the drawing, often cannot generate the proper view.

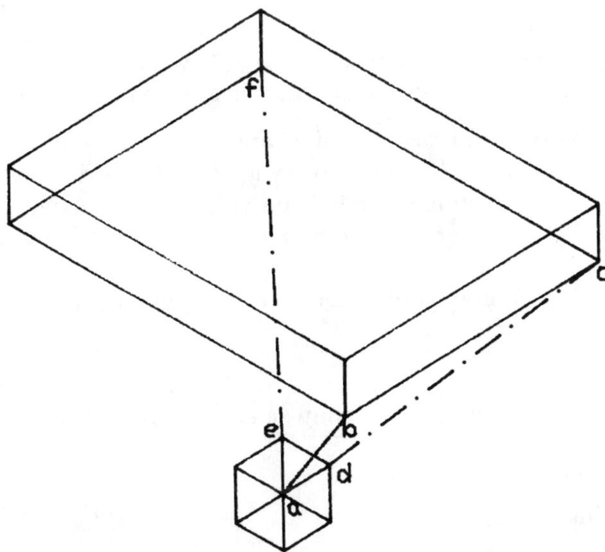

Figure 15.13 Bin 3-D faces.

Save the view naming it 3d so it can be easily restored later:

`View` <pick> `View` <pick> `Save` <pick> `View name to save:` **3d** <return>

The view should be similar to that illustrated in Fig. 15.13.

15.9.1 Lines in space

Standard AutoCAD for Windows or DOS has a command called 3Dface. That command allows you to draw faces (plates) in space. AutoCAD LT does not support the 3Dface command and the sides of the bin will be drawn using the 3dpoly command (or the Line command). The difference is not visible unless the Hide command is invoked. When Hide is invoked portions of entities behind 3Dfaces are hidden, giving a view like the isometric view in Fig. 15.12. If the line command is used to draw the sides of the bin, the sides appear as wire frames and the back sides are visible. In this exercise hatching will be used to "Hide" entities behind another.

To draw the sides of the bin, the running Intersection object snap is to be set to allow snapping onto the corners of the extruded lines defining the plates at the top and bottom opening of the bin. The running object snap is set as follows:

`Assist` <pick> `Object Snap...` <pick>

The Running Object Snap dialogue box shown in Fig. 5.2 is displayed. Choose the `Intersection` object snap and then press OK.

Side abcd (Fig. 15.13) of the bin is drawn as follows (enter 3dpoly from the keyboard):

3dpoly <return> `From point:` Place the Intersection object snap aperture on point a in Fig. 15.13. <pick> `Close/Undo/<Endpoint of line>:` Place the Intersection aperture on point b. <pick> `Close/Undo/<Endpoint of line>:` Place the Intersection aperture on point c. <pick> `Close/Undo/<Endpoint of line>:` Place the Intersection aperture on point d. <pick> *Close/Undo/<Endpoint of line>:* `Close` (Toolbar, see Fig. E.11) <pick> <return> `Close/Undo/<Endpoint of line>:`

Repeat the process selecting points c, d, e, and f and then entering c (Close). If you make an error, enter U (Undo) and try again. We need a closed polyline for each of the four sides around the bin. That will make it easier for hatching later. With a closed polyline an area to be hatched is selected by picking one point on the polyline.

The Intersection object snap is no longer required, and should be turned off:

`Assist` <pick> `Object Snap...` <pick>

Select `None` from the running object snap selection box and then press OK.

15.9.2 Suppressing hidden lines

Choose the following:

`View` <pick> `Hide` <pick>

AutoCAD LT generates a hidden line view; however, only the top and bottom sections of the bin are interpreted as solid surfaces, and the sides are interpreted as wire frames. A simulated solid surface will be done using hatching.

15.10 Drawing Coordinate Systems

AutoCAD LT uses a fixed *World Coordinate System* (WCS) and an arbitrary *User Coordinate System* (UCS). The WCS is a fixed Cartesian coordinate system illustrated in Fig. 15.14. All drawings completed in earlier chapters of this book are done on the WCS.

Positive rotational angles about an axis are based on the right-hand rule. For example, positive rotation about the z-axis is determined by pointing the thumb of your right hand in the positive direction of the axis (out of the screen) and curling your fingers. The direction in which the tips of your fingers point is the direction of positive rotation about the z-axis.

The UCS is a Cartesian coordinate system which may be defined in any plane of the drawing and is done to facilitate drawing entities on that plane—for instance, on the sloping roof of a house. Any number of UCSs may be defined. The UCS origin is at a location specified by the drafter when the plane is defined.

15.10.1 Coordinate system icon

AutoCAD LT displays a coordinate system icon to show the positive direction of the x and y axis along with other relevant information about the UCS. If the current UCS is the WCS a W appears in the Y arm of the icon as illustrated in Fig. 15.15*a*. If the icon is located at the UCS origin a + is displayed in the base of the icon as shown in Fig. 15.15*a* and *b*. If the UCS is viewed from above, a box is formed at the base of the icon (Fig. 15.15*a, b,* and *c*); whereas, if viewed from below, the box is missing (Fig. 15.15*d*). If either the x or y axis of the UCS is within one degree of perpendicular to the screen, the icon displayed is a broken pencil to indicate the UCS is being viewed on edge; therefore, pointing to locations on the screen may be meaningless (see Fig. 15.15*e*).

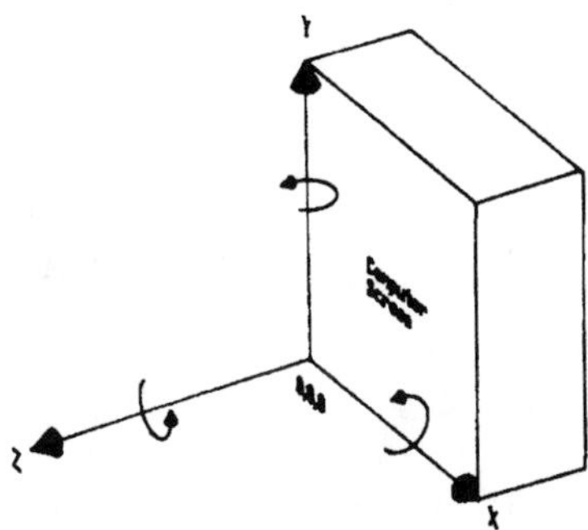

Figure 15.14 WCS and UCS Cartesian coordinate system.

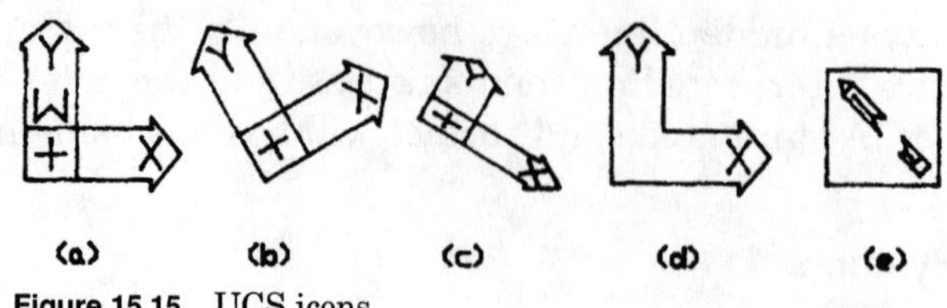

Figure 15.15 UCS icons.

15.10.2 World coordinate system

If the WCS icon (Fig. 15.15*a*) is not displayed on the screen, enter the following:

> `Assist` <pick> `UCS icon` <pick> `ON/OFF/All/Noorigin/ORigin/<OFF>:` **on** <return>

The WCS icon is probably located in the left corner of the screen. In order to follow the various settings to be done it should be located at its origin, as shown in Fig. 15.16:

> `Assist` <pick> `UCS icon` <pick> `ON/OFF/All/Noorigin/ORigin/<ON>:` **or** (Origin) <return>

15.10.3 User coordinate system

In order to hatch a three-dimensional surface properly, it should be plane to the current user coordinate system. A UCS is created on the right side of the bin as follows (select object snaps from the toolbox):

> `Assist` <pick> `Set UCS` <pick> `3 Point` <pick> `Origin point <0,0,0>: INTERSECTION` <pick> `of` Place the Intersection aperture box on point a (Fig. 15.13).

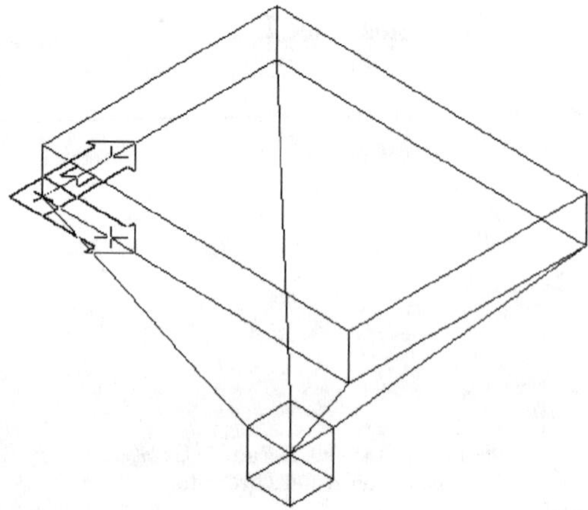

Figure 15.16 WCS origin.

<pick> Point on positive portion of the X-axis <default>: INTERSECTION <Pick> *of* Place the Intersection aperture box on d (D), setting the x axis of the UCS along line a-d. <pick> Point on positive-Y portion of UCS XY plane <default>: INTERSECTION <pick> of Place the intersection aperture box on b (B), setting the y axis along plane a-b. <pick>

The UCS icon should appear as illustrated in Fig. 15.17, on the right side of the bin. Before continuing, name the Right UCS so it can be recalled later:

Assist <pick> Named UCS... <pick>

The UCS Control box illustrated in Fig. 15.18 is displayed. The Current (Cur) UCS is named *NO NAME*. Click on it to highlight it. Then move the cursor to the Rename To: edit box and change the name in the box from *NO NAME* to **Right** as shown. Click the Rename To: box, and the name in the listing changes from *NO NAME* to RIGHT. Notice the name is *not* changed in the list until the Rename To box is clicked. If the name Right is listed in the UCS list box click OK. If it is not, repeat the above steps.

Now, create the front UCS shown in Fig. 15.19 and change its name from *NO NAME* to FRONT.

15.10.4 Hatching on a 3-D plane

Click on the current layer name button in the buttons bar and select the layer name HATCHF (hatch front) from the drop-down box. This sets the current layer to HATCHF, listing that name in the current layer button box.

It will be easier to select the surface to be hatched if a plan view of the Front UCS is displayed:

View <pick> 3D Plan View <pick> Current UCS <pick>

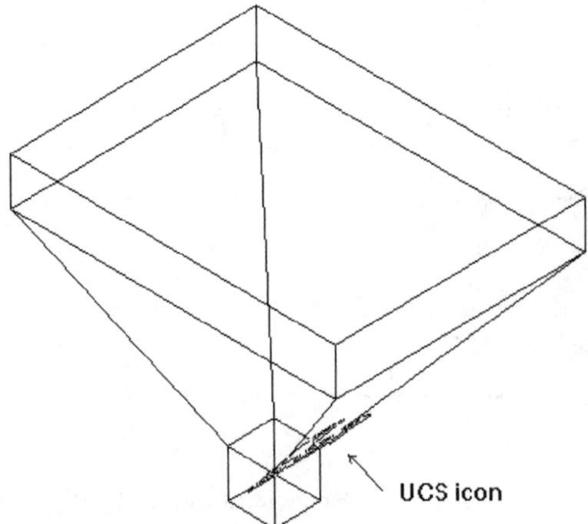

Figure 15.17 Right-side UCS.

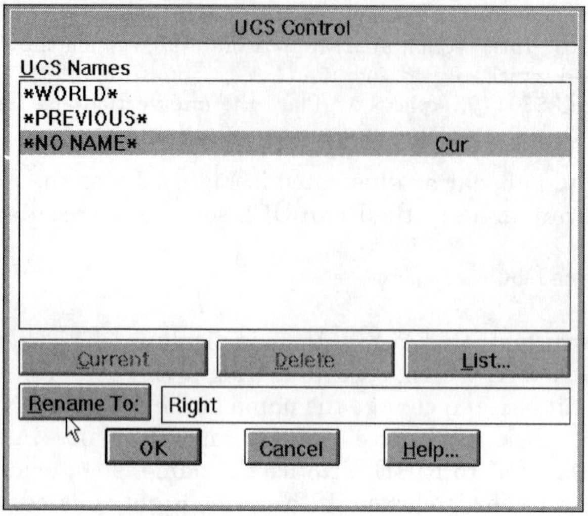

UCS Control

UCS Names

WORLD
PREVIOUS
NO NAME Cur

Current Delete List...

Rename To: Right

OK Cancel Help...

Figure 15.18 Naming a UCS.

The plan view of the front UCS plane similar to that shown in Fig. 15.20 is drawn on the screen (without the hatching). Choose the following to hatch the front side of the bin:

`Draw` <pick> `Hatch...` <pick>

The Select Hatch Pattern box shown in Fig. 6.15 is displayed. Select the `ansi37` pattern (second from the top on the right side of the box). AutoCAD LT continues with:

`Pattern (? or name/U style): ansi37`
`Scale for pattern <1>:` **15** <return>

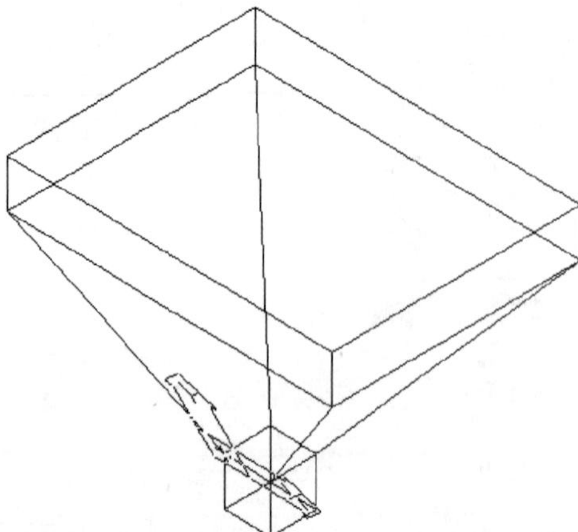

Figure 15.19 Front UCS.

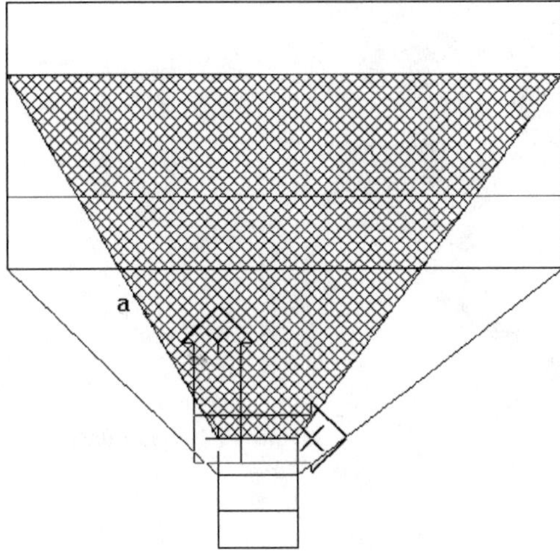

Figure 15.20 Plan of front UCS.

`Angle for pattern <0>:` <return>
`Select objects:` Digitize a point on the polyline outlining the side to be hatched—point a in Fig. 15.20. <pick>

If the hatching is incorrect Undo it and try again. If you have trouble selecting the correct polyline, use a selection window. Then use the Remove option in the Assist Select menu to remove other entities selected. The Add option in the Select menu takes you out of the remove mode and back into the add mode of selection.

When the hatching is correct restore the 3D view to see if it appears OK in that view.

`View` <pick> `View` <pick> `Restore` <pick> `View name to restore:` **3d** <return>

If the hatching is not correct, enter Undo twice and retry the hatching.

When the front sloping side is hatched correctly, set HATCHR as the current layer and freeze layer HATCHF (to get it out of the way). Then choose the following:

`Assist` <pick> `Named UCS...` <pick>

Click on the `RIGHT` UCS in the list box and then press the `Current` button to make RIGHT the current UCS. Then press `OK`. Repeat the procedure outlined above to hatch the right-side sloping surface of the bin. When it is hatched, thaw layer `HATCHF` and then restore the `3D` view. Enter the `Hide` command. The bin should appear as shown in Fig. 15.21.

15.11 Dynamic View

The 3D Dynamic View option (Dview command) in the View menu allows you to view models three-dimensionally and dynamically control all aspects of the

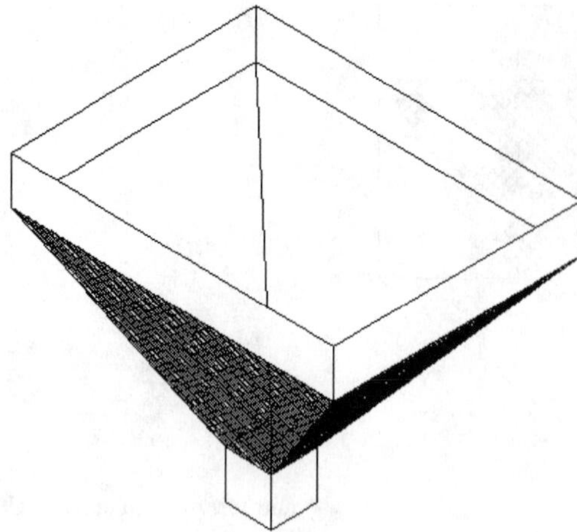

Figure 15.21 Simulated hidden view.

view. The viewer's eye location is called the *camera,* and the focus point is the *target.* The line between these two points is the line of site. The line of site is adjusted by moving the camera and/or the target. You can zoom on the object using a slider bar, and the object can be panned or twisted around the line of site. Finally, you can create a perspective view where the focal lines converge on a distant point giving a real-life look of depth.

15.11.1 Setting the camera and target

The camera option allows you to specify the camera position along the line of site:

`View` <pick> `3D Dynamic View` <pick> `Select objects:` Place a selection window around the entire storage bin. <pick> `Select objects:` <return> `CAmera/TArget/Distance/POints/PAn/Zoom/TWist/CLip/Hide/Off/Undo/<eXit>:`

Note that the WCS is displayed (see Fig. 15.16). The control of the 3-D view is based on the WCS. If the view is too large on your screen, enter the Z (Zoom) option and enter a zoom factor to reduce the object size; e.g., 0.5 reduces the object to half its size. The camera position is set entering:

ca <return> `Toggle angle in/Enter angle from XY plane <35.26>:`

The first angle requested is the vertical rotation of the camera. A 0 angle places the camera pointing parallel to the XY plane. Move the cursor up (positive) and you look down on the XY plane (into the bin). Move the cursor down (negative) and you look up from below the XY plane (below the bin). The angles are displayed dynamically in the coordinate display window. Enter a value of **15.** AutoCAD LT continues with:

`Toggle angle in/Enter angle in XY plane from X axis <-45.00>:`

The next angle requested is the horizontal rotation of the camera. A 0 angle places the camera looking directly into the X axis (icon). Moving the cursor to the right (positive) walks the camera to the right (counterclockwise) around the object. Moving the camera to the left (negative) walks it to the left (clockwise) around the object. Enter a value of **–60.** AutoCAD LT continues with:

```
CAmera/TArget/Distance/POints/PAn/Zoom/TWist/CLip/Hide/Off/Undo/
<eXit>: ta <return> Toggle angle in/Enter angle from XY plane <15>:
```

Entering ta (TArget) allows you to move the target around the camera which remains stationary. The first angle requested is the vertical rotation of the target. Moving the cursor up (positive) rotates the target (object) above the camera, and the line of site is toward the bottom of the bin. Moving the cursor down (negative) is like rotating the target (object) below the camera, and the line of site is into the bin. Enter a value of **–20.** AutoCAD LT continues with:

```
Toggle angle in/Enter angle in XY plane from X axis <120>:
```

The next angle requested is the horizontal rotation of the target. A 0 angle places the target looking directly along the x axis (icon), and the line of site is horizontal. Moving the cursor to the right (positive) walks the target (object) to the right (counterclockwise) around the camera. Moving the target to the left (negative) walks it to the left (clockwise) around the camera. Enter a value of **150.** The current view on the screen is seen in Fig. 15.22.

An easier way to set the camera and target is using the POints option:

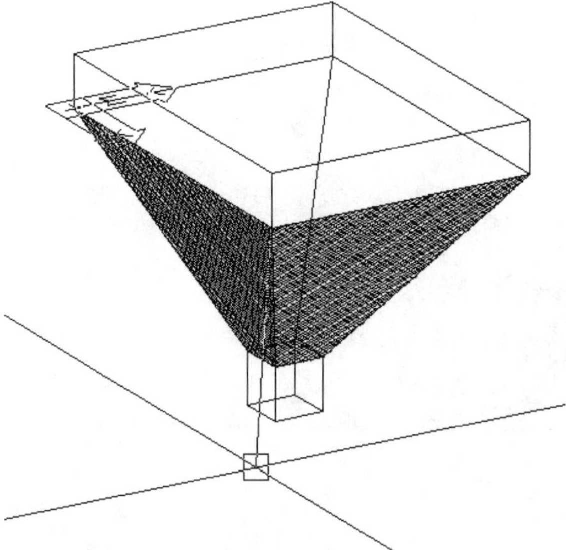

Figure 15.22 Camera/Target positions.

CAmera/TArget/Distance/POints/PAn/Zoom /TWist/CLip/Hide/Off/Undo/ <eXit>: **po** <return> Enter target point <9′-3 3/4″,9′-0 1/4″,-2′-1″>: INTERSECTION <pick> of **Click the Intersection object snap aperture box on the target (corner of bin) shown in Fig. 15.22.** <pick> Enter camera point <10′6″,8′4″,1′7″>: select a point as shown in Fig. 15.22 (cursor box). <pick>

The Zoom option allows you to zoom on object:

CAmera/TArget/Distance/POints/PAn/Zoom/TWist/CLip/Hide/Off/Undo/ <eXit>: **z** <return> Adjust zoom scale factor:

AutoCAD LT displays a slider bar across the top of the screen, ranging from 0x to 16x. Moving the cursor towards 0x reduces the size of the object, and moving toward 16x enlarges the size. Set a reasonable zoom size on your screen.

15.11.2 3-D perspective view

A perspective view with lines converging on a distant point is created using the Distance option:

CAmera/TArget/Distance/POints/PAn/Zoom/TWist/CLip/Hide/Off/Undo/ <eXit>: **d** <return> New camera/target distance <43′8″>:

A slider bar along the top allows you to move the camera distance from the target. Select a distance of about 28 ft. The drawing is regenerated as a perspective view, indicated by the perspective icon in the lower-left corner of the screen, illustrated in Fig. 15.23. The convergence of the lines depends on the length of the object in comparison to the camera/target distance.

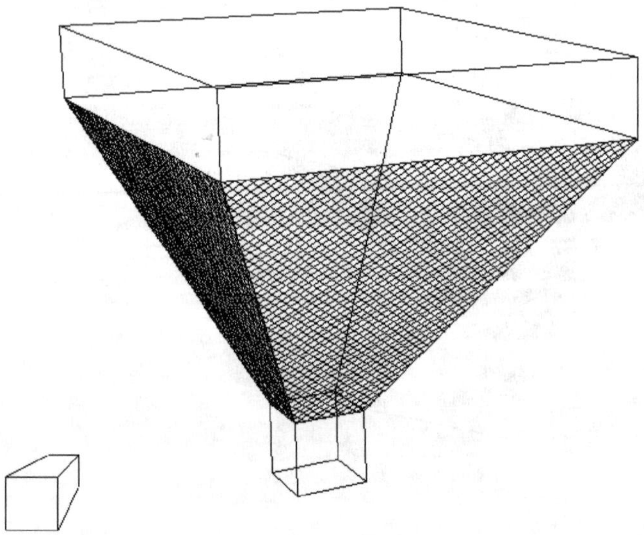

Figure 15.23 Perspective view.

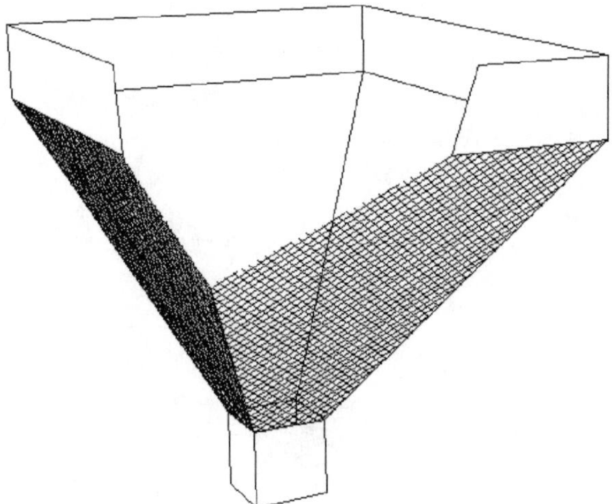

Figure 15.24 Clipped view.

15.11.3 Clipping parts of the object

The front or back of the object can be cut off using clipping planes. A clipping plane is perpendicular to your line of site, and a specified distance from the target. Positive distances are in front of the target, and negative distances are behind the target. Enter the following:

CAmera/TArget/Distance/POints/PAn/Zoom/TWist/CLip/Hide/Off/Undo/
<eXit>: **CL** <return> Eye/<Distance from target><27′–9″>:

A slider bar is displayed across the top of the screen. Move along the slider bar and select a distance of about –2′–4″ reading the value in the coordinate display window. The clipped view is shown in Fig. 15.24.

Try clipping the back of the object. Choosing Off, turn off front and back clipping. The eXit (x) option exits the 3D Dynamic View (Dview) command and regenerates the drawing using the last view established.

If you enter <return> instead of selecting an object when the 3-D Dynamic View option is initially selected, AutoCAD LT displays a small house for you to use to set a desired view. When the command is exited your model replaces the house using the last view established. In a complex drawing it is often easier and faster to establish a view this way.

Chapter

16

Multiview Drawings

Objective. Complete a three-dimensional multiview drawing of an industrial building, user-coordinate systems, viewports in model space and paper space, layer visibility in viewports, and dimensioning in viewports.

Drawing. Begin a new drawing named Proj-16. Set the units to decimal (mm) with zero digits to the right of the decimal. The drawing is to be plotted on a B-size (280 by 430) sheet using a scale of 1:200. The screen limits are based on the floor-plan dimensions of 18,000 by 22,000 mm. In order to allow room for dimensions, set the screen limits as 0,0 and 28000,32000. The completed drawing is illustrated in Fig. 16.1.

16.1 Viewports in Model Space

The computer drawing screen can be divided into multiple viewports. Each viewport can contain a different view of the drawing and can be zoomed or panned independently. If you modify the drawing or add entities to one viewport, the changes are reflected in each of the other viewports. Because a viewport has a smaller screen area than the full screen, drawing with viewports is only advantageous when the extra view(s) of the entity assist in visualizing and drawing the entity. For instance, because points for an entity can be selected in any viewport, it is easy to envision how the additional views can simplify the drawing of some three-dimensional objects.

Although you can display multiple viewports, only one viewport is the current one. When the cursor is moved into the current viewport, the familiar cross hairs are displayed. If the cursor is moved out of the current viewport into an adjacent one, the cross hairs change to a small arrow pointing in a northwest direction. Changing the current viewport is done by pointing to the desired viewport and pressing the <pick> button on the mouse. The keyboard cursor control keys move the cursor only within the current viewport and cannot be used to select a new viewport.

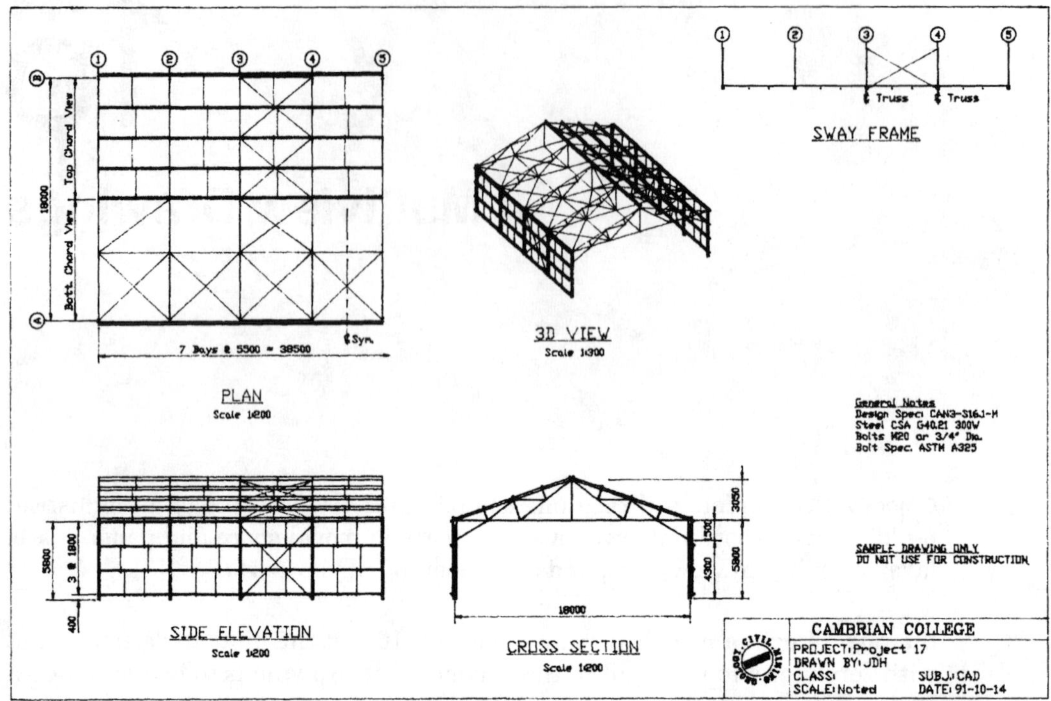

Figure 16.1 Industrial building.

16.2 Industrial Building

A three-dimensional view of the industrial building to be drawn will fit within a box 18,000 mm wide, 22,200 mm long, and 5800 mm high (at the eave). Prior to drawing the structure, the outline of this box is drawn on a construction layer. Make a new layer named Constr. If you have a color monitor, set the color of Constr as yellow so the construction lines stand out from the object lines. If you have a monochrome monitor, set the line type as Dot. The Ltscale is calculated using Eq. (6.2) as: (also see App. C, Table C.2.B)

$$\text{PLot scale} \times \text{LTSCALE} = 1 \text{ in} \times \text{conversion} \times \tfrac{3}{4}$$
$$\tfrac{1}{200} \times \text{LTSCALE} = 1 \times (25.4/1000) \times \tfrac{3}{4}$$
$$\text{LTSCALE} = 3810$$

The front side of the box is drawn as follows:

`LINE` (Toolbox) <pick> `From point:` **5000,5000** <return> `To point:` **@22000 <0** <return> `To point:` **@0,0,5800** <return> `To point:` **@22000 < 180** <return> `Close` (Buttons bar) <pick>

Notice that the third point entered is 5800 mm along the z axis (perpendicular to the screen). The Copy command is used to draw the back side:

COPY <pick> Select objects: Place a selection window around the front wall. <pick> Base point or displacement: **0,18000** <return> Second point of displacement: <return>

The end walls are easier to draw on a three-dimensional view of the structure. The Vpoint command is used to view the structure from a point –30 degrees in front of the plan (the negative indicates a clockwise rotation on the *x,y* plane) and 30 degrees above the plan (positive is counterclockwise from the *x,y* plane) as follows:

View <pick> 3D Viewpoint <pick> Rotate <pick> Enter angle in X-Y plane from X axis <270>: **–30** <return> Enter angle from X-Y plane <90>: **30** <return>

Complete the box by adding the top and bottom lines on each end wall using the Line command and the Intersection object snap. Then save the View using the name **3d.** This view will be used throughout the drawing as a reference view illustrating the entire building.

16.2.1 Coordinate system icon location

The default location of the UCS icon (see Fig. 15.15) is in the lower-left corner of the monitor or viewport. When defining a UCS, it is easier to visualize what is being done if the icon is located at the origin of the UCS. The Ucsicon command is used to locate the icon at the UCS origin as follows:

Assist <pick> UCS icon <pick> ON/OFF/ALL/Noorigin/Origin <OFF>: **On** <return> <return> ON/OFF/ALL/Noorigin/ORigin <ON>: **OR** (ORigin) <return>

The ORigin option tells AutoCAD LT to display the icon at the origin of the UCS, provided the origin is on the screen. If the origin is off the screen or too close to the edge of the screen, the icon is displayed in the lower-left corner of the screen.

The All option is used when you have already created viewports and the UCS icon setting being made is to apply to all viewports. If All is not selected prior to entering an option, the option applies only to the current viewport.

The Noorigin option tells AutoCAD LT to display the icon in the lower-left corner of the viewport.

Because the display currently fills the viewport, the UCS origin is close to the screen edge and, although the ORigin option was selected, the icon is displayed in the lower-left corner of the viewport. It will be displayed at the UCS origin if the size of the display is reduced as follows:

View <pick> Zoom <pick> Scale <pick> All/Center/Extents/Previous/Window/ <Scale (X/XP)>: **.9x** <return>

The current UCS is the WCS, so the icon is displayed at point 0,0,0 based on the screen limits set. The zoom value .9X was entered to zoom 0.9 times the current screen.

16.2.2 Defining user-coordinate systems

User-coordinate systems (refer to Chap. 15.10) are to be defined on the top (of the box), front side, right side, and sloping roof planes of the building. The origin of the UCS on the top of the box is to have its origin at the left corner on the top of the box and is created as follows:

> `Assist` <pick> `Set UCS >` <pick> `Origin` <pick> `Origin point <0,0,0>: INTERSECTION` <pick> `of` Place the Intersection object snap aperture on the far left corner of the top of the box. <pick>

The UCS icon will move to the top of the box in the far left corner. Save the coordinate system using the name Roofplan as follows:

> `Assist` <pick> `Named UCS...` <pick>

The UCS Control dialogue box illustrated in Fig. 16.2 is displayed. *WORLD* in the list box is the World UCS which has its origin at the 0,0,0 limits defined at the opening of the drawing. *PREVIOUS* is the previous UCS which also happens to be the WCS (*WORLD*). *NO NAME* is the current UCS (note Cur to the right of the name in the list box) which has not yet been named. Choose `*NO NAME*` by clicking on it. Then move the cursor into the Rename To: edit box and enter **Roofplan.** Then press `Rename To:` to rename the *NO NAME* UCS to Roofplan. Press `OK` to exit the dialogue box.

Now following the procedure outlined above move the UCS origin to the front view, directly below its current position, using the Intersection object snap to ensure the UCS is on the intersection point.

The relocated UCS is to be on the plane of the front view, so it must be rotated by 90 degrees in a positive direction about its x axis (based on the right-hand rule), to appear as shown in Fig. 16.3.

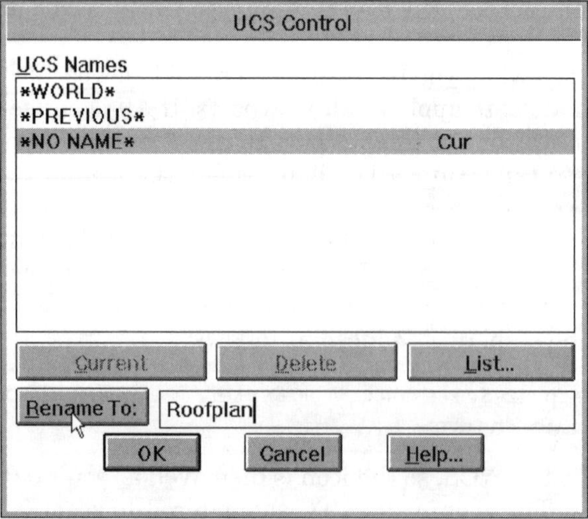

Figure 16.2 UCS Control dialogue box.

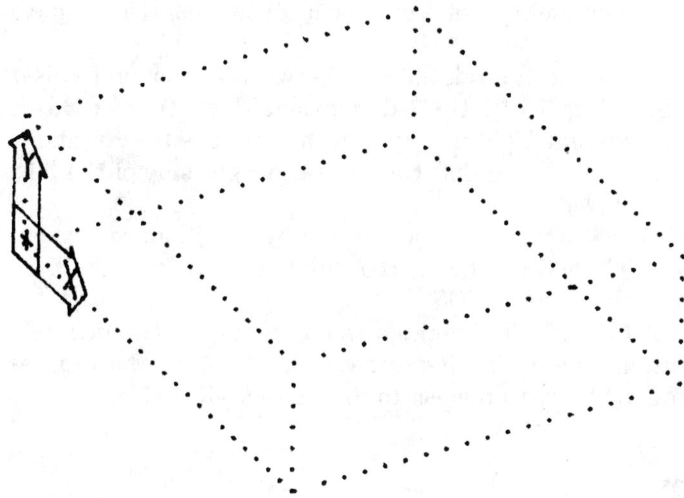

Figure 16.3 UCS Front.

`Assist` <pick> `Set UCS >` <pick> `X Axis Rotate` <pick> `Rotation angle about X axis <0.0>:` **90** <return>

Display the UCS Control box. The current UCS is named *NO NAME*. Rename it to **Front.**

Define a UCS on the right-side end of the box by moving the UCS origin to the bottom-right corner of the front view of the box. Then rotate the UCS 90 degrees about the *y* axis. The view should appear as illustrated in Fig. 16.4. Name the UCS **Rightside.**

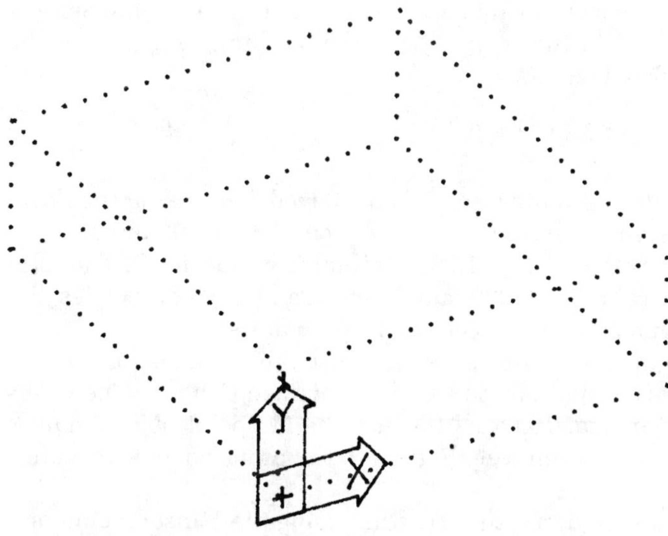

Figure 16.4 UCS Rightside.

The UCS in the plane of the sloping roof is created after the roof trusses have been drawn.

It is important you understand the relationship between a view and a user coordinate system, UCS. In Fig. 16.4 a three-dimensional View (named 3d) of the box is displayed. The current UCS in Fig. 16.4, however, is the Rightside UCS, which has its origin in the lower-left corner of the right side of the box, where the UCS icon is displayed.

The View command is used to view an object from any direction, regardless of the current UCS. The UCS defines the x,y coordinate system, and the UCS icon graphically indicates the current UCS.

When you invoke an AutoCAD LT command to create an entity, such as a line, you define its position by entering its x,y,z coordinates. The coordinates are interpreted by AutoCAD LT with respect to the current UCS.

16.3 Columns and Roof Trusses

Building columns are vertical primary structural members that support the building and rest on the footings. Roof trusses are horizontal primary structural members that, in this building, span between columns and support the roof loads. A roof truss is composed of a number of individual members connected in a geometric pattern to form a single member.

The structural framework is to be drawn on a layer named **SS** (structural steel). Use the Layer control dialogue box to make the new layer and set it as the current layer.

16.3.1 Columns

The columns are added to the structure by creating a block and inserting it into the drawing using the Minsert (multiple insert) command. The column block is to be drawn on elevation 0 in the plan view of the building, which is on the WCS. The WCS is recalled as follows:

```
View <pick> 3D Plan View <pick> World UCS <pick> Assist <pick> Set UCS
<pick> World <pick>
```

A plan view of the World coordinate system is displayed. Now using the Zoom and Window commands, zoom on a clear area of about 500 by 500 units.

Draw the column illustrated in Fig. 16.5*a* (excluding dimensions). The total height (thickness) of the column is 6025 mm. Using the Change Properties dialogue box, change the thickness of the column to 6025 units.

After the column height (thickness) is changed, use the Block Definition dialogue box (Fig. 10.4) to save the column as a block named Column. The insertion point is illustrated in Fig. 16.5*a* as IP—use the Midpoint object snap to select the midpoint of the 250-mm web. Return to the previous view by entering Zoom and Previous.

The Column block is inserted into the structure using the Minsert command which is entered at the command line as follows:

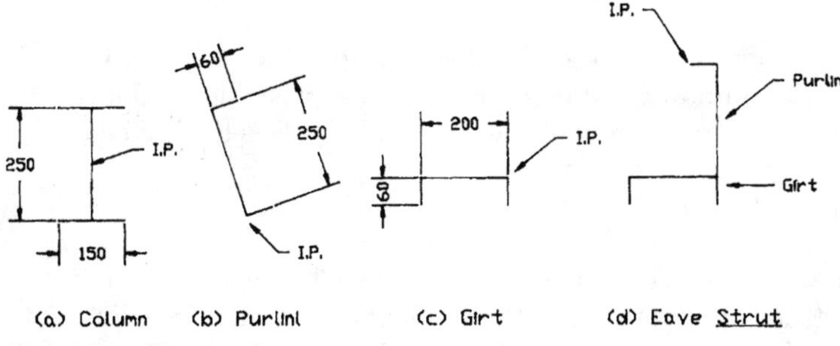

Figure 16.5 Structural components.

Minsert <return> `Block name (or ?):` **Column** <return> `Insertion point: INTERSECTION` <pick> `of` **Place the object snap target over the lower-left corner of the structure.** <pick> `X scale factor <1>/Corner/XYZ:` <return> `Y scale factor (default = X):` <return> `Rotation angle <0>:` <return> `Number of rows (---) <1>:` **2** <return> `Number of columns (|||) <1>:` **5** <return> `Unit cell or distance between rows (---):` **18000** <return> `Distance between columns (|||):` **5500** <return>

To see if the columns have been inserted properly, the 3-D view created earlier is recalled:

`View` <pick> `View` <pick> `Restore` <pick> `View name to restore:` **3d** <return>

The screen view should appear as illustrated in Fig. 16.6.

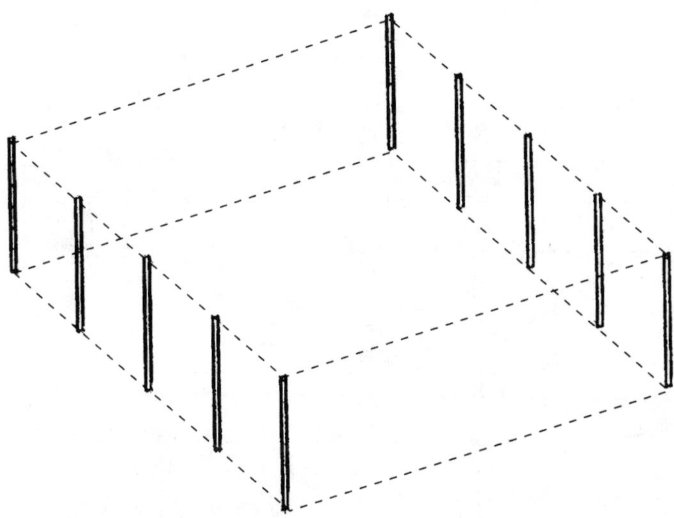

Figure 16.6 3D view with columns inserted.

16.3.2 Roof trusses

The roof trusses are drawn as a block and inserted into the building in each bay using the Minsert command. Prior to drawing the truss block, the Rightside UCS is restored, and a plan view of the Rightside UCS is displayed:

`Assist` <pick> `Named UCS` <pick>

The UCS Control dialogue box (Fig. 16.2) is displayed. Choose `RIGHTSIDE` in the list box and then click on Current to make Rightside the current UCS. Click `OK` to close the dialogue box. Choose the following to get a plan view of the current UCS:

`View` <pick> `3D Plan View` <pick> `Current UCS` <pick>

Use the Pan command from the Toolbox to pan the monitor so the building is located in the middle area of the screen.

The Rightside UCS origin (coordinate 0,0) is at the center of the base of the left column. The roof truss' top and bottom chord lines intersect at the center line of the left column 5800 mm above its base. The truss width is 18,000 mm, and its peak height is 3050 mm. The truss top and bottom chords are drawn as follows:

`LINE` <pick> `From point:` **0,5800** <return> `To point:` **@18000<0** <return> `To point:` **@–9000,3050** <return> `To point:` **C** <return>

The truss web members intersect the top chord at its quarter points, and are perpendicular to the top chord of the truss (see Fig. 16.7). Prior to drawing the members the drawing snap angle is to be rotated parallel to the top chord of the truss. The Drawing Aids dialogue box is normally used to set snap, but it does not allow you to enter the snap rotation on the screen. Enter snap at the command line by typing it in (select object snaps from the toolbox):

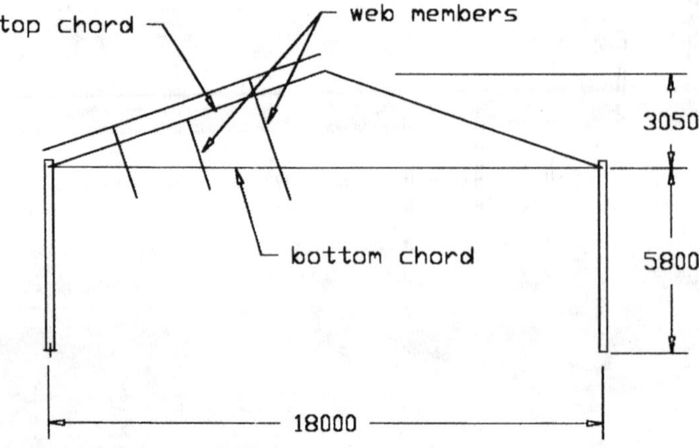

Figure 16.7 Truss components.

snap <return> `Snap spacing or ON/OFF/Aspect/Rotate/Style <1>:` **r** (Rotate) <return> `Base point: ENDPOINT` <pick> `of` Place the Endpoint aperture box near the bottom end of the top chord on the left side of the truss. <pick> `Rotation angle <0>: ENDPOINT` <pick> `of` Place the Endpoint aperture box on the same line near the peak of the truss. <pick>

The cursor x axis is now aligned with the top-left chord of the truss.

16.3.3 Copying a line using grips

Grips are small squares that appear at defined points on objects, and can be used to edit the objects. Pick a point on the top chord on the left side of the truss. The entity selected is highlighted (dotted) and small blue boxes appear on the top chord member as illustrated in Figure 16-8. The small blue boxes are grips. Highlighted entities are manipulated using the grips.

If the grips did not appear, set the Grips system variable to 1 as follows and retry the preceding:

```
COMMAND: grips
New value for GRIPS<0>: 1 <return>
```

The cursor will have a small target box at its intersection indicating that the Grips system variable is set to 1. Move the target box onto the middle grip (Fig. 16.8) on the line and press <pick>. The grip fills in and becomes hot (red) indicating it will serve as the basis for editing. The command line appears as follows:

```
**STRETCH**
<Stretch to point>/Base point/Copy/Undo/eXit:
```

Move the cursor around noting how the line stretches. Do *not* press pick. Grip commands are Stretch, Move, Rotate, Scale, and Mirror. The commands

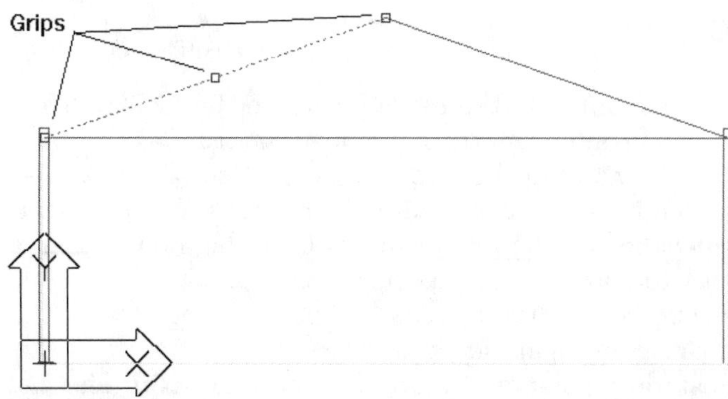

Figure 16.8 Grips.

are changed by pressing <return>. Press <return> once and the Move command is available (if not, keep pressing <return> until it is available). The Copy option is selected in the following so a copy of the line is moved and the original line remains:

```
**MOVE**
<Move to point>/Base point/Copy/Undo/eXit: c <return> **MOVE (multiple)**
<Move to point>/Base point/Copy/Undo/eXit:
```

Pick the Ortho mode button on (it will appear white) in the tool bar. Now pick a point *about* 500 units above the current line, copying the top chord as shown in Fig. 16.7. Press <return> to exit the grips command. Then press ^C (Cancel) in the toolbar twice to remove the grips. Refer to App. A.2, for more information on using grips.

Use the Break command to break the copied line at its midpoint:

Modify <pick> Break <pick> Select objects: MIDPOINT <pick> of Place the midpoint object snap aperture box on the new line copied above the truss. <pick> Enter second point (or F for first point: @ (from the toolbar) <pick>

Although it is not visible there is a small break in the line at its midpoint, so it is now two lines. Draw the web members illustrated in Fig. 16.7 (Ortho is to be on):

LINE <pick> From point: MIDPOINT <pick> of Place the Midpoint aperture box on the top chord line on the left side of the truss. <Pick> To point: Move the cursor below the bottom chord of the truss. Ortho is on so the line is perpendicular to the snap; i.e., perpendicular to the top chord of the truss. <pick> To point: <return> <return> Line From point: MIDPOINT <pick> of Place the midpoint aperture box on one side of the copied line. <pick> To point: Move the cursor below the bottom chord drawing the next web member. <pick>

Draw the remaining web member. Then Rotate snap back to 0 degrees with its origin at 0,0. Erase the copied construction line. Then use the Trim command to trim the web members:

Modify <pick> Trim <pick> Select cutting edge(s) ... Select objects: Pick the top and bottom chords of the truss. <Pick> <return> Select objects to trim: Pick the ends of the web members that are to be trimmed off. <pick>

Turn the ortho mode off using the Ortho mode button in the toolbar. Then complete the remaining web members on the left side of the truss as shown in Fig. 16.9. Use the Mirror command in the Construct menu (see Chap. 9, Sec. 9.4.2) to mirror the web members about the center of the truss. When indicating the mirror line, turn Ortho on. The mirror line is from the intersection of the top chords of the truss, and an orthogonal line directly below.

Draw the left-side knee brace from the intersection point on the truss to the UCS coordinate 0,4300. Draw the right-side knee brace.

Using the View and Restore commands, restore the view named **3d.** The roof truss is to be saved as a block, and inserted into the structure using the multi-

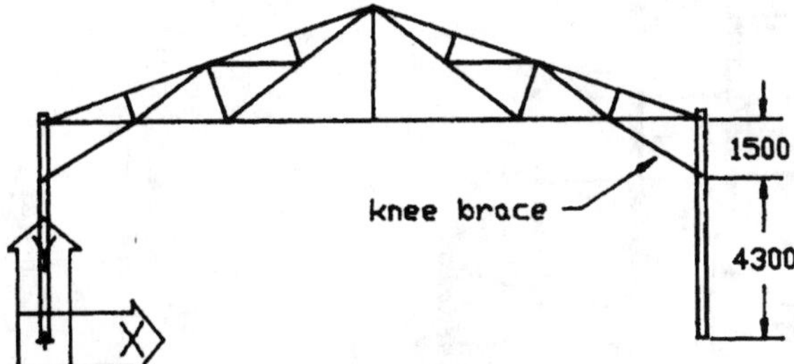

Figure 16.9 Roof truss and knee brace.

ple insert (Minsert) command. Before creating the block, however, you must determine what UCS is to be current when the block is to be inserted. If the UCS current when the block is created does not match the UCS to be current when block is inserted, the block will not be aligned properly. The Minsert command allows you to insert a block as an array along the *x* and/or *y* axis. The truss is to be inserted along the length of the building and spanning between columns. Consequently the *x* and *y* axis must fall along the roof plan plane when the truss is inserted, which is the Roofplan UCS.

Use the UCS Control box to set the current UCS as `Roofplan`. You should now have a three-dimensional view of the building displayed with the UCS icon at the far left column, which is the origin (0,0,0) of the Roofplan UCS.

Note: Turn the `Constr` layer off.

Save the roof truss and knee brace as a block named **Truss.** Use a window to select the truss, and the knee braces. Entities selected will be drawn dotted by AutoCAD LT. If the building columns are accidentally selected, use the Remove command to remove them from the selection set. If you make a mistake, use the Undo command to undo the commands and then try again. The block insertion point is at the intersection of the top and bottom chords on the left side of the truss.

The Truss block is to be inserted into the structure using the Minsert command. Prior to inserting the Truss block, use the Zoom command and enter a magnification of 0.8×. This is necessary because the Truss block is complex and if part of the truss is off the screen when it is being inserted, your system may be slowed considerably while entering the block.

Use the Minsert command to insert the block named **Truss.** The insertion point is the origin of the Roofplan UCS, point 0,0. There are to be 1 row and 5 columns, and the spacing of the columns is 5500 mm. If the trusses are not inserted properly, use the Undo command and try again. Your drawing should appear as illustrated in Fig. 16.10.

16.4 Defining the Topchord UCS

A UCS is required on the plane of the top chord of the truss to facilitate drawing entities on that plane. Because there are two sides to the truss, two top

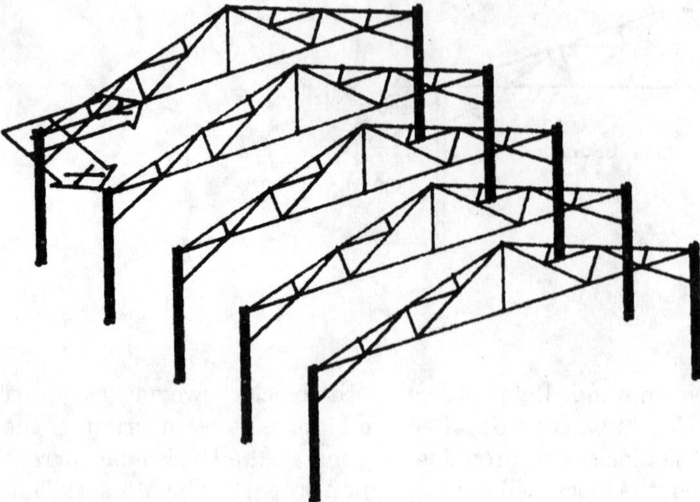

Figure 16.10 Structure with trusses inserted.

chord planes will be defined using the names **Topchordl** (left) and **Topchordr** (right)—as viewed from the right side of the building.

The current UCS origin is the top of the building's front-left column as illustrated in Fig. 16.10. The Topchordl UCS is defined by rotating the UCS origin so that it lies in the plane of the truss' top chord.

To facilitate the selection of points, use the Zoom and Window commands, or the Aerial View window, to enlarge a view that includes the current UCS icon and the left half of the roof truss located at the left end of the building.

After the view is enlarged, the new UCS is defined using the 3point option as follows:

> `Assist` <pick> `Set UCS` <pick> `3Point` <pick> `origin point <0, 0, 0>: END-POINT` <pick> `of` Place the target on the left side of the top chord of the end truss. <pick> `Point on positive portion of the X axis:` The X axis is not being changed so accept the default. <return> `Point of positive-Y portion of the UCS X-Y plane: ENDPOINT` <pick> `of` Place the target on the top chord of the truss near the peak of the truss.

The UCS icon should be displayed at the left end of the truss with its *x,y* axis on the plane of the truss top chord as illustrated in Fig. 16.11. If your UCS icon is located in the lower-left corner of the screen, your view might be too close to the edge of the screen (see Sec. 16.1.1). Try panning the view slightly to the right. If you have other problems, enter Undo and retry the commands, being more careful when selecting points.

Name the UCS **Topchordl** (left). Use similar procedures to define a UCS named **Topchordr** (right). Its origin is the *peak* of the truss, and the *x,y* axis is to lie on the plane of the top chord on the right side of the truss, with the *y*

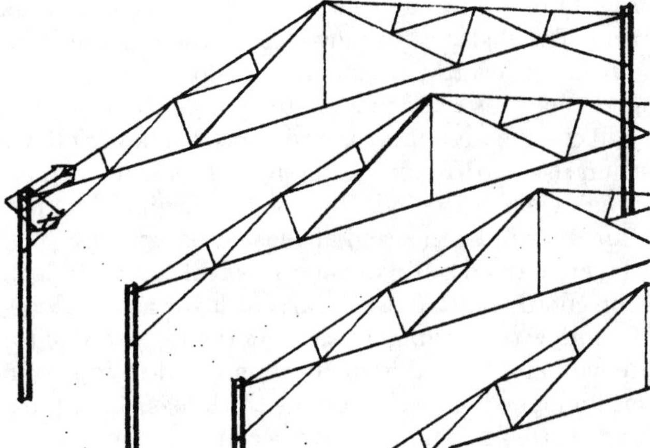

Figure 16.11 UCS Topchord.

axis pointing to the intersection of the top and bottom chord at the right side of the truss. Name the UCS.

16.5 Roof Purlins

Roof purlins are members on the roof of a structure, spanning between roof trusses, and used to support the roof sheeting. The purlins are to be drawn on the Rightside UCS in the right-end bay of the front of the building. Restore the UCS named **Rightside,** and display the plan view of the UCS.

After the plan view of the Rightside UCS is displayed, use the Zoom and Window commands to enlarge a view of the left half of the truss. The drawing plane is then rotated parallel to the top chord of the truss as follows:

> **snap** <return> `Snap spacing or ON/OFF/Aspect/Rotate/Style <1>:` **r** (Rotate) <pick> `Base point <0,0>:` <pick> `ENDPOINT` <pick> `of` Place the target near the left end of the top or bottom chord of the truss. <pick> `Rotation on angle:` <pick> `ENDPOINT` <pick> `of` Place the target on the top chord near the peak of the truss. <pick>

The truss members are currently drawn as single lines that represent the centroid of the truss members. The roof purlins, however, sit on the top chord of the truss and should be drawn 40 mm above the truss top chord line to account for the actual thickness of the truss member above its centroid.

A line representing the outside edge of the truss top chord is to be drawn 40 mm above the top chord on a layer named SSLine. Using the Layer Control dialogue box make a new layer named **Ssline,** set its color as yellow, linetype as continuous, and make it the current layer (see Chap. 6 if you need to review working with Layers).

Now, Zoom on the top chord on the left side of the truss. Snap is set parallel to the top chord of the truss. Turn the Ortho mode on, and then using grips copy the top chord 40 units (mm) above the current top chord. Make sure you use the Copy option. The distance to move (copy) the top chord is **@40 < 190** (the angle is read from the coordinate display window).

Use the Change Properties dialogue box to change the copied line to layer **Ssline.** The line will change to that layer and appear yellow. Following the procedures used earlier, use the Break command to break the copied line at its midpoint. Then break each of the half lines so the original line is broken into quarter section. Purlins will be inserted at these break points.

Make two new layers named **Sstcl** (structural steel top chord left) and **Sstcr** (structural steel top chord right). Set the current layer as **Sstcl.**

Now zoom on a window containing a section of the top chord of the truss and sufficient room above it to draw the purlin illustrated in Fig. 16.5*b*. Use the Change Properties dialogue box to change the thickness of the purlin to –5500 mm (the c/c spacing of trusses, and negative because it is into the *z* axis). Save the purlin as a block using the name **Purlinl** (purlin left). The insertion point is illustrated in Fig. 16.5*b*.

Insert the Purlinl at the ¼, ½, and ¾ break points along the yellow line, using the Endpoint object snap to snap onto the points. Do not insert the purlin at the truss peak.

The purlin at the top peak of the truss is located 80 mm below the peak along the yellow line. To facilitate this locate the last point of the cursor as the top end of the yellow line using the ID command:

`Assist` <pick> `ID Point` <pick> `ID point: ENDPOINT` <pick> `of` Place the Endpoint aperture box on the top end of the yellow line. <pick>

AutoCAD LT reports the coordinates of the point; however, we only wanted to locate a known last point. Now we need to know the angle of the line from its top end:

`LINE` <pick> `From point:` @ (from buttons bar) <pick> `To point:`

Move the cursor along the yellow line noting its angle in the coordinate display box as 199 degrees. Choose `^C` from the buttons bar to cancel the command.

Now insert Purlinl. Specify the Insertion Point parameters on the screen by entering **@80 < 199.**

Set the current layer as **Sstcr** (SS top chord right), and draw the purlins on the right side of the truss. Do not be tempted to use the mirror command here. Purlinr must be on layer **Sstcr.** If you mirrored Purlinl it would be on the wrong layer. When you have completed the right side of the truss, use the View and Restore commands to restore the view named 3D. The completed structure should appear as illustrated in Fig. 16.12. Set the current layer as **Ss** and turn the **Ssline** layer off.

16.6 Wall Girts and Eave Struts

Girts are members on the exterior walls of a structure, spanning between columns, and used to support the wall sheeting. The girts are initially to be

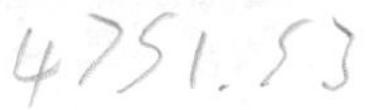

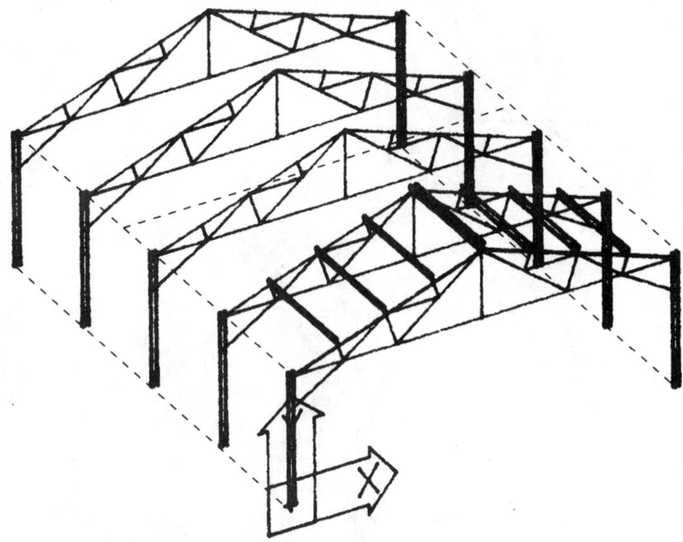

Figure 16.12 Purlins in end bay.

drawn on the Rightside UCS. Restore the **Rightside** UCS and then display the plan view.

Enlarge a view of the left column using the Zoom and Window commands.

In an open space, draw the **Girt** block illustrated in Fig. 16.5*c*. The thickness is –**5500** mm, and the insertion point is noted.

The Rightside UCS origin is at the center of the base of the left column. The first girt is to be inserted 400 mm above the column base on the outside face of the 250-mm-wide column, so the insertion point is –125,400. The other two girts are spaced 1800 mm and 3600 mm, respectively, above the first girt. Insert the three girts on the left column using the Minsert command.

The eave strut is a member at the eave of the structure, spanning between columns, and is used to support the roof sheeting and the wall siding.

Enlarge a view as illustrated in Fig. 16.13 and draw a line parallel to the top chord by first rotating the snap parallel to the top chord and turning the orthogonal mode on. Use an object snap to snap onto the roof purlin.

Set snap to 0 degrees and draw the eave **Strut** block illustrated in Fig. 16.5*d*. It has a thickness of –**5500** mm and an insertion point as noted. Insert the strut at the eave of the building as illustrated in Fig. 16.13, and erase line *a*.

Do not draw the girts and eave strut on the back wall of the building yet.

16.7 Sagrods

Girts and purlins are constructed from members that are deep and narrow (see Fig. 16.5). As a result they tend to sag about their weak axis and must be supported by sagrods as illustrated in Fig. 16.14.

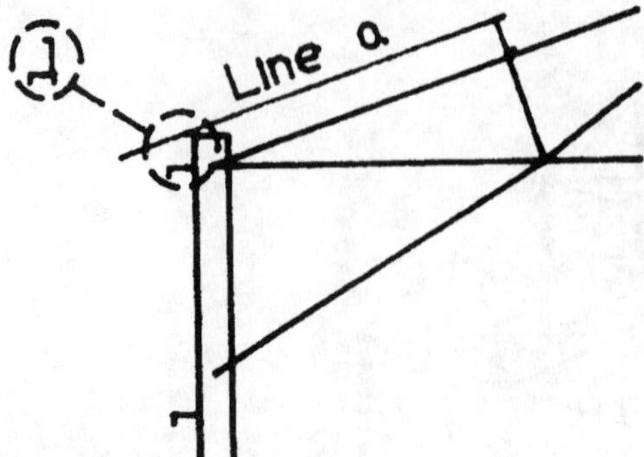

Figure 16.13 Eave strut.

16.7.1 Viewports

The wall sagrods are easiest to draw if points can be concurrently selected from both the front and right side views. Those two views are displayed in viewports as follows:

> `View` <Pick> `Viewports` <pick> `2 Viewports` (see App. E, Fig. E.4.2) <pick>
> `Horizontal/<Vertical>:` **V** (Vertical) <return>

AutoCAD LT divides the screen into two equal-size viewports with the previous screen displayed in each. The viewport enclosed by the heavier border is the current viewport. Move the cursor in that viewport and the familiar horizontal and vertical cursor lines are displayed. Move the cursor into the other viewport and the cursor is changed to a small arrow pointing in the northwest

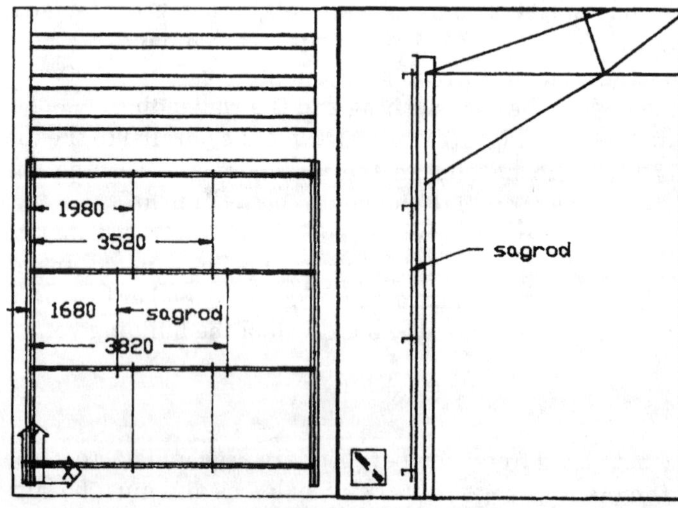

Figure 16.14 Wall sagrod viewports.

direction. To make that viewport the current one press the <pick> button on the mouse.

Make the viewport on the right side of the screen the current one by moving the cursor into it and pressing <pick>. Enter the following commands to display the Rightside UCS in that viewport:

`Assist` <pick> `Named UCS` <pick>

The UCS Control dialogue box (Fig. 16.2) is displayed. Choose `RIGHTSIDE` in the list box and then click on Current to make Rightside the current UCS. Click `OK` to close the dialogue box. Choose the following to get a plan view of the current UCS:

`View` <pick> `3D Plan View` <pick> `Current UCS` <pick>

AutoCAD LT draws the Rightside UCS plan in the right viewport. Notice that the view is zoomed to its extents. Use the Zoom and Window commands to enlarge a view of the column similar to that illustrated in the right viewpoint in Fig. 16.14.

Make the left viewport current. Then display the plan view of the **Front** UCS in that viewport. Next, enlarge a view of the bay at the right end of the building similar to that illustrated in Fig. 16.14 (sagrods have not been drawn yet). When the Front UCS is the current one, the icon in the right viewport becomes a broken pencil, indicating the UCS is being viewed on edge and pointing to locations on that viewport might be meaningless.

The origin of the front UCS is shown in Fig. 16.14. It will be easier to select points in the left viewport if the UCS origin (point 0,0,0) is moved to the bottom of the left column in the viewport as illustrated in Fig. 16.14. That column is three bays to the right of the current UCS origin, and the column spacing is 5500 mm, so the origin is to be moved 16,500 mm (3 × 5500) along the x axis. This is done as follows:

`Assist` <pick> `Set UCS` <pick> **Origin** <pick> `Origin point <0,0,0>:` **16500,0,0** <return>

The x distances to the sagrods on the front wall are shown in the left viewport in Fig. 16.14. (The locations are 150 mm left or right of the one-third points along the girts, to facilitate the connection of the sagrod to the girt.) The z position of the sagrods is at the center of the girts as illustrated in the right viewport in Fig. 16.14. When drawing the sagrods, the x,y coordinate is selected in the left viewport, and the z coordinate is selected in the right viewport. The top row of sagrods are drawn as follows:

Press `O` (Ortho on) in the toolbar <pick> `LINE` <pick> `From point: [Shift->2B]` (Floating cursor menu) `XYZ Filters` <pick> `.XY` <pick> `of`

The XY filter is used to allow entry of the x,y coordinates separately from the z coordinate. The x coordinate is 1980 mm (from Fig. 16.14), and the y coordinate is determined by moving the cursor to a point slightly above the eave strut and reading the y coordinate from the monitor (press Ctrl-D if the cursor coordinates are not updated as the cursor is moved). The author read the y coordinate as 5850. The entries continue as follows:

> **1980,5850** <return> `(need Z) :` Move the cursor to the right viewport. <pick> Pick a point at the middle of the girt web. <pick> `To point:` Move the cursor to the left viewport. <pick> Digitize a point below the middle girt so that the sagrod appears as illustrated in Fig. 16.14. <pick> `To point:` <return>

Recall the Line command by pressing Enter, and draw the next sagrod in the top row. The x coordinate is 3520 and the y coordinate is 5850. Use an XY filter. The z coordinate is picked in the right viewport. Draw the remaining sagrods illustrated in Fig. 16.14. Do not add the dimensions to your drawing.

16.7.2 Back wall girts and sagrods

The girts, eave strut, and sagrods on the front wall are copied to the back wall of the structure using the Mirror command. The mirror line is a vertical line through the center of the truss in the right side view and must be in the plane of the x,y axis. Use the UCS command to make the **Rightside** UCS current. Next, make the right viewport current and enter Zoom and All to display a full view of the truss in the right viewport.

If the orthogonal mode is not on, press O in the toolbar to turn it on.

Use the Mirror command to mirror the girts, sagrods, and eave strut. When selecting the objects, digitize them in the left viewport. Use the right viewport and the Midpoint object snap to select the mirror line at the center point of the truss bottom chord.

Restore the 3D view in the right viewport to visually ensure that all the purlins and sagrods and the eave strut were mirrored correctly (zoom as required). If necessary use the Undo command to undo sufficient commands to retry the Mirror command.

16.7.3 Roof sagrods

To draw the roof sagrods on the left side of the roof, you are to display the plan view of the **Topchordl** UCS in the left viewport and the plan view of the **Rightside** UCS in the right viewport. Zoom on the views as illustrated in Fig. 16.15. (The left viewport illustrates the front half of the roof in the right-end bay of the building.) The current UCS is the **Rightside.**

Set the current layer as **SSTCL** (SS top chord left). Move the cursor into the right viewport and press <pick> making that viewport current (displaying the **Rightside** UCS). Draw the horizontal sagrod connecting the two purlins at the roof peak as follows:

> Press `O` (Ortho on) in the toolbar <pick> `LINE` <pick> `From point: [Shift->2B]` (Floating cursor menu) `XYZ Filters` <pick> `.XY` <pick> `of` Digitize point a. <pick> `(Need Z):` **–2900** <return> `To point: [shift->2b] XYZ Filters` <pick>`.XY` <pick> `of` Digitize point b.<pick>`(Need Z):` **–2900** <return> `To point:` <return> `O` (Ortho off) <pick>

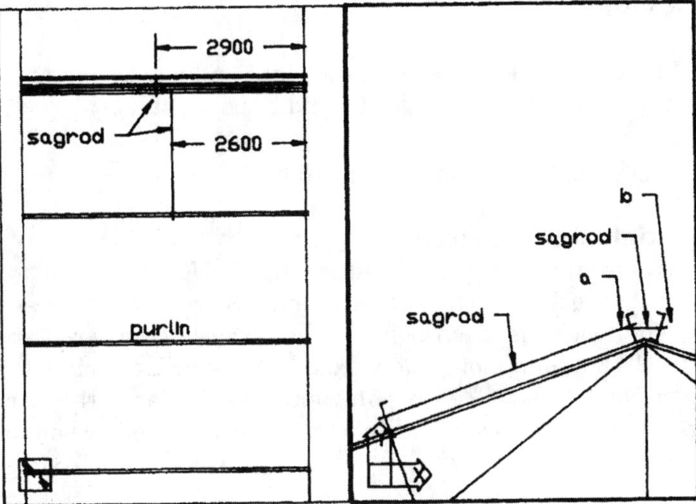

Figure 16.15 Roof sagrod viewports.

The left viewport is not being used to select points. It acts as a visual reference so you can see that the sagrods are being installed correctly.

Prior to drawing the sagrods along the sloping left side of the truss, rotate Snap parallel to the roof slope. Then turn the orthogonal mode on.

Draw the sagrods by selecting the *xy* coordinate from the right viewport and entering the *z* coordinate from the keyboard. The *z* coordinate is –2600 or –2900, as illustrated in Fig. 16.15, to stagger the sagrods and allow room for their connections to the purlins. To draw the sagrods further down the slope of the roof, you will have to Pan the view in the right viewport to display the purlins that the sagrod spans between. Don't forget to draw the last sagrod connecting the eave strut and the lower purlin.

Set the current layer as **SSTCR** (SS top chord right). Draw the sagrods on the right side of the truss by displacing the plan view of the **Topchordr** in the left viewport and the right side of the truss in the right viewport. Turn the orthogonal mode off and rotate Snap parallel to the right side of the truss. Then, turn the orthogonal mode on and draw the sagrods following the same procedure used for the other side of the roof.

Restore the **3D** view and ensure that everything drawn is correct before continuing. Leave the 3-D view on the screen. Set the current layer as **SS.**

16.8 PGS (Purlins/Girts/Sagrods) Block

The girts, purlins, sagrods, and eave struts in the end bay are to be blocked and inserted into the bays of the building. To do so, a number of views of the structure are required. Using `View` <pick> `Viewports` <pick> create four viewports and display the following in each viewport:

Upper-left viewport. **Roofplan** UCS plan.

Lower-left viewport. **Front** UCS plan. Zoom on the right end bay to enlarge a view containing only the wall girts, wall sagrods, and the eave strut.

Upper-right viewport. **3D** view. Zoom magnification 0.9×.

Lower-right viewport. **Rightside** UCS plan.

Before continuing, restore the **Front** UCS as the current UCS.

A block composed of the purlins, girts, sagrods, and eave struts in the end bay is to be created. The block insertion point is the lower-left corner of the panel, which is a point 16,500 mm along the x axis. When asked to select the objects, the Crossing option is used. The Crossing option is similar to the Window option; however, it selects all objects within or crossing the window boundary. The commands are:

`Construct` <pick> `Make Block...` <pick>

The Block Definition dialogue box (see Fig. 10.4) is displayed. Set the Block Name as **PGS.** The Retain Entities check box should be off (no X in it). Enter the insertion Base Points as X: **16500,** Y: **0,** and Z: **0.** Then press the `Select Objects <` button. The drawing screen is returned:

> `Select objects:` Make the lower-left viewport current by clicking on it. Use a crossing window (the first point of the selection box is on the right side, and the second point is to the left of it), to select the entities with the crossing window's sides crossing the girts and the eave struts, and with all wall sagrods enclosed in the window. <pick> `Select objects:` Make the upper-left viewport current by clicking on it. Use a crossing window with the sides crossing all purlins and the roof sagrods enclosed in the window. <pick> `Select objects:` <return>

If all of the girts, purlins, sagrods, and eave struts do not disappear from the screen, use Undo to undo the Block command, and then retry the block entries.

Use the Minsert (multiple insert) command to insert the **PGS** block into the four bays of the structure. The insertion point is the Frontview UCS origin, point 0,0,0. The multiple insert is for one row and four columns.

16.9 Bracing

Bracing is used in a structure to prevent the building from collapsing under horizontally applied loads such as wind. It also prevents twisting and racking of the building and must be installed on all planes of the structure.

Create the two viewports illustrated in Fig. 16.16. Turn layers **SSTCL** and **SSTCR** off to provide a clear view of the bottom chord of the truss. Create two new layers named **SSBCL** (SS bottom chord left) and **SSBCR** (SS bottom chord right), and draw the bottom chord bracing illustrated in Fig. 16.16. Bracing on the truss bottom chord along the frontside of the building is to be on layer SSBCL, and bracing along the backside of the building is to be on layer

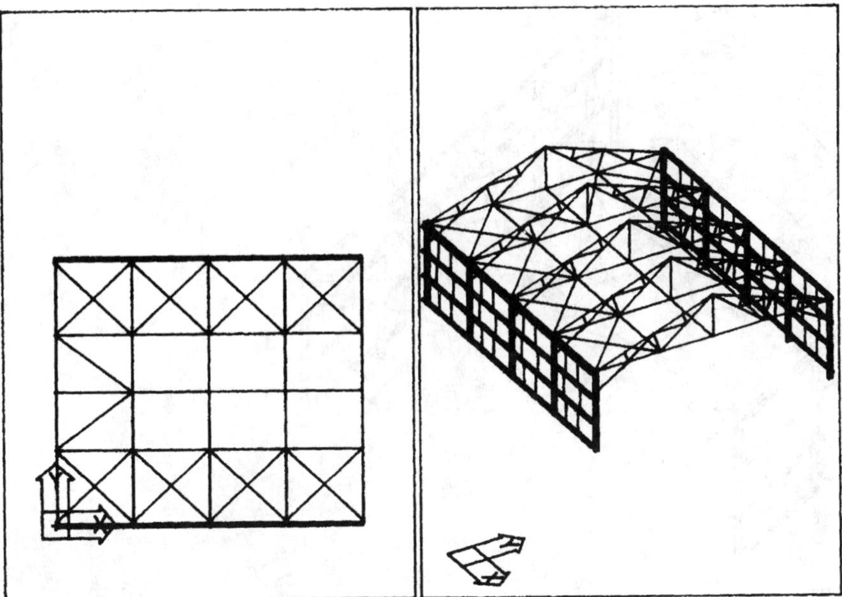

Figure 16.16 Bottom chord bracing.

SSBCR. Use the Zoom command in the view menu and/or XYZ filters to pick difficult points on the screen. Draw one panel of bracing, save it as a block, and use the Minsert command to insert it into the structure; however, do the front and back bracing separately because they are to reside on different layers.

The third bay of the building is to act as a rigid braced frame. Display the view named **3d** in a single viewport as illustrated in Fig. 16.17, and add the side wall and truss top and bottom chord X-bracing to the third bay of the structure, also illustrated in Fig. 16.17. The bracing along the top and bottom chords of the truss extends across the full width of the building. (In Fig. 16.17 the SSTCL, SSTCR, and SSBCR layers are turned off for clarity. You are to draw bracing on both sides of the bay. Table 16.1 lists the UCS to use when drawing the bracing and the layer on which the bracing is to reside.)

Complete the structure by adding the vertical sway frame to layer SS, connecting the third and fourth trusses. To draw the sway frame, move the **Front** UCS to point 11000,5800,–9000 creating the UCS shown in Fig. 16.18. The X-brace lines are drawn by entering *x,y,z* coordinates from the keyboard (the UCS origin is always point 0,0.0).

16.10 Multiview Drawing Using Viewports in Paper Space

Viewports in paper space behave very different from the viewports in model space used earlier in this chapter. The viewport feature allows you to create a multiview drawing by opening viewports in paper space and displaying different views in each viewport. This offers several advantages:

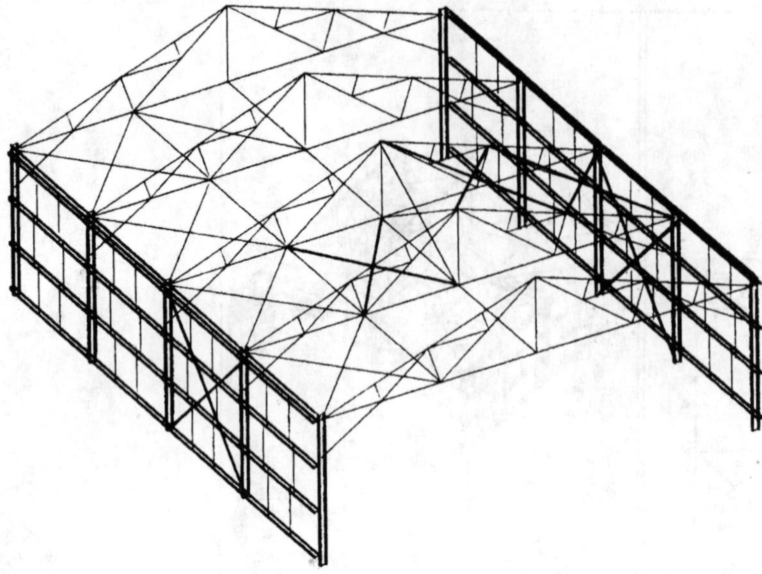

Figure 16.17 Third bay bracing.

- The object is drawn full-size in model space.
- The drawing border and title block is created in paper space for the plot sheet size desired without exiting the drawing.
- Each viewport opened in paper space can display a different view of the object.
- A multiscale drawing is created by scaling the object individually in each viewport.
- Viewports in paper space can overlap and can be edited using commands such as Move, Stretch, Erase, and Scale.
- A layer can be frozen in one viewport, and visible in others.
- Viewports can be turned off to allow plotting of a subset of viewports in a drawing.

TABLE 16.1 Third Bay Bracing

UCS	Layer	Comments
Front	SS	Front wall (use x,y filter, $z = 0$)
Rightside	SS	Back wall (mirror front bracing)
Roofplan	SSBCL	truss bottom chord, left side
Roofplan	SSBCR	Truss bottom chcrd, right side
Topchordl	SSTCL	Truss top chord, left side
Topchordr	SSTCR	Truss top chord, right side

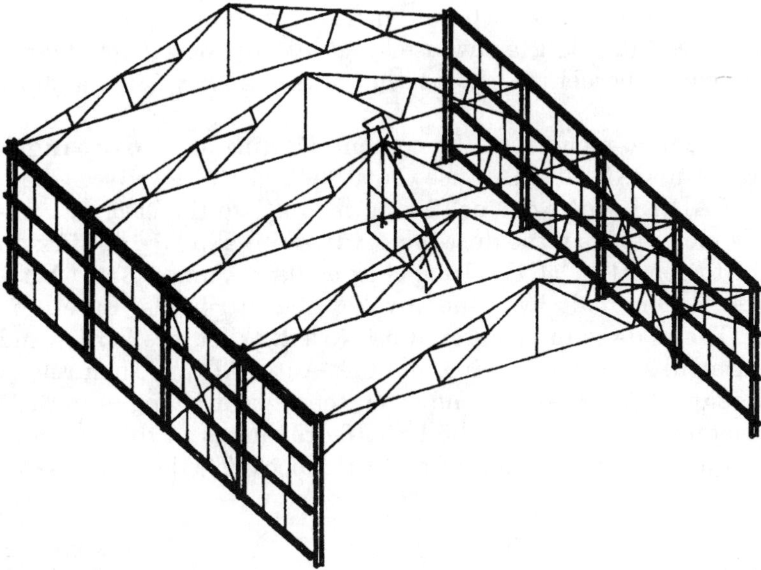

Figure 16.18 UCS sway frame.

16.10.1 Initial setup

Prior to entering paper space, ensure that you are working from the same settings as the author. You should currently be working in model space, indicated by the model space icon displayed in the lower-left corner of the screen. You should have a single viewport open on the screen with the View named 3D displayed as illustrated in Fig. 16.18.

Use the UCS command to restore the user coordinate system named **FRONT.** Turn on all of the working layers **SS, SSTCL, SSTCR, SSBCL,** and **SSBCR** and set layer **SS** as current.

16.10.2 Drawing the border in paper space

To enter paper space the Tilemode system variable must be set off:

`View` <pick> **Paper Space** <pick> `New value for TILEMODE <1>: 0 Entering Paper Space. Use MVIEW to insert Model Space viewports.`

A tick mark is added in front of Paper Space in the View menu indicating Tilemode is 0. The paper space icon is displayed in the lower-left corner of the screen and the paper space button in the toolbar is displayed pressed on (white).

The 3-D view displayed in model space is no longer on the screen. To see the view a viewport will be opened later. Move the cursor on the screen noting that the drawing limits are 0,0 and about 12,9.

If at any time you change the Tilemode system variable back to 1, the model space screen is returned, and the border—or any other items drawn in paper space—is no longer displayed on the screen.

If you added the B-size (430 by 280 mm) or A3-size border option to your menu in Chap. 12, Sec. 12.7.3, it is now used to draw a border. If you did not create the B-size metric border, set the screen limits to 430 by 280 and draw one now.

To load your aclt2.mnu menu save the current drawing as **c:\drawings\proj-16,** and exit AutoCAD LT. Then use the ACADLT PROTO1 icon (see Chap. 12) to load AutoCAD LT with your aclt2.mnu menu. Use the Open... command in the File menu to open the drawing **c.\drawings\proj-16.** Click on Title Blk in the toolbar (Fig. 11.11). Then click on Metric and B Size. AutoCAD LT inserts the bm-hbdr.dwg, and invokes the attributes. Enter the requested data. The scale is to be entered as **Noted.** When the border and title block are drawn, save the drawing and exit AutoCAD LT. Then reload the standard version of AutoCAD LT and Open the same drawing. AutoCAD LT's standard menu is available and the Proj-16 drawing is on the screen in paper space with a B-size metric border and title block. The building is not yet visible.

16.10.3 Viewports in paper space

When the system variable Tilemode is set to 1 the working space is model space. In model space the viewports function as outlined earlier in this chapter—filling the graphics screen and lying side by side like tiles on a floor. In model space, viewports are referred to as *tiled viewports.*

When Tilemode is set to 0 the working space is paper space. In paper space viewports behave quite differently from those in model space. They can overlap and they can be edited using commands such as Move, Stretch, Erase, and Scale. Because they do not have to lie side by side they are referred to as *nontiled viewports.*

Tilemode is currently set to 0 making the working space paper space. Prior to opening a viewport, create a new layer named **Viewlyr1** (view layer 1) for the viewport which is to be opened to reside on. Set the color of Viewlyr1 as magenta, and make Viewlyr1 the current layer.

The current layer name box in the toolbar should indicate that the current layer is Viewlyr1.

A viewport is to be opened in the top-left quadrant of the drawing to display the plan view of the building as illustrated in Fig. 16.19. When the viewport is initially opened, the 3-D view that was on the screen in model space is visible:

> View <pick> Viewports (See App. E, Fig. E.4.2*b*, noting that the menu displayed is different from that for model space; see Sec. 16.7.1.) <pick> Make Viewport <pick> First point: INTERSECTION <pick> of Place the Intersection object snap aperture on the top-left corner of the drawing border. <pick> Other corner: Pick a point in approximately the middle of the screen so the viewport takes up about ¼ of the screen space. The size is not critical because it can be modified as required. <pick>

The Hideplot option in the Viewports menu instructs AutoCAD LT to perform hidden line removal when plotting the contents of the designated viewport.

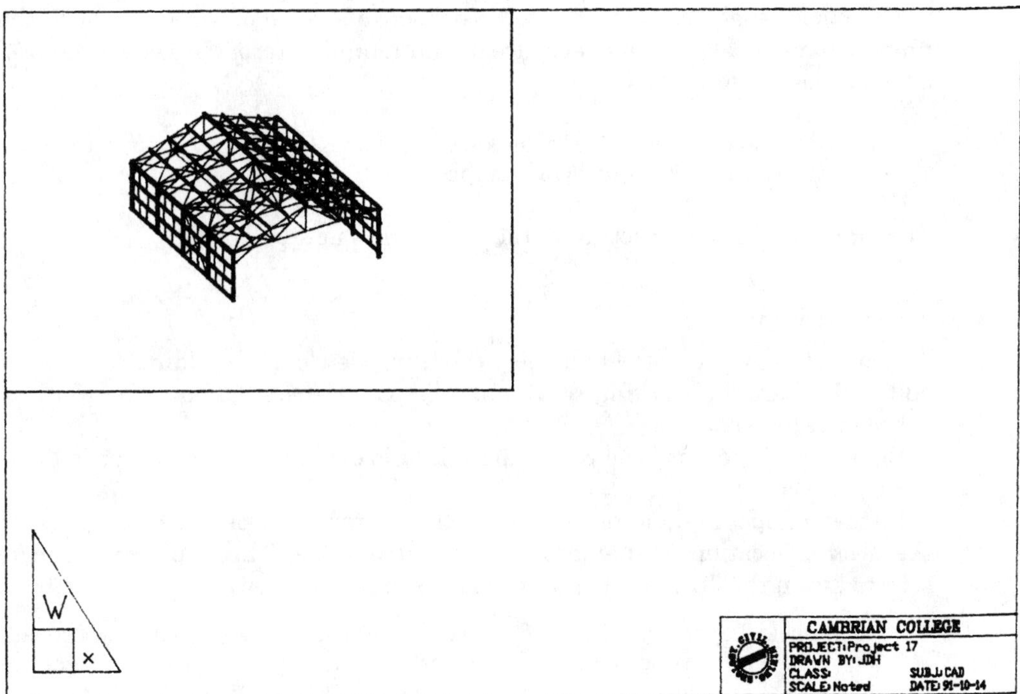

Figure 16.19 Viewport No. 1.

16.10.4 Scaling the model

The roof plan of the building is to be displayed in the open viewport at a scale of 1:200. To change the UCS to **Roofplan**. To scale the model (object) in the viewport, the working space must set to model space:

Press the P button off in the buttons bar

The model space icon is now at its origin in the viewport indicating the current working space is model space. Move the cursor on the screen observing that the standard cursor is displayed within the viewport, and the cursor becomes an arrow when moved outside of the viewport. Also the drawing limits apply only within the viewport, which is the current working screen.

Set the current UCS to Roofplan:

Assist <pick> Set UCS <pick> Restore <pick> ?/Name of UCS to restore: **Roofplan** <return>

Display a plan view of the Roofplan UCS in the viewport as follows:

View <pick> 3D Plan View <pick> Named UCS <pick> ?/<Name of UCS>: **Roofplan** <return>

The model space plan view is to be drawn to a scale of 1:200. Because the units of paper space and model space are both millimeters, the scale is entered as ¹⁄₂₀₀ times paper spaces:

View <pick> Zoom <pick> Scale <pick> All/Center/Extents/Previous/Window/<Scale (X/XP)>: **1/200xp** <return>

The plan view of the structure in the viewport is now complete.

16.10.5 Copying a viewport

A viewport is to be created to display the front view of the building. To open or edit a viewport the working space must be paper space. Change the working space to paper space.

Do not continue until the paper space icon is displayed in the lower-left corner of the screen.

Instead of opening another viewport, the current viewport will be copied to the desired location. Either procedure is acceptable. The Copy command is selected from the Toolbox. The viewport is copied as follows:

COPY <pick> Select objects: Pick a point on the magenta-colored viewport window. The viewport window should become dotted. <pick> Select objects: <return> <Base point or displacement>/Multiple: INTERSECTION <pick> of Place the object snap selection box on the lower-left corner of the viewport window. <pick> Second point of displacement: INTERSECTION <pick> of Select the lower-left corner of the drawing border. <pick>

The drawing should appear as illustrated in Fig. 16.20. Notice that the viewports overlap, hence the reason why paper space viewports are referred to as nontiled.

The new viewport currently displays the plan view of the Roofplan UCS. To modify the model to display the plan view of the Front UCS in the new viewport, the working space must be model space.

Change the working space to model space. The model space icon must be displayed in each viewport before continuing.

Pick a point in the bottom left viewport to make it current. When the cursor is located in the lower-left viewport the standard cross hair cursor is displayed. Move the cursor outside the current viewport and it becomes an arrow indicating you are outside of the current model space viewport.

Following the procedure outlined in Sec. 16.10.4 display a plan view of the Front UCS in the current viewport.

Following the procedure outlined in section 16.10.4 scale the model to ¹⁄₂₀₀ times paper space.

16.10.6 Stretching a viewport

The lower-left viewport displays the plan view of the Front UCS. The viewport is larger than it need be, so it will be stretched to a more appropriate size.

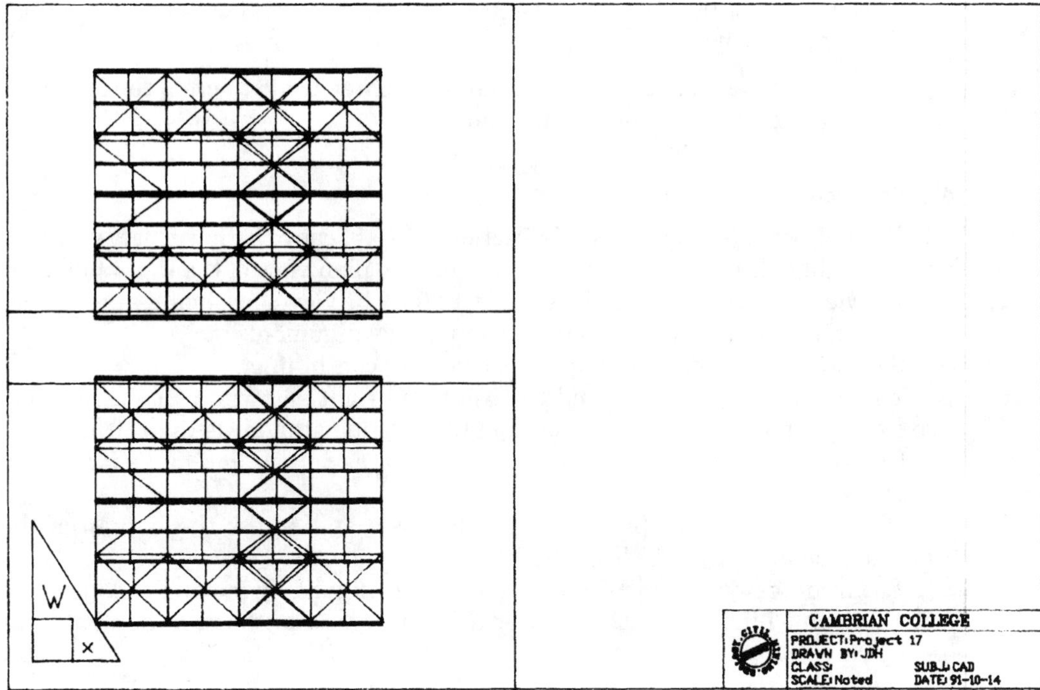

Figure 16.20 Viewport No. 2.

Because viewports reside in paper space, the working space must be changed to paper space before the viewport can be edited. Set the working space to paper space.

The Stretch command can be selected from the Modify menu in the menu bar or the Toolbox. The stretch command requires you to select the objects to be stretched, with a crossing window. When selecting a viewport, both a horizontal and vertical viewport window line must be included in the crossing window. The pull-down menu commands are as follows:

> `Modify` <pick> `Stretch` <pick> `Select objects to stretch by window or polygon...Select objects:_c` Select a point so the crossing window crosses the top, bottom, and right side of the lower-left viewport window. <pick> `Next corner:` Select the other corner of the crossing window. The viewport window should go dotted. <pick> `Select object:`

If the viewport window for the top viewport is dotted, or if the drawing border is dotted, select the Remove command (in the Assist/Select menu) and then pick a point on those lines to remove them from the selection set. The selection is completed as follows:

> `Select objects:` <return> `Base point:` Pick a point on the top line of the window for the front view viewport. <pick> `New point:` Pick a point where you want

the top line of the viewport to be relocated. See Fig. 16.21 showing the author's Front elevation viewport. <pick>

If you want to retry the Stretch command, enter Undo to undo the last command and then reenter the Stretch command.

16.10.7 Aligning models in viewports

Following procedures outlined in section 16.10.5, copy the lower-left viewport to the right side of the border. Then display the plan view of the Rightside UCS in the viewport and scale it to a scale of 1:200. The viewport should appear similar to that illustrated in Fig. 16.21 (minus the alignment line).

Set the working space to paper space before continuing.

The top and front views, and the front and right side views of the building are to be aligned following orthographic projection standards in drafting.

Create a new layer name **Align,** set its color as yellow, and make it the current layer.

Draw the alignment line along the left side and across the bottom of the drawing as illustrated in Fig. 16.21.

The front view in the lower-left viewport is aligned by moving the viewport so that point 1 in Fig. 16.22 is located at the intersection of the alignment lines

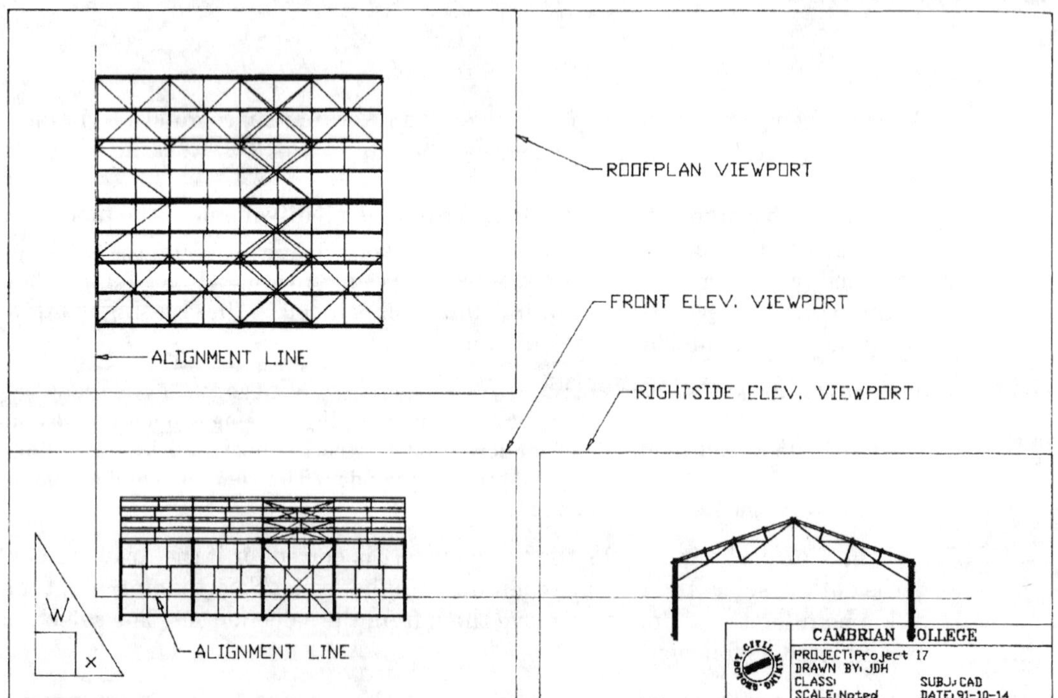

Figure 16.21 Viewports.

shown as point 2. Use the Zoom and Window commands to zoom on a window illustrated in Fig. 16.22, encompassing the alignment lines, the bottom line of the viewport window and the lower-left corner of the front view of the building. The window should be tight enough so you will not have difficulty placing the cursor on point 1, which is the center of the column base. If the bottom of the viewport window is not displayed use the Pan command to pan the view up slightly.

The viewport is moved as follows:

> `Modify` <pick> `Move` <pick> `Select object:` Select the magenta-colored viewport window as illustrated in Fig. 16.22. You cannot select the structure as it is drawn in model space and not visible to AutoCAD LT when the working space is paper space. <pick> `Select objects:` <return> `Base point or displacement:` Very carefully select point 1, which is the intersection of the column center line and base. You cannot use the intersection object snap because AutoCAD LT does not recognize the model when in paper space. <pick> `Second point of displacement:` `INTERSECTION` <pick> `of` Place the intersection cursor on point 2. The alignment lines were drawn in paper space so their intersection is located by AutoCAD LT. <pick>

Enter Zoom and Previous to restore the entire drawing. The lower-left viewport will have moved, and will probably cross the drawing border. When layer Viewlyr1 is turned off later, the viewport windows will not be visible.

The model was not moved in model space because it would move by the same amount in all of the viewports, and it is necessary to move each viewport by a different amount to align the models.

Use a similar procedure and align the roof plan and the right side viewports with the alignment line.

If you have problems, enter Undo to undo the command and try again. If you somehow mess up a view, follow procedures discussed earlier to display the proper plan view and scale the view with respect to paper space. Once the

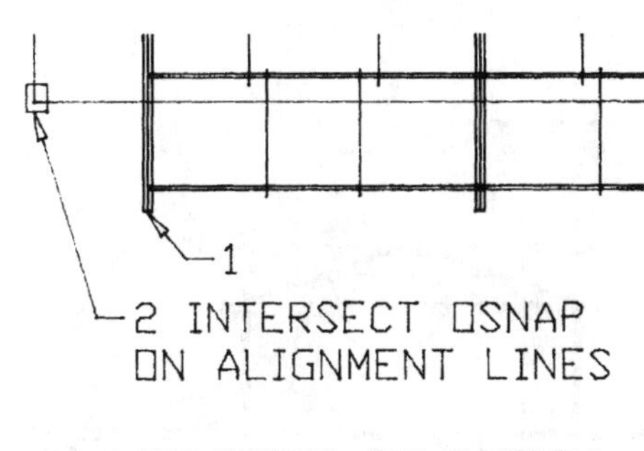

Figure 16.22 Alignment of front view.

viewports are aligned, if you must move one, move the adjacent one concurrently to maintain the alignment.

Set the current layer to **Viewlyr1** and freeze the **Align** layer.

Once the viewports are aligned each view should be saved so it can be restored if it gets out of alignment. Click in the Roofplan viewport making it current, and choose the following:

`View` <pick> `View` <pick> `Save` <pick> `View name to save:` **Roofplan** <return>

Follow the same procedure to name the Front and Rightside views. You can restore a named view at any time using the Restore option.

Set the working space to paper space.

The drawing should appear as illustrated in Fig. 16.23 (minus the 3-D and sway frame viewports).

Use the Viewports menu to make a Viewport for the 3-D view by selecting the viewport window boundaries to match those in Fig. 16.23.

The scale for the 3-D view is to be 1:300.

Edit the viewport as required to display the entire 3-D view.

Use the Viewports menu to make a Viewport in the top-right corner of the border to display a side view of the roof in the Front UCS as illustrated in Fig. 16.23. The scale is 1:200. Edit the viewport so that the sway frame bracing fits

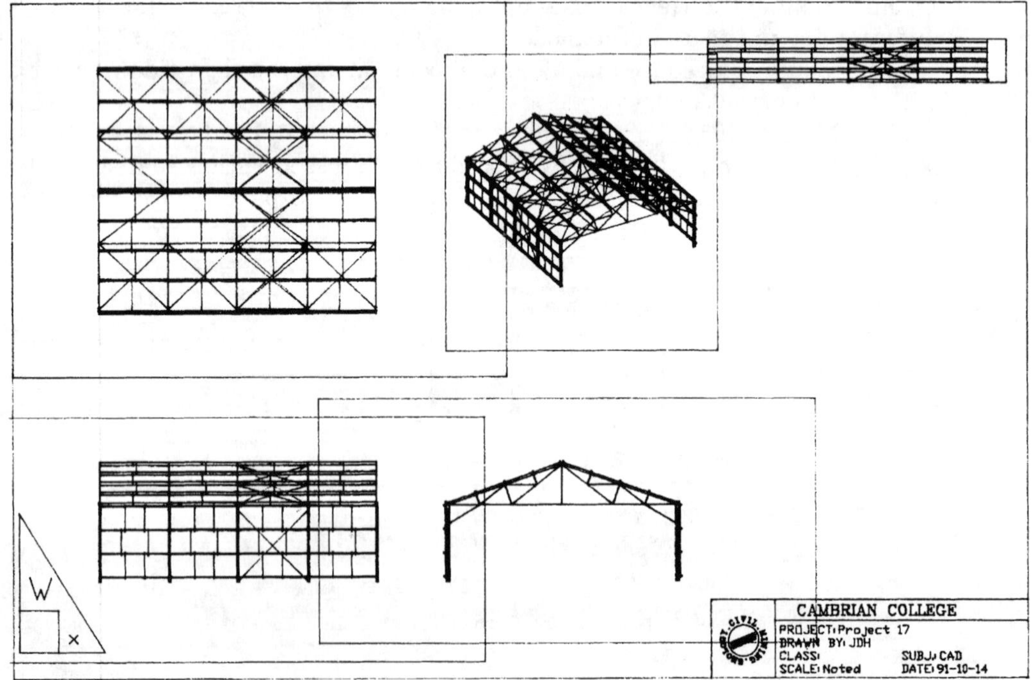

Figure 16.23 Final viewports.

within the viewport as illustrated. If you zoom on the viewport to stretch it you will have to include enough of the viewport to be able to select it with the Stretch commands crossing window.

Viewports can be edited at any time as required.

16.10.8 Controlling layer visibility in viewports

The On/Off and Freeze/Thaw options of the Layer command set the visibility of layers globally, in all viewports. The Vplayer command allows you to set layer visibility by viewport, so a layer can be off in one viewport and on in other viewports.

The Plan view of the building (see Fig. 16.1) is to display in the top half of the plan, bracing and purlins, which are on the top chord of the truss; and in the bottom half of the plan, bracing, which is on the bottom chord of the truss. This is accomplished using the Vplayer command to turn layers SSBCR off and SSTCL off in the viewport displaying the Plan view. These layers are also to be turned off in the Side Elevation and 3-D View. In the Cross Section layers SSBCR and SSTCL are to be turned on.

Using the Layer Control dialogue box turn layers **SS, SSTCL, SSBCL, SSTCR** and **SSTCL** on.

The Vplayer command can be invoked in model or paper space. If the current working space is model space, AutoCAD LT switches to paper space when Vplayer is invoked and returns to model space after the command is exited. The Vplayer command is entered as follows:

`View` <pick> `Viewport Layer Visibility` (App. E, Fig. E.4.3) <pick>

Options to the Vplayer command are:

List?	List frozen layers in a selected viewport
Freeze	Freeze layers in selected viewports
Thaw	Thaw layers in selected viewports
Reset	Resets layer visibility to global setting in selected viewports
Newfrz	Creates new layers that are frozen in all viewports
VP Default Visibility	Sets default frozen thawed state for layers in new viewports when they are created

The Freeze option is invoked as follows:

`Freeze` <pick> `Layer(s) to Freeze:` **SSTCL** <return>
`All/Select/<Current>:`

The options are: *All* freezes layer SSTCL in All viewports; *Select* allows you to select the viewports on which layer SSTCL is to be frozen; and *Current* (default) freezes layer SSTCL in the current viewport. Enter Select to select viewports in which layer SSTL is to be frozen:

> **S**(select) <return> `Select objects:` Pick each of the following viewport windows in which layer SSTCL is to be frozen—Plan, Side Elevation, 3-D View, Sway Frame <pick>
> `?/Freeze/Thaw/Reset/Newfrz/Vpvisdfit:`

Freeze layers SSBCR in the viewports displaying the Plan, Side Elevation, 3-D View, and Sway Frame. Then freeze layers SSTCR and SSBCL in the viewport containing the Sway Frame.

Press <return> to exit the command. The viewports should appear as illustrated in Fig. 16.1.

16.10.9 Dimensioning variable settings

As discussed in Chap. 4, Sec. 4.4, the dimension variable Dimscale is a global factor applied to all numeric dimension variables. If Dimscale is set to 0.0, however, AutoCAD LT computes a reasonable value for Dimscale for each viewport based on the scaling between the current model space viewport and paper space. The height of dimension text, for instance, will be 0.18 inches (the default value) in the *plotted* drawing regardless of the zoom scale used for the model in the viewport. For dimensions done in paper space AutoCAD LT calculates the numeric dimension variables as though Dimscale is 1.0.

The default dimension variables are inch units. This drawing is done in millimeter so some of the dimension variables must be changed to get millimeter-sized dimension constituent parts. Variables are converted from inches to millimeters by multiplying them by 25.4. (Also see Chp. 6, Sect. 6.13)

Some drawing situations will require that you work with different dimension variable settings throughout the course of the drawing. Dimension settings can be named and recalled at any time. The current default dimension variables are saved using the name STANDARD as follows:

> `Settings` <pick> `Dimension Style...` <pick>

The Dimension Style and Settings dialogue box similar to that shown in Fig. 16.24 is displayed. The current dimension style is *UNNAMED* in the Dimension Styles list box. Move the cursor into the Dimension Style edit box and enter the name **STANDARD** and press <return>. The name *UNNAMED* is changed to STANDARD as shown. Press `OK`.

AutoCAD LT dimension variables are in inch units, and are to be converted to millimeter units by multiplying by 25.4. The default dimension text height is 0.18 inches, which converted to millimeter units is $0.18 \times 25.4 = 4.57$ mm. If the desired plotted text height is 2.5 mm instead of 4.57 mm, the metric conversion factor is $25.4 \times (2.5/4.57) = 13.89$. Applicable dimension variables are converted to millimeter units in the following table by multiplying them by 13.89:

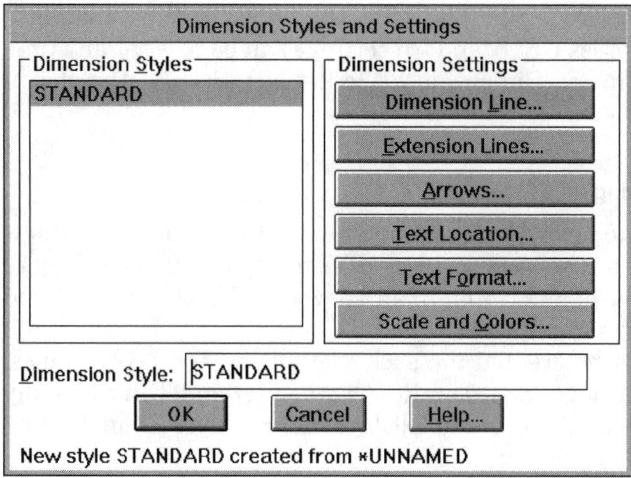

Figure 16.24 Naming a dimension style.

Dimension Setting box	Dimension function	Imperial value*	Metric value
Dimension Line . . .	Text Gap	0.09	1.25
	Baseline Increment	0.38	5.3
Extension Lines . . .	Extension Above Line	0.18	2.5
	Feature Offset	0.0625	0.87
Arrows . . .	Arrow Size	0.18	2.5
Text Location . . .	Text Height	0.18	2.5

* Values are rounded to one decimal place in AutoCAD LT dialogue boxes.

Choose `Dimension Style...` in the settings menu to display the Dimension Style and Settings dialogue box (Fig. 16.24). Set the dimension variables outlined in the above table to their metric values. Also set the variables indicated in the following table:

Dimension Setting box	Item	Setting
Text Location . . .	Vertical	Above
	Horizontal	Force Text Inside
	Alignment	Align With Dimension Line

Next, choose `Scale and Colors...` to display the Scale and Colors dialogue box (Fig. 4.3), and click the check box beside `Use Paper Space Scaling` turning it on—there is to be an X in the box. Press `OK` to return to the Dimension Style and Settings dialogue box. Move the cursor into the `Dimension Style` edit box (Fig. 16.24) and enter the name **METRIC** and press <return>. The name METRIC will be listed in the Dimension styles list box. The previous settings are saved under the dimension style Standard. To use metric settings highlight METRIC in the list box and press OK. Standard settings can be reset at any time by selecting STANDARD in the Dimension Style list box. Set the Dimension Style to METRIC and press OK.

16.10.10 Creating viewport dimensioning layers

Usually it is not desirable to have dimensions that are drawn on a specific view also show up on other views. The Viewport Layer Visibility menu's New Freeze option is used to create new layers frozen in all viewports. The layers are then thawed in specific viewports as required.

Dimension layers are to be created for each view using the layer names: DimT (top view), DimF (front view), DimRS (right side) and DimSF (sway frame). The layers are created frozen on all layers, and layer Dimt is then thawed for the Roof Plan (top view) as follows:

> View <pick> Viewport Layer Visibility <pick> New Freeze <pick> New Viewport frozen layer name(s): **dimt,dimf,dimrs,dimsf** <return> ?/Freeze/Thaw/Reset/Newfrz/Vpvisdfit: **t** (Thaw) <return> Layer(s) to Thaw: **dimt** <return> All/Select/<Current>: **s** (Select) <return> Switching to paper space. Select objects: Pick a point on the viewport window for the Roof Plan <pick> Select objects: <return> Switching to Model space. ?/Freeze/Thaw/Reset/Newfrz/Vpvisdfit: <return>

Use the Layer Control dialogue box to set the color of layers Dimt, Dimf, Dimrs, and Dimsw to cyan. Set Dimt as the current layer.

16.10.11 Dimensioning the roof plan

Dimt should be displayed in the buttons bar as the current layer.

To dimension the Roof Plan it will have to be zoomed on the screen. If you use the zoom command while in model space, the area selected will be zoomed only in its viewport. To zoom on the viewport, the working space must be paper space. Do the following:

- Change the working space to paper space.
- Zoom on the Roof Plan viewport window.
- Change the working space to model space.

Set the current UCS to **Roofplan.**

The horizontal dimension "7 Bays @ 5500 = 38500" in the roof plan is added as follows:

The Aerial View Window is to be used to assist in selecting the first point of the extension line. First, check that the current viewport is the one with the roof plan in it by moving the cursor in that viewport. If the cursor is an arrow, click in the viewport. The viewport is current when the standard cursor is displayed. Next, if the aerial viewport is not displayed, click on its icon (Fig. 5.6) in the buttons bar. Move the aerial view window to the top right corner of the screen, and the toolbox to the bottom right corner by moving the cursor onto its title box, then press and hold the pick button and move the window by sliding the cursor. Release the pick button when you have the window in the desired location.

The current view in the Aerial View Window should be that shown in Fig. 16.25 (minus the zoom window). Now start the dimensioning:

> `Draw` <pick> `Linear Dimensions` <pick> `Horizontal` <pick> `First extension line origin or RETURN to select:`

Move the cursor into the Aerial View Window and press Zoom and then place a window around the lower left column as shown in Fig. 16.25. When the second corner of the zoom window is picked the windowed area is displayed (enlarged) on the drawing screen. Move the cursor back onto the drawing screen and continue:

> `First extension line origin or RETURN to select:` **Digitize a point in line with the column center line.** <pick> `Second extension line origin:`

Move the cursor into the Aerial View Window and place a window around the front part of the plan as shown in Fig. 16.26. When the second corner of the zoom window is picked the windowed area is displayed on the drawing screen. Continue the dimension:

> `Second extension line origin:` **Pick a point to the right of the roof plan as shown in Fig. 16.1.** <pick> `Dimension line location:` **Pick the dimension line location.** <pick> `Dimension text <some value>:` **7 Bays @ 5500 = 38500** <return>

The dimension completed will have an extension line on the right-hand side, which is not desired. It is removed by choosing `Extension Lines...` in the Dimension Styles and Variables dialogue box. Set the Visibility to `Suppress Second` (Fig. 16.27) to suppress the second extension line drawn. Press `OK` to exit each dialogue box. Then choose the following to update the dimension to the latest setting:

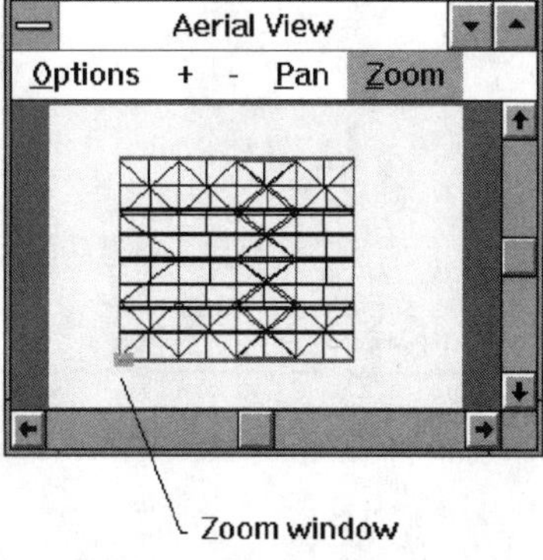

Figure 16.25 Zoom in—aerial view.

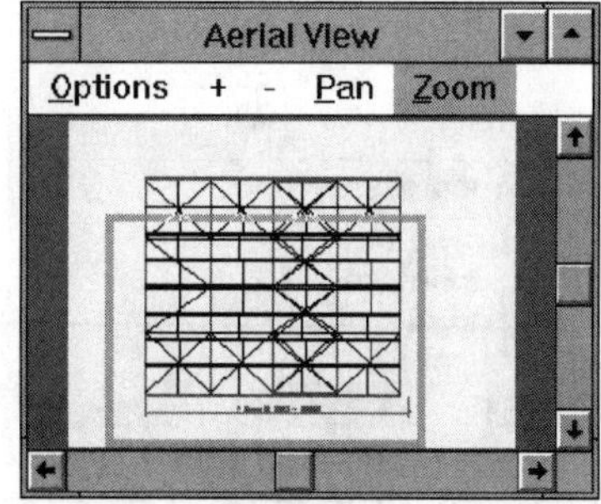

Figure 16.26 Zoom out—aerial view.

Modify <pick> Edit Dimensions <pick> Update Dimensions <pick> Select object: Pick a point on the dimension to be updated. <pick>

The dimension is regenerated without the second extension line. The current dimension style is named *UNNAMED by AutoCAD LT, since it has been changed. Display the Dimension Styles and Variables dialogue box (Fig. 16.24) and highlight METRIC in the list box and then press OK to make that the current style.

Add the remaining dimensions to the Roofplan. Do not add the view's title and scale yet.

When the dimensions are complete on the Roofplan view, restore the view to ensure it is realigned with the other views:

View <pick> View <pick> Restore <pick> View name to restore: **Roofplan** <return>

Dimension the other views as illustrated in Fig. 16.1. Prior to dimensioning in a new viewport complete the following sequence:

1. Set the working space to paper space.
2. Zoom on the desired viewport(s).
3. Set the working space to model space.
4. Set the viewport as current by picking a point in it.
5. Set the appropriate UCS.
6. Set the dimension layer visibility (see the following).
7. Set the dimension layer as current.

Prior to dimensioning the Side Elevation (front view) it is set as the current viewport, layer DIMF (dimension front view) is thawed for the current viewport and set as the current layer. All other layers are to be frozen in the current viewport.

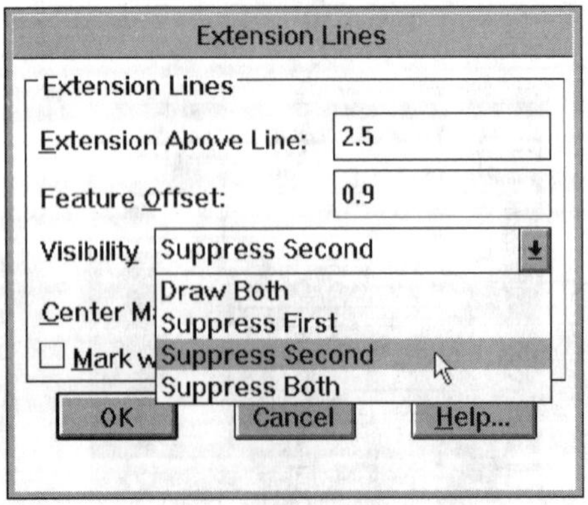

Figure 16.27 Suppressing an extension line.

The viewport layer visibility can be set using the Viewport Layer Visibility command as illustrated in Sec. 16.10.10 or using the Layer Control dialogue box. Setting a layer's visibility for the current viewport using the Layer Control dialogue box is done as follows: (see Fig. 16.28):

- Current settings are model space, the current viewport is the front view and the UCS is Front as described earlier.
- Display the Layer Control dialogue box illustrated in Fig. 16.28. Using the slider bar display the listings for layers DIMF, DIMRS, DIMSF, and DIMT in the list box.
- Click on layer name DIMF in the list box highlighting its row.
- Note the Cur VP and New VP Thw and Frz boxes. These boxes allow you to set the visibility (Freeze or Thaw) of the current viewport and new viewports not yet created. Press the Cur VP Thw box, thawing layer DIMF in the current viewport (the front view of the building). AutoCAD LT removes the C from the list box in the DIMF layer row indicating the layer is not frozen in the current viewport. The N indicates layer DIMF will be frozen in any new viewports created.
- Layers DIMRS, DIMSF, and DIMT should have a letter C in their listing indicating they are frozen in the current viewport.

Note that the C and N settings only relate to the current viewport. These settings may change with each viewport selected as current.

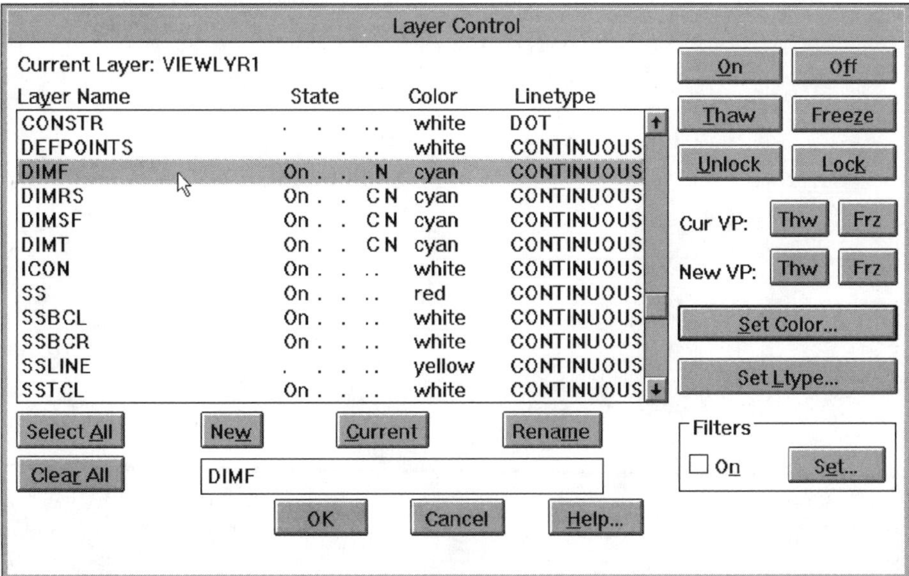

Figure 16.28 Setting viewport layer visibility.

In model space it is often difficult to zoom on a desired view, particularly when dimensioning. If you are confronted with that problem, set the working space to paper space, zoom tightly on the largest view desired, and then return the working space to model space. While dimensioning use the Aerial View window to assist in selecting points.

When dimensioning is complete change the working space to paper space. Enter zoom all to zoom on the entire drawing. Do not add the text to the drawing yet, because text on the drawing is usually done in paper space.

Freeze layer **Viewlyr1** to make the viewport windows invisible.

Add text to the drawing in paper space on a layer named **Txt.** In paper space the screen limits are the plot sheet size, and the text height is the actual text height desired on the plot, which is 2.5 mm. Titles should be 4 mm in height.

Plot the drawing in paper space on an B-size sheet using a scale of 1 = 1.

Chapter

17

Slide Show

Objective. Use AutoCAD LT's slide show facility to display the sequence of operation for a construction or production operation; create a script file to automatically invoke commands; demonstrate further applications of view command.

Drawing. A series of slides (drawings) that outlines the erection sequence for a precast concrete bridge are to be produced. A script file will then be used to display the slides in sequence, demonstrating the bridge erection procedure.

Boot AutoCAD LT and begin a new drawing named c:\Drawings\Proj-17. Set the limits at 0,0 and 110,70, and invoke the Zoom and All commands.

The drawing is to be done in foot (decimal) units. Set the units to decimal with one digit to the right of the decimal. Angle units can be set at decimal degrees with zero fractional places for the display of the angle.

For drawings of this type a color monitor is advantageous. The purpose of the slide show is to illustrate the location of various components during the erection of a bridge girder. A color monitor allows the drafter to separate components in the drawing by color, thereby helping the user interpret the views. If you have a color monitor, you should use a new layer for each color. The layers to use are specified below. If you do not have a color monitor, you can draw all the items on one layer unless you intend to plot the views and use a different pen for each component. Create the following layers:

Item	Name	Color	Line type
Misc. data	Const	White (7)	Continuous
Bridge piers	Pier	White (7)	Continuous
Overhead gantry	Gantry	Blue (5)	Continuous
Bridge girders	Girders	Red (1)	Continuous
Gantry supports	Sups	Yellow (2)	Continuous

17.1 Bridge Component Blocks

The overhead gantry (see Fig. 17.1) is a box truss arrangement that is used to support the moving hoists for the bridge. The gantry itself is a movable system that creeps along the bridge as the bridge girders are erected between piers.

17.1.1 Gantry

The total length of the gantry is to be 60 ft. Initially, a 15-ft-long section will be drawn and stored as a block. The Array command will then be used to replicate the block four times, creating the 60-ft gantry.

Set Gantry as the current layer. Zoom on an area about 20 by 10 units, and draw the outside rectangle of the gantry 15 by 2.6 units, as illustrated in Fig. 17.1. Do not dimension the gantry.

Because the web members divide the gantry length into 12 sections, the horizontal distance for each diagonal is 1.25 (15/12) units. The depth of the gantry truss is 2.6 units. The commands to draw the web members are:

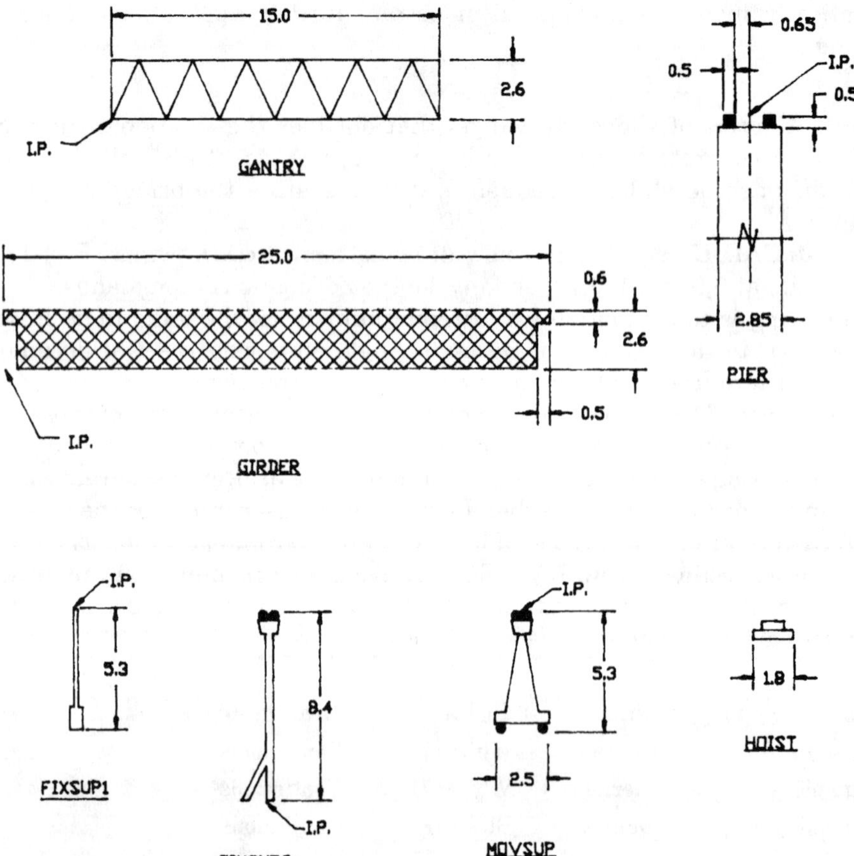

Figure 17.1 Bridge components.

Draw <pick> Line <pick> From point: INTERSECTION <pick> of Place the target over the lower-left corner of the gantry. <pick> To point: **@1.25,2.6** <return> To point: **@1.25,–2.6** <return> etc.

Save the gantry as a Block named Gantry. Designate the lower-left corner as the insertion point, using the INTERSECTION object snap to digitize the point.

17.1.2 Girder

Girders are the bridge members that span from pier to pier and support the roadway. The slide show to be created will illustrate the procedure for erecting a precast concrete bridge girder.

Set the current layer as **Girder**. Zoom on an area that is approximately 30 by 50 units. Draw the outline of the girder, as illustrated in Fig. 17.1. Do not dimension the girder.

Rather than selecting an AutoCAD LT pattern for hatching, a new pattern will be defined. The pattern will be at an angle of 45 degrees, spaced 0.5 units, and double-hatched. To define a pattern enter Hatch at the command prompt:

hatch <return> Pattern (? or name/U,style):

The U option allows you to define a pattern "on the fly":

u <return> Angle for crosshatch lines <0>: **45** <return> Spacing between lines <1>: **0.5** <return> Double hatch area?<N>: **y** <return> Select objects: Place a selection window around the girder. <pick> <return>

Save the girder as a block named **Girder.** Select the lower-left corner as the insertion point (indicated as I.P. in Fig. 17.1). Be sure that the cursor is exactly on the imaginary lower-left corner when selecting the insertion point.

17.1.3 Pier

The piers support the girders of the bridge, as illustrated in Fig. 17.2, and transfer the load to the ground.

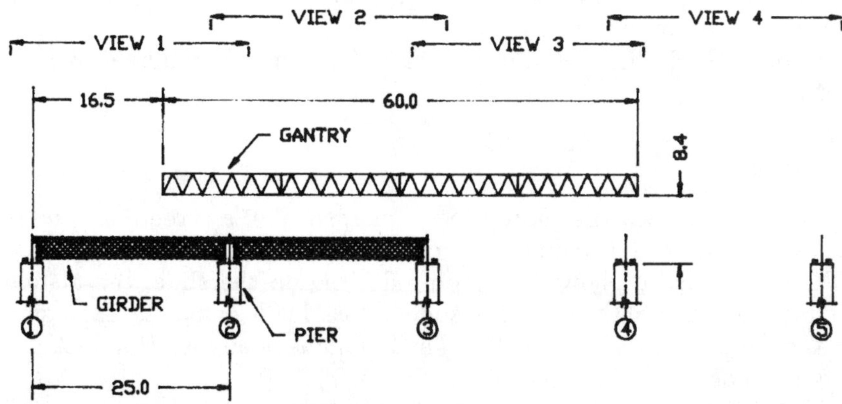

Figure 17.2 Initial position of gantry and view locations.

Set the current layer as **Pier.** Draw the pier, as illustrated in Fig. 17.1. Rather than use another layer with a center linetype, draw the center line using solid line segments.

The bearing pads are the solid squares on the top of the pier. To draw the pads, first draw one using the Line command. To solidly fill the pad after it is drawn, enter the following:

To fill the bearing pads use:

> `Draw` <pick> `Solid` <pick> `First point:` Digitize the upper-left corner of the pad. <pick> `Second point:` Digitize the upper-right corner of the pad. <pick> `Third point:` Digitize the lower-left corner of the pad. <pick> `Fourth point:` Digitize the lower-right corner of the pad. <pick> `Fifth point:` <return>

Draw the second support pad by using the Copy command to make a copy of the first.

Save the pier as a block with the name **Pier.** The insertion point is the middle point of the top line of the pier, as illustrated in Fig. 17.1.

17.1.4 Gantry supports

The gantry has three supports: Fixsup1, the far-left support; Fixsup2, the far-right support; and Movsup, the middle support. They are illustrated in Figs. 17.1 and 17.3.

Set the current layer as **Sups.** Prior to drawing the gantry supports, a roller will be created and stored as a block. The roller can then be inserted onto the supports as required.

> `Draw` <pick> `Donut` <pick> `Inside diameter:` **0** <return> `Outside diameter:` **0.4** <return> `Center of doughnut:` Digitize a point in a clear space on the monitor. <pick> `Center of doughnut:` <return>

Save the solid circle as a block with the name **Roller.** Select the bottom of the circle as the insertion point.

Draw each of the gantry supports and save each as a block. The critical dimension is the overall height of each, which is illustrated in Fig. 17.1. The other dimensions can be estimated.

Draw the hoist block illustrated in Fig. 17.1. The hoist should be drawn on the **Const** layer.

17.2 AutoCAD LT Slides

An AutoCAD LT slide is a file containing a "snapshot" of a screen. A slide is produced by creating the drawing desired using ordinary AutoCAD LT commands. When the screen shows everything desired on the slide, the Mslide command is used to create the snapshot slide file. Slide files have the extension .sld after the name specified for the file. The file name is any legitimate AutoCAD LT file name.

Slide files contain only information describing the snapshot saved and cannot be altered. Do not try to alter a slide. If a slide is loaded and alterations are attempted, the alterations will appear on the drawing that was on the screen prior to the displayed slide file.

The only way to change a slide file is to redraw the picture desired and use MSLIDE to save the new picture using the same slide file name.

To view a slide the Vslide command is used. A slide show can be produced by creating a Script file (see Sec. 17.8) which contains a sequence of Vslide commands that load sequential files. AutoCAD LT's script facility allows a sequence of commands to be read from a text file. The procedure is discussed later in this project.

17.3 Slide Dwg-1

Dwg-1 shows the initial position of the gantry on the bridge, as illustrated in Fig. 17.3*a*. The relative dimensions for the items in the initial position are illustrated in Fig. 17.2.

Set the current drawing layer as Const. Use the Zoom and All commands to zoom to the initial limits set for the screen (0,0 and 110,70). Press Ctrl-D (or F6) to display the cursor coordinates.

The coordinates 6,20 will be used for the insertion point of the first pier. Because there are five piers to be inserted at a spacing of 25 units center to center, the Minsert (multiple insert) command is used to insert an array as follows (enter Minsert from the keyboard):

INITIAL POSITION OF GANTRY ON BRIDGE.

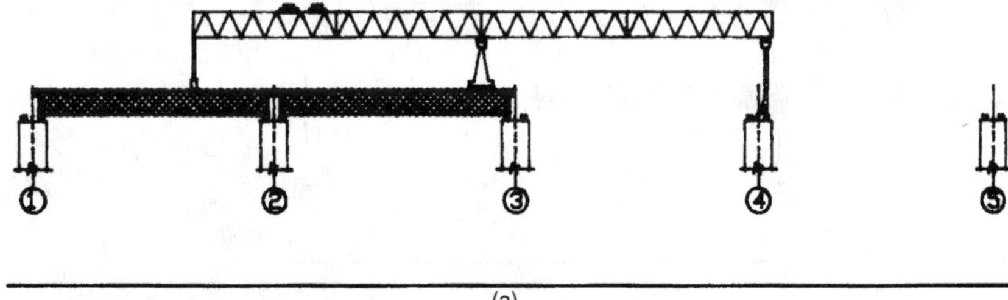

(a)

MOVE NEW GIRDER INTO BAYS 2 & 3 (ZOOMED VIEW).

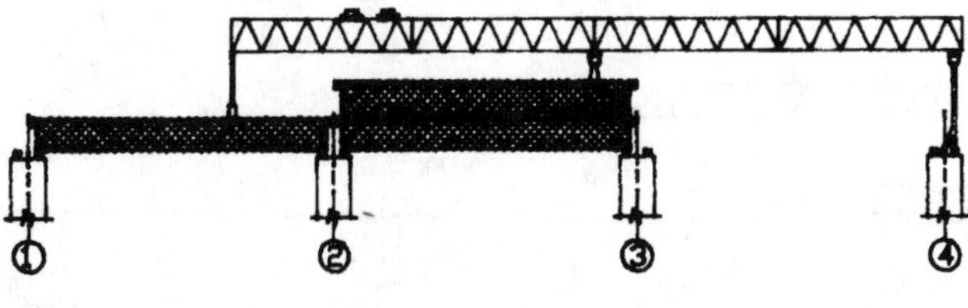

(b)

Figure 17.3 Slide show views.

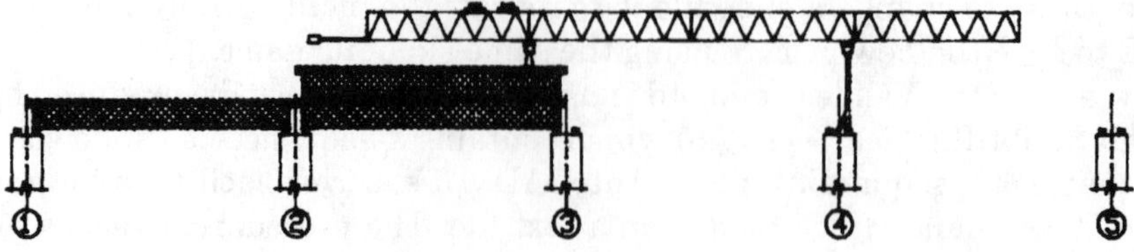
RAISE LEFT FIXED SUPPORT &
MOVE GANTRY 15 FEET TO THE RIGHT.
1
2
3
4
5

(c)

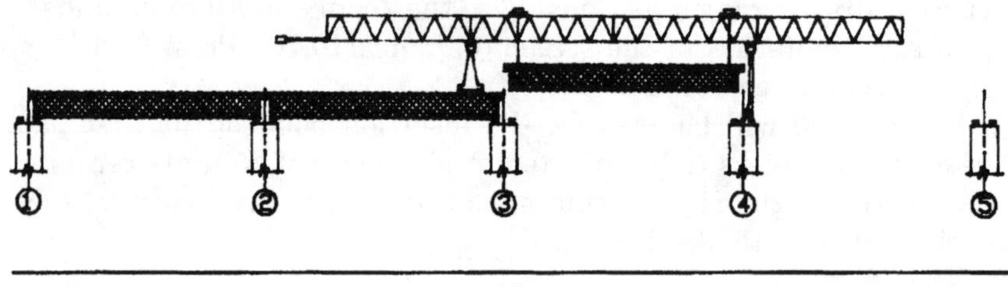
USING HOISTS, MOVE GIRDER INTO POSITION BETWEEN BAYS 3-4.
1
2
3
4
5

(d)

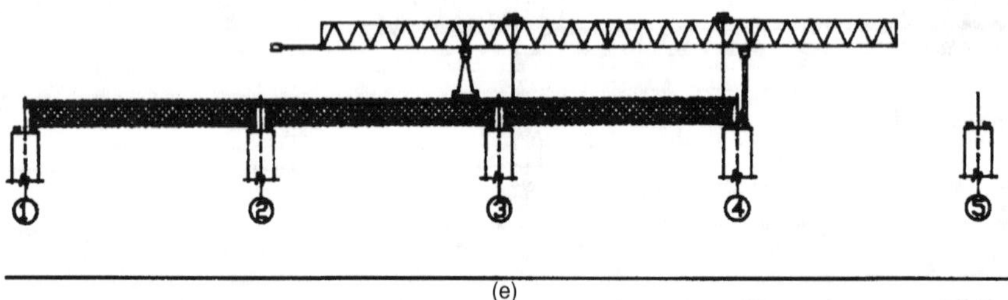
LOWER GIRDER INTO PLACE.
1
2
3
4
5

(e)

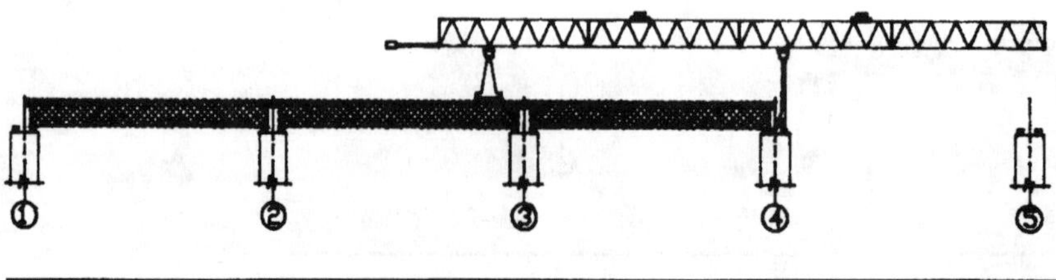
RELEASE HOIST CABLES &
MOVE GANTRY 10 FEET TO THE RIGHT.
1
2
3
4
5

(f)

Figure 17.3 *(Continued)*

ZOOMED VIEW OF BAYS 2-5.
LOWER LEFT FIXED SUPPORT &
MOVE MIDDLE SUPPORT TO THE RIGHT.

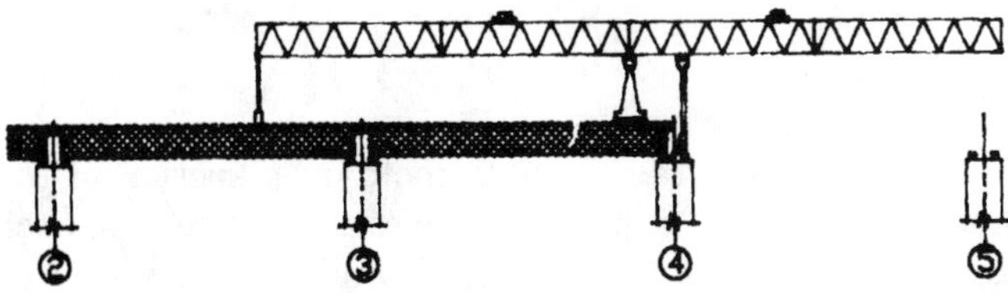

MOVE RIGHT SIDE SUPPORT FROM PIER 4 TO PIER 5.
ZOOMED VIEW

(g)

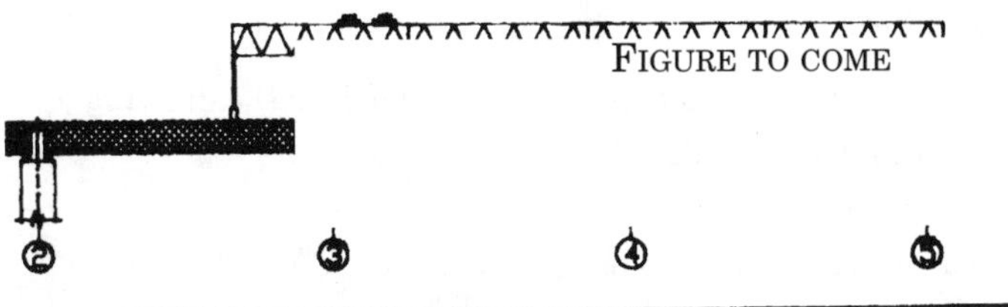

FINAL POSITION OF SEQUENCE.
START POSITION OF NEXT SEQUENCE.

(h)

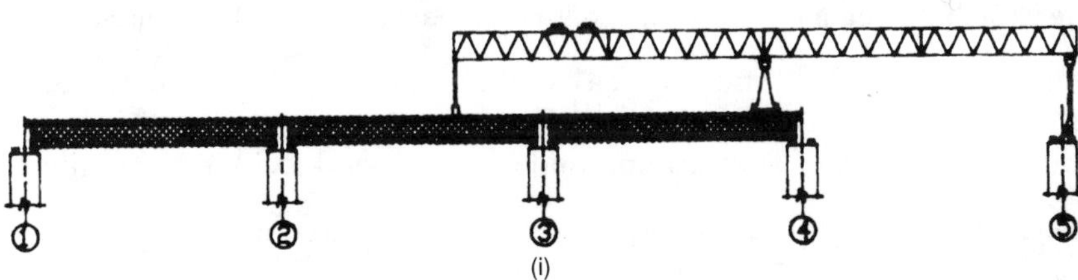

(i)

Figure 17.3 *(Continued)*

MINSERT <return> Block name: **pier** <return> Insert point: **6,20** <return> X scale factor <1>/Corner/X/Y/Z: <return> Y scale factor (default = X): <return> Rotation angle <0>: <return> Number of rows (---) <1>: <return> Number of columns (|||) <1>: **5** <return> Distance between columns (||): **25** <return>

Insert the two girders using the Minsert command. The insertion point is the same as for pier 1 (6,20), and the spacing of the girders is 25 units.

The 60-m gantry can also be inserted using the Minsert command. The insertion point is 22.5,27.9 (where $x = 6 + 16.5$ and $y = 20 + (8.40 - 0.5)$). Refer to Figs. 17.1 and 17.2 to understand the calculations used to determine the coordinates. A single gantry section is 15 units long, so there will be four columns in the Minsert array.

17.3.1 Designate views

As the drawing is continued, you will often have to zoom on a section of the bridge to locate points more accurately. To speed up the drawing process, each of the bays will be enlarged with the Zoom command, and the view will be named using the View command. After a view is named, it can be quickly recalled using the View and Restore commands.

`View` <pick> `View` <pick>

The options are listed below:

List? Produces a list of the view names currently saved for the drawing

Delete Used to remove a view from the list of saved views

Restore Used to display a saved view

Save Allows the user to save the current screen view

Window Allows the user to save a view by placing a window around the desired view area

The Window command will be used to specify the view. The view is to be named 1 (reducing the typing required):

`Window` <pick> `View Name:` **1** <return> `First point:` Place a window around the bridge area enclosing piers 1 and 2. See View 1, marked in Fig. 17.2 <pick>

Recall the View command, and then save views 2, 3, and 4, as illustrated in Fig. 17.2.

To display view 1, the Restore command is used. Recall the View command:

`View` <pick> `View` <pick> `Restore` <pick> `View name:` **1** <return>

Insert Fixsup1 at the lower-left corner of the gantry. Use the INTERSECTION object snap to digitize the point of insertion.

Restore view 2 and insert Movsup 30 units to the right of the left end of the gantry. Because the last point was the left end of the gantry, the insertion point is entered relative to that point as @30 < 0.

Insert the first hoist on top of the gantry at coordinates 32.5,30.4, and insert the second hoist at coordinates 35.5,30.4.

Restore view 3, and insert Fixsup2 using an insertion point at the left side of the right support pad on pier 4 (see Fig. 17.3*a*).

17.3.2 Use attributes to draw pier column numbers

The pier mark numbers will be enclosed in a 1.25 unit-radius circle, which will allow room for a 1.5-unit-high number inside the circle:

Draw <pick> Circle <pick> Center/Radius <pick> 3P/2P/TIR <Center point>: Digitize a point on the screen outside of the current drawing. <pick> Radius **1.25** <return>

Attributes are used to allow insertion of each pier column number block with a different number. The Attribute Definition is shown in Fig. 17.4. Press Pick-Point< to enter the insertion point, which is the center of the 1.25 radius circle.

The attribute tag T will now be displayed inside the 2.5-unit circle. Use the Move command to locate it properly in the circle (unless it is already centered).

Save the block. The insertion point should be the top of the circle.

Regenerate view 1 and insert the pier column number at the bottom center line of the pier, as illustrated in Fig. 17.2. Add the pier column numbers to each of the other piers.

17.3.3 Adding text

Use the Zoom and All commands to obtain a view of the entire bridge. The start location for the text will be coordinates 6,50. The text height will be selected as 1.5 units to adequately allow reading of the text when the views are displayed.

Draw <pick> Text <pick> Justify/Style/<start point>: **6,50** <return> Height: **1.5** <return> Rotation angle <0.0>: <return> Text: **INITIAL POSITION OF GANTRY ON BRIDGE.** <return>

17.3.4 Saving the slide

Be sure that the drawing includes all of the items illustrated in Fig. 17.3*a*. This drawing will be the first slide, which is to be named Dwg-1.

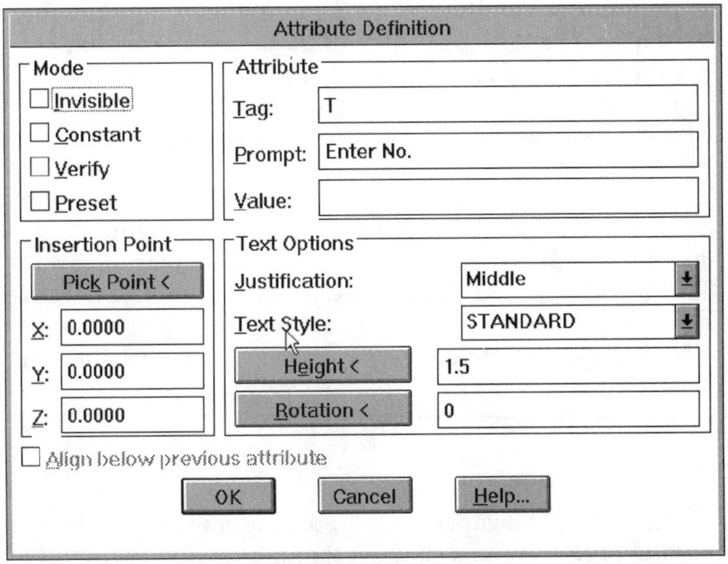

Figure 17.4 Attributes.

File <pick> Import/Export <pick> Make slide... <pick>

A file dialogue display box will be displayed. The directory will match that used to store the drawing file, which is assumed to be c:\drawings, unless you are using another file path. If you want to change the directory, move the cursor to the directory box and enter the desired directory.

The file name is the current drawing name. Because there will be more than one slide, a new file name is to be entered. Move the cursor to the file name edit box and enter the file name as **Dwg-1.** Then press the OK button.

The screen is now saved as a slide file with the name DWG-1.SLD. The file size will be small because only information locating the vectors on the screen is saved.

Although it is not necessary, you might now want to save a drawing file copy of this screen. Remember that slides cannot be altered—if you later want to change the slide and you have saved the screen in a drawing file, you can change the drawing file and then resave the slide. The only real problem in saving the drawing file is that it will contain all the information about the drawing and hence use up disk space. If you do want to save the screen, use the Save As command and use an original name such as Fig. 17.1. This can be done for each slide (using consecutive names Fig 17.2, Fig 17.3, etc.). When the project is complete and the slides are considered final, the drawing files can be erased.

17.4 Slide Dwg-2

Dwg-2 illustrates the positioning of a new girder in preparation for lifting into bays 3 and 4 (see Fig. 17.3*b*). This girder is located 25 units to the right and 3 units (girder depth plus 0.4 units for rollers) above the insertion point of the first pier. The cursor's last position will be set on the insertion point of the first pier, and you can then insert the new girder @25,3 units relative to that position. The cursor's last position is set as follows:

Assist <pick> ID Point <pick> INS (Toolbox) <pick> of Place the target over the insertion point of the first pier. <pick>

Insert the new girder @25,3 units relative to the cursor's last point.

Use the Zoom command to enlarge a view of the bridge from piers 1 to 4.

At coordinates 31,50, add the text "MOVE NEW GIRDER INTO BAYS 2 & 3."

Use the Make Slide dialogue box to save this screen, using the file name c:\drawings\dwg-2.

17.5 Slide Dwg-3

In Dwg-3, Fixsup1 is raised and the gantry is moved 15 units to the right.

Use the View command to Restore view 2 (bays 2 and 3).

To raise Fixsup1, use the Rotate command as follows:

Modify <pick> Rotate <pick> Select objects: Digitize Fixsup1 <pick><return> Base point: INS <pick> of Digitize Fixup1 <pick> <Rotation angle>/Reference: **–90** <return>

Move the gantry, hoists, and Fixsup1 15 units to the right, as illustrated in Fig. 17.3*c:*

Modify <pick> Move <pick> Select objects: Place a window enclosing the gantry, hoists, and Fixsup1. <pick> <return> Base point or displacement: **@15 < 0** <return>

Use the Zoom and All commands to view the entire bridge. Add the following text to the drawing:

DTEXT <pick> Justify/Style/<Start point>: **6.50** <return> Height <1.5>: <return> Rotation angle <0.0>: <return> Text: **RAISE LEFT FIXED SUPPORT &** <return> Text: **MOVE GANTRY 15 FEET TO THE RIGHT.** <return> <return>

Save the slide using the name c:\drawings\dwg-3.

17.6 Slide Dwg-4, Dwg-5, and Dwg-6

In Dwg-4 the girder is picked up by the hoists and moved into position over and between piers 3 and 4. The Move command is used to move the girder 25 units to the right. To select the object to be moved, digitize a point on the girder. The "Base point or displacement" is entered as @25 < 0.

The left hoist is then moved 10 units to the right (@10 < 0), and the right hoist is moved 29 units to the right.

Use the View command to view bays 3 and 4 (view 3), and then use the Line command to add cables connecting the hoists to the girder, as illustrated in Fig. 17.3*d.*

Enter Zoom and All and then add the text "USING HOISTS, MOVE GIRDER INTO POSITION BETWEEN BAYS 3–4." Save the slide as c:\drawings\dwg-4.

In Dwg-5 the girder is lowered (moved) into position (@3 < 270). Add the text to the screen as illustrated in Fig. 17.3*e,* and save the slide as c:\drawings\dwg-5.

In Dwg-6 the hoist cables are erased and the gantry, including the hoists and the left gantry support, is moved 10 units to the right. Add the text illustrated in Fig. 17.3*f* and save the slide as c:\drawings\dwg-6.

17.7 Slide Dwg-7, Dwg-8, and Dwg-9

Both Dwg-7 and Dwg-8 are zoomed views of the bridge from bays 2 to 5.

Remember to use views 1 to 4 to provide enlarged views of the bridge bays when drawing.

In Dwg-7, the Fixsup1 is rotated 90 degrees, as illustrated in Fig. 17.3*g.* The Movsup is then moved 25 units (@25 < 0) to the right.

Add the text to the drawing at coordinates 31,50 and save the slide using the name c:\drawings\dwg-7.

In Dwg-8, the Fixsup2 is moved from pier 4 to pier 5 by 25 units (@25 < 0). The hoists are then moved back to the left end of the gantry in preparation for the next girder to be installed. They are moved back by the amount they were moved forward in Dwg-4, i.e., the left hoist is moved @–10 < 0 and the right hoist is moved @–29 < 0.

Add the text illustrated in Fig. 17.3*h* and save the slide as c:\drawings\dwg-8.

Dwg-9 is a Zoom All view of Dwg-8 with the text illustrated in Fig. 17.3*i* added.

17.8 Writing the Script

A script file is a text file with the extension .scr, which contains a list of AutoCAD LT commands incorporating a sequence of drawing operations that can be read by AutoCAD LT.

The script file will be written using the Windows' Notepad program (see Chap. 11, Sec. 11.3). The syntax for writing script files is different in many ways from that used in menu files. In both, a space invokes the Enter key; however, the semicolon (;) does not invoke the Enter key in script files. Other menu file commands such as \ and + also do not apply to script files. Lines that begin with a semicolon (;) are considered comment lines by AutoCAD LT.

The script file for the slide show is listed below. A discussion of the file follows the listing. Read the discussion before writing the file. The number and the colon at the front of each line are used to support the discussion and are not part of the file.

Exit AutoCAD LT. Do not save the drawing. Load Notepad from Windows Accessories window. A script file must have the extension .scr. The script file is to be named c:\drawings\bridge.scr:

```
1: layer make const
2:
3: limits 0,0 110,70 zoom all
4: line 10,10 100,10 100,60 10,60 c
5: text c 55,40 2 0
6: PRECAST CONCRETE BRIDGE CONSTRUCTION
7:    BY
8:    EASY CONSTRUCTION INC.
9: vslide *c:\drawings\dwg-1
10: delay 2000
11: vslide
12: vslide *c:\drawings\dwg-2
13: delay 4000
14: vslide
15: vslide *c:\drawings\dwg-3
16: delay 4000
17: vslide
18: vslide *c:\drawings\dwg-4
19: delay 4000
20: vslide
21: vslide *c:\drawings\dwg-5
```

```
22: delay 4000
23: vslide
24: vslide *c:\drawings\dwg-6
25: delay 4000
26: vslide
27: vslide *c:\drawings\dwg-7
28: delay 4000
29: vslide
30: vslide *c:\drawings\dwg-8
31: delay 4000
32: vslide
33: vslide *c:\drawings\dwg-9
34: delay 4000
35: vslide
36: delay 6000
37: rscript
```

Be sure that the file you have written is exactly the same as the one illustrated (without the number and colon at the start of the line). Then save the file as c:\drawings\bridge.scr, and exit Notepad. A discussion of the script file follows:

Line 1. Calls the Layer command, makes a new layer called Const. and sets the current layer as Const. The other layers used in the script drawings do not have to be created because this will be done automatically when the entities on them are inserted into the drawing. Making the current layer Const eliminates the possible problems resulting if layer 0, which was not used in the slide drawings, was turned off when creating the slides. The space between commands invokes the Enter key and is required to call a command.

Line 2. This is a blank line to invoke the Enter key required to exit the Layer command. When writing script files, you must be very familiar with the syntax of AutoCAD LT commands; i.e., in this case the Layer command is not exited unless the Enter key is called. Refer to using Help in App. A.4, which gives information on AutoCAD LT commands.

Line 3. Sets the drawing limits and zooms.

Line 4. Draws a rectangle on the screen with a 10-unit border.

Line 5. Calls the Text command with the C (center) option. The center point is then specified as coordinates 55,40, the text height is 2 units, and the rotation angle is 0 degrees.

Line 6. This is the text to be printed on the screen.

Lines 7 and 8. These lines begin with two blank spaces which invoke the Enter key to recall the previous Text command. Remember that when Text is recalled, it uses the same height and angle as used for the initial command and places the next text directly below the previous line—in this case, centered because the initial command was for centered text. The text is then printed out.

Line 9. The Vslide command is used to call a slide. In this case, the slide file name is preceded with an asterisk (*) indicating that the slide file is to be loaded but not shown yet. It will be shown when Vslide is next encountered. If the file name is not preceded with an asterisk, the file is loaded and shown immediately. This preloads the slide, thereby eliminating the delay caused by AutoCAD LT having to read the file from the disk when it is to be shown.

Line 10. The Delay command is used to delay the slide show, allowing the viewer to see the current screen before viewing the next screen. The current screen contains the rectangle which encloses the text of lines 6, 7, and 8. A Delay of 1000 takes about 1 second, so a delay of about 2 seconds is invoked.

Line 11. This Vslide command causes AutoCAD LT to display the slide c:\drawings\Dwg-1 that was preloaded in line 9.

Line 12. Preloads c:\drawings\dwg-2.

Line 13. Delays AutoCAD LT operations for about 4 seconds to allow the viewer to see the current slide c:\drawings\dwg-1.

Lines 14 to 35. A continuous sequence of displaying a preloaded file, preloading the next, and delaying the AutoCAD LT sequence for about 4 seconds.

Line 36. Delays the AutoCAD LT operation for about 6 seconds to allow the viewer to see the last slide in the slide show.

Line 37. Enters the Rscript command which repeats the script.

17.8.1 Invoking the script

Boot up AutoCAD LT and begin a new drawing named c:\drawings\bridge. When the drawing editor is loaded, use the Script command to load the file Bridge.scr:

```
File <pick> Run Script... <pick>
```

A script file dialogue display box is displayed showing the directory as c:\drawings the pattern of *scr. Select the file named bridge.scr from the file list and press OK to load the file.

The file will now be invoked and the slide show will be displayed. If the show is interrupted because of an error in the script file, exit AutoCAD LT and correct the error in the script file using Notepad. If you want to see the remainder of the file prior to making the corrections, enter the Resume command.

You can interrupt a slide show at any time by pressing Ctrl-C or the Backspace key. To continue the show enter Resume.

Chapter

18

AutoCAD LT in the Windows Environment

Objective. To run multiple applications, and transfer data from one application to the other.

18.1 Working in Multiple Windows

AutoCAD LT works in the Windows environment which allows you to open multiple applications. Boot AutoCAD LT. When AutoCAD LT is loaded hold down the Alt key and press and release the Tab key. Each time the Tab key is pressed (while the Alt key is held down) the title of an open application is displayed on the screen. When the title of the desired application is displayed release the Alt key and the application will appear in the foreground. Toggle to Program Manager, and then back to AutoCAD LT.

When you have multiple documents open, all documents should be closed before turning the computer off. To ensure this happens close Windows by clicking on the control menu box (the dash in the top-left corner of the window) in the Program Manager Window. This allows you to exit to DOS and ensures all Windows applications are closed.

18.2 Using Windows Clipboard

Windows Clipboard acts as an storage area in the transfer of data between applications working in the Windows environment. The following commands in AutoCAD LT copy entities to the Clipboard:

Copy Image. Copies the selected image from AutoCAD LT in bitmap format. Bitmap images are composed of a pattern of dots and the image cannot be scaled. There may be degradation in the quality of the image. Most Windows applications support bitmap images.

Copy Vectors. Copies entities in both AutoCAD LT format and Windows metafile format. This process is used to transfer information to an AutoCAD LT drawing or an application that supports Windows Metafile format (WMF). When you paste the entities the correct format is automatically used. Both formats contain screen vector information. Data is transferred without loss of resolution, and entities can be scaled. When you paste entities into AutoCAD and AutoCAD LT they are inserted into the current UCS as a block, and the prompts are the same as those for the Insert command allowing you to scale and rotate the block.

Copy Embed. When you embed an AutoCAD LT drawing in another document, a copy of the drawing is stored in the destination document. Embedded drawings can be modified. The embedded drawing, however, is no longer associated with the original drawing and, if the embedded drawing is modified, the original source drawing is not affected.

Copy Link. When you link entities from an AutoCAD LT drawing to another document you create a link between the two applications. The link tells the destination document where to find the original drawing. Linked drawings are automatically updated as the drawing is modified.

18.2.1 Copying images to Windows clipboard

Images are copied from AutoCAD LT to another application in bitmap format as follows:

```
Edit <pick> Copy Image <pick> Select an area of the screen:
```

The cursor changes to a "+" shape. Pick two corners of the area you want to copy. You are not limited to the graphics area and may include any part of the toolbar, toolbox, and command line. The image is transferred to Clipboard, and you may paste it into other applications. This will be discussed in the following sections.

18.2.2 Copying vectors to Windows clipboard

Vectors are copied from AutoCAD LT to another application in AutoCAD and Windows Metafile Format as follows:

```
Edit <pick> Copy Vectors <pick> Select objects:
```

Use any standard AutoCAD LT procedure to select entities to be copied to Clipboard. The Paste command is used to insert the entities into another document. This process is discussed in the following sections.

18.2.3 Embedding an AutoCAD LT drawing

Vectors are copied from AutoCAD LT to embed into another application in AutoCAD or Windows Metafile Format. Draw two joined lines on the screen and then choose the following:

`Edit` <pick> `Copy Embed` <pick> `Select objects:` Select the two lines <pick>

The Paste command is used to insert the entities into another document; for example, use the current drawing:

`Edit` <pick> `Paste` <pick> `Insertion point:` Drag the block to a desired point. <pick> `X Scale factor <1>/Corner/XYZ:` **1** <return> `Y Scale factor (default = x):` <return> `Rotation angle <0>:` <return>

List the data for the block:

`Assist` <pick> `List` <pick> `Select objects:` Select the entity that was pasted. <pick> `Select objects` <return>

AutoCAD LT lists data for the entity. Note that it is a block named WMF0. If another entity is inserted it is named WMF1, etc. Choose Explode in the Modify menu to explode the block. List the data again, noting the lines are now single entities and are polylines.

Embedded items can be edited following procedures outlined in the following section. Unlike linked drawings though, if an embedded entity is modified the original drawing is not affected.

18.2.4 Linking an AutoCAD LT drawing

Open the Proj-16 drawing. Set the current working mode to model, and click on the viewport with the 3-D view, making it the current viewport. This view was saved with the name 3-D (Chap. 16, Sec. 16.2). Prior to Linking a view it should be named. If the view is not named, AutoCAD LT gives it a name such as OLE1. The Copy Link option in the edit menu is grayed until the drawing is named. Prior to linking the 3-D view, freeze the layer named Viewlyr1. If this view is on, the viewport outlines may be included in the linked drawing in some form. Choose the following to link the 3-D view:

`Edit` <pick> `Copy Link` <pick>

The Copylink command is echoed at the command line and the view is transferred to Clipboard. The view is linked to another application—in this case Windows Write program—as follows:

- Hold down the Alt key and press and release the Tab key repeatedly until the Program Manager title is displayed. Then release the Alt key. Windows Program Manager is in the foreground. Click on the Accessories window bringing it to the foreground as shown in Fig. 18.1.
- Double-click on the Write icon as shown in Fig. 18.1. The Write program is loaded. Choose the following:

  `Edit` <pick> `Paste Link` <pick>
- The 3-D view appears in the Word document at the location of the cursor.

Editing linked views. The linked 3-D view is edited as follows:

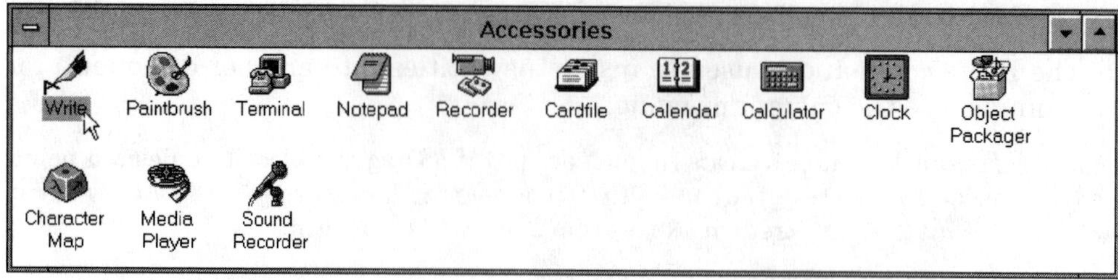

Figure 18.1 Accessories window.

- Double-click on the 3-D view in the Write document. Windows OLE locates the originating program AutoCAD LT, loads it, and opens the drawing Proj-17. Make sure you are in model space, and layer Viewlyr1 is frozen. Click on the Front view making it current.
- Hold down the Alt key and press the Tab key as required to return to the Write document.
- Choose the following:

  Edit <pick> **Links...** <pick>

- The links dialogue box (Fig. 18.2) is displayed. Press the Update Now box, and the 3-D view is updated and replaced with a plan view of the front UCS.

If you save the current document and exit Write, the next time the document is opened in Write you will be asked if you wish to update the links (Fig. 18.3). If you choose yes, OLE boots the originating program and the file containing the linked view. You may have to reset the UCS in order to get the proper view in the destination document. Toggle to the Write document as outlined in the preceding.

18.2.5 Pasting text from Windows clipboard

Text can be imported from a Windows word processor to AutoCAD LT as follows:

Links
Links:
AutoCAD Drawing PROJ-17A.DWG OLE1 Automatic
Update: Automatic Manual
Update Now Cancel Link Change Link...
OK
Cancel
Activate
Edit

Figure 18.2 Links dialogue box.

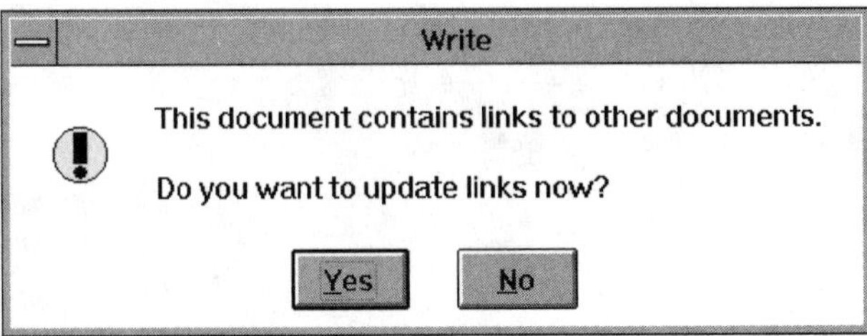

Figure 18.3 Updating links box.

- Boot AutoCAD LT
- Hold down Alt and press Tab and toggle to Windows Program Manager.
- Bring the Accessories Window (Fig. 18.1) to the foreground and open Notepad by clicking twice on its icon. Type some text into Notepad. Select the text by holding down the select button on the mouse as you slide the cursor through the text. The selected text is highlighted.
- Choose Copy (or Cut) in Notepad's edit menu.
- Toggle to AutoCAD LT, and choose the following:

  `Draw` <pick> `Text` <pick> `Justify/Style/<Start point>:` Digitize the start point of the text. <pick> `Height <0.2>:` <**return**> `Rotation angle <0>:` <return> `Text:` `Edit` <pick> `Paste Command` <pick> `Text:` <return>

18.3 Importing/Exporting Windows Metafile Format Files

AutoCAD LT entities can be saved to a WMF file and then imported into other applications.

To create a WMF file in AutoCAD LT:

- Choose Import/Export in the File menu, then choose WMF Out . . .
- The Export WMF dialogue box is displayed. Enter a file name and then press OK.
- Select the entities to export to the WMF file.

To import a WMF to AutoCAD LT:

- Choose Import/Export in the File menu, then choose WMF In . . .
- The Import WMF dialogue box is displayed. Select a file to import and then press OK to import the file.

The WMF . . . command displays the Import WMF dialogue box. Set the directory to c:\acltwin\symbols and click the preview button on. WMF symbols provided with AutoCAD LT in the architec, business, electron and engineer subdirectories can be previewed (by clicking on their file name) and inserted into the drawing like blocks.

Appendix

Trouble-Shooting Hints

A.1 General Hints

1. Always make backup copies of important drawing files. Remember that diskettes are a volatile storage device and data can easily be lost. Very important data should have two backups. Each backup should be stored in a different location.

2. AutoCAD LT normally places its temporary files in the file directory containing the drawing. If you use a floppy diskette for your drawing directory, you need space on the diskette for the drawing file plus the backup file and AutoCAD LT's temporary files. If the drawing size is greater than one-third of the diskette capacity you might have a crash.

3. If you must use a floppy diskette for your drawing directory (often necessary in a classroom situation) you should set the temporary file location to the hard drive as follows. Boot AutoCAD LT and choose the following:

`File` <pick> `Preferences...` <pick>

The Preferences dialogue box illustrated in Fig. A.1.1 is displayed. Press the `Temporary Files...` button to display the Temporary Files dialogue box illustrated in Fig. A.1.2. Click the `Use Drawing Directory` check box off (there will not be an X in it). Then enter the directory for the temporary files in the Directory box. This setting will become the default.

4. AutoCAD LT can be set to do automatic saves at specified intervals using the Preferences dialogue box (Fig. A.1.1). The file name for automatic saves also can be set. Don't forget to click the Automatic Save Every box on.

5. If you are not using AutoCAD LT on a network, turn File Locking off in Preferences dialogue box (Fig. A.1.1).

6. If you work in S.I. units you may want to change the Measurement units to Metric in the Preferences dialogue box. The setting becomes default so remember to change the units back to English if you work in Imperial on a

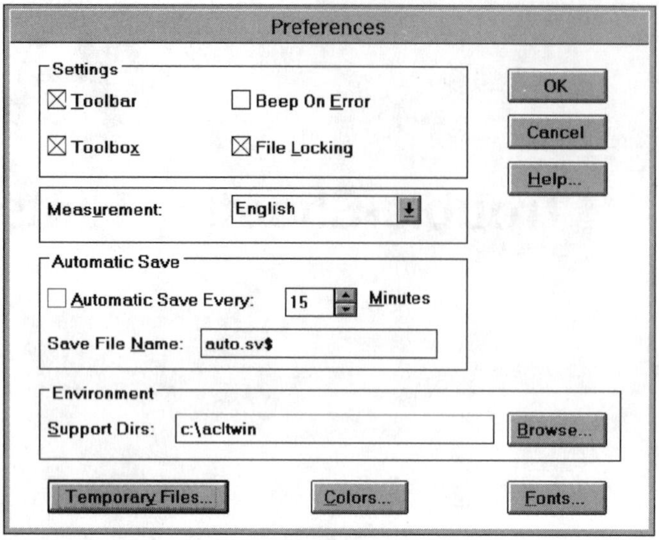

Figure A.1.1 Preferences dialogue box.

drawing. In Chap. 16, Sec. 16.10.9, you could set the measurement units to Metric in lieu of changing the dimension variables. Also see Chap. 6, Sect. 6.13.

7. If AutoCAD LT rejects a point you are selecting and reports it is outside the limits, enter `Limits` <pick> `Off` <pick> to turn limits checking off.

8. If you press the Enter key or <pick> button to digitize a point and AutoCAD LT does not "see" the point, press the backspace key a few times. Then try entering the point again. You might have inadvertently pressed another key prior to pressing Enter.

9. If you plot a drawing and your noncontinuous lines are plotted as continuous lines, you probably have not set the Linetype Scale (Ltscale) properly. This is often forgotten when inserting drawings into another drawing (see Chap. 12, Sec. 12.7.2).

10. If parts of your border are not plotting, enter the actual sheet size when entering plot data (i.e., enter 11 by 8.5 inches for an A-size sheet rather than selecting AutoCAD LT's A size or MAX size).

11. If something on your drawing does not plot, and everything around it is plotting, check that the item not plotting is not on layer Dimaso. Layer Dimaso

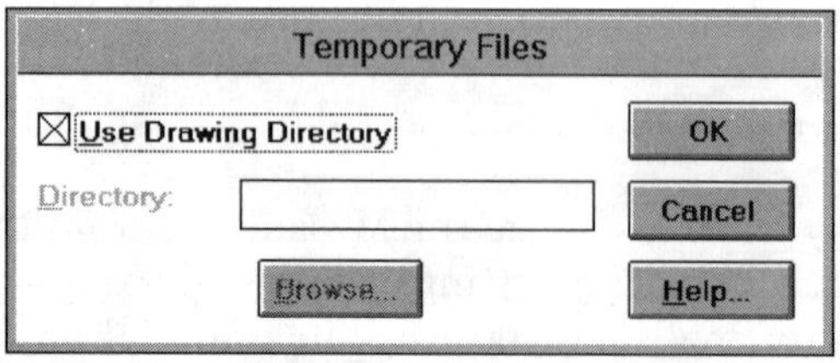

Figure A.1.2 Setting the temporary file directory.

is created for AutoCAD LT's associate dimension control points and items on that layer do not plot.

12. When working on a large drawing:

- Set Linetype Scale (Ltscale) to a large value so all lines appear as continuous. This speeds up drawing regeneration and also simplifies screen picks. Alternatively set all linetypes as continuous. Then prior to plotting set the desired linetypes.
- Leave all hatching until the end to speed up drawing regeneration.
- Freeze layers not required to be displayed. Thaw them prior to printing.
- If the drawing contains a lot of text, enter Qtext at the command line, and specify On. Prior to plotting turn Qtext Off.

13. If you are experimenting use Undo to set a marker. You can then Undo to that marker:

`Undo` <return> `Auto/Back/End/Group/Mark/<Number>:`

Entering `Mark` places a mark at the current location.

Entering `Back` takes the drawing back to the last Mark.

Entering a number specifies the number of preceding operations to be undone.

14. If an entity on a layer does not have the layer color or linetype you may have set color and/or linetype by entity. That is done in the Entity Modes dialogue box (Fig. 15.2). To turn color back to By Layer choose the following:

`Settings` <pick> `Entity Modes...` <pick>

Choose `Color...` in the Entity Modes dialogue box (Fig. 15.2) and then set the Logical Colors to `Bylayer` in the set Color dialogue box (Fig. 6.10). To fix entities that were drawn with the wrong color see the next hint.

15. If you have entities with their color or linetype set to by entity they can be changed to Bylayer as follows:

`Modify` <pick> `Change Properties` <pick> `Select object:` Digitize the entities to be changed. <pick>

The Change Properties dialogue box (Fig. 15.1) is displayed. Change the color or layer to `BYLAYER`.

16. If you have entities you don't want to accidently change when working in detail on a drawing, place those entities on a separate layer(s), and then Lock the layer in the Layer Control dialogue box (Fig. 6.6).

17. The Purge command in the Modify menu can be used at the start of a drawing session to remove unused blocks, dimension styles, layers, and text styles from the drawing database. Purge must be invoked before any other command.

18. Minserted blocks cannot be exploded.

19. The Scale command can be used to rescale an entire drawing. For example, to change a drawing from inches to millimeters, set the screen limits to suit the larger metric drawing (multiply them by 25.4), and choose the following:

Modify <pick> Scale <pick> Select object: Place a selection window around the entire drawing. <pick> Select objects: <return> Base point: **0,0** (or the lower-left corner of the drawing if it is not 0,0) <return> <Scale factor>/Reference: **25.4** <return>

20. The size of a drawing file can often be reduced considerably by creating a Wblock (Block Out . . . in the File menu) using the name of the drawing for the file name. When asked for the block name press Enter. Use an insertion point of 0,0, and use a selection window to select the entire drawing when selecting objects.

Do not Wblock (Block out) a drawing when you are using user coordinates (UCS). If you do, the current UCS becomes the WCS and all UCSes, named views, and viewport configurations are deleted from the Wblocked file.

21. If the paper space icon is replaced by a broken pencil icon, set the UCS to World.

22. If you are in paper space (Chap. 13, Sec. 13.1) you cannot toggle to model space by clicking the P (paper space) toggle button in the buttons menu until you have opened a viewport.

23. Linetypes are scaled according to drawing units by setting Ltscale as outlined in Chap. 6, Sec. 6.7.1. In this case the same linetype might look different in each viewport in paper space, depending on the scale of that viewport. To rectify this see the next hint.

24. In paper space linetypes can be scaled to look uniform in all viewports (even if viewports have different scales) as follows:

Settings <pick> Linetype Style <pick> Pspace LT Scale <pick>

This sets linetype dash lengths based on paper space units even for entities in model space.

25. Dashed pattern linetypes often appear continuous around the vertices of a 2-D polyline. To set the dashes to appear as a continuous pattern choose the following:

Settings <pick> Polyline Style <pick> Linetype Generation <pick>

26. When plotting to a printer, AutoCAD LT scans you drawing from top to bottom, sending the data to the printer as horizontal strips. Consequently drawings without a border can often be printed quicker than ones with a border. If the border is not necessary, for example on a test plot, put it on a different layer and turn the layer off prior to plotting.

27. Plotter settings for a drawing can be saved to file and retrieved from the file the next time you print the drawing. To save the settings to file, set the desired plot settings in the Plot Configuration dialogue box (Fig. 7.1). Then choose Print/Plot Setup & Default Selection..., which displays the dialogue

box illustrated in Fig. 7.2. Press `Save Defaults to File...` and enter the file name. The file name is often set the same as the drawing name. The file extension in the dialogue box is PCP. The plot settings are retrieved by choosing `Get Defaults From File` in the Print/Plot default Selection dialogue box. If you use the same settings for a number of drawings create standard plot files which can be retrieved as required.

A.2 Grips

Grips are introduced in Chap. 16, Sec. 16.3.3. Following are more applications for grips. Load AutoCAD LT and draw the circle and two lines illustrated in Fig. A.2.1. Next pick a point on the right side line and the circle. Both entities are highlighted and small blue boxes, grips, appear on the entities. Highlighted entities are manipulated by use of the grips.

If the grips did not appear, set the GRIPS system variable to 1 and retry the preceding:

```
Command: grips
New value for GRIPS<0>: 1 <return>
```

The cursor will have a small target box at its intersection indicating that the GRIPS system variable is set to 1. Move the target box onto the grip on the right side of the circle as illustrated in Fig. A.2.2, and press <pick>. The grip fills in becoming hot (red), indicating it will serve as the basis for editing. The first grip mode is Stretch. Move the cursor to the right and the circle is stretched. Press Enter to complete the stretch.

Choose Undo in the toolbar (App. E, Fig. E.11). Now make the grip at the top of the line hot and stretch the highlighted line as illustrated in Fig. A.2.3. Press enter to complete the command.

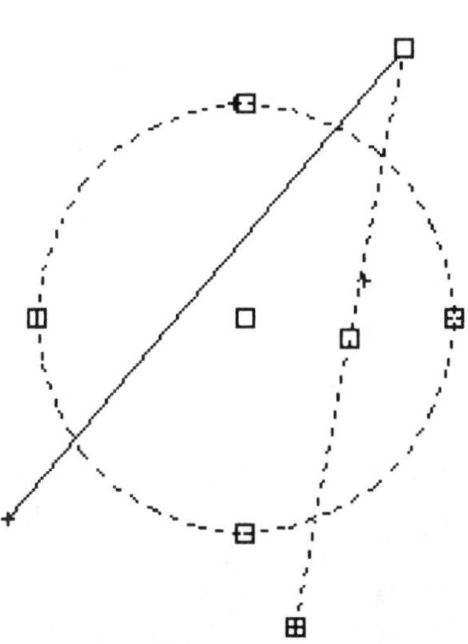

Figure A.2.1 Grips.

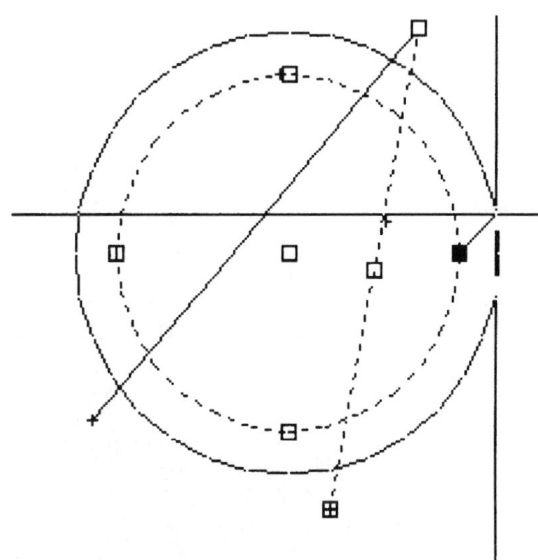

Figure A.2.2 Hot grips.

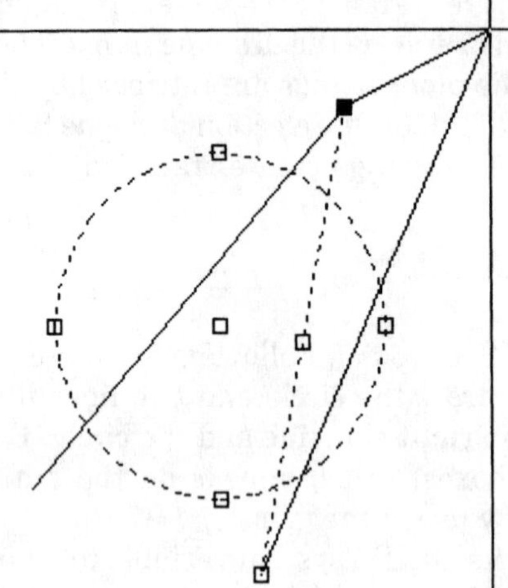

Figure A.2.3 Stretching a line.

Undo the last command. Pick a point on the left line to highlight it. Now make the grip at the top of the lines hot and stretch it as illustrated in Fig. A.2.4. Both lines stretch as a system since the hot grip was on both entities.

Undo the last command and stretch the right line as illustrated in Fig. A.2.5. Since the line is stretched from its midpoint it moves with the hot grip rather than elongating or shortening. The options at the Command line are as follows:

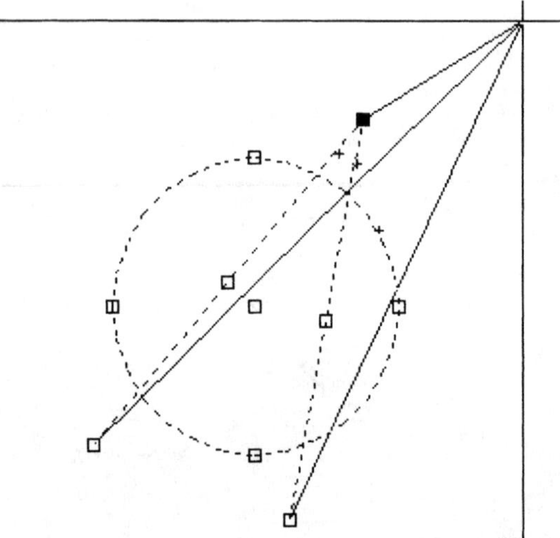

Figure A.2.4 Stretching a system of entities.

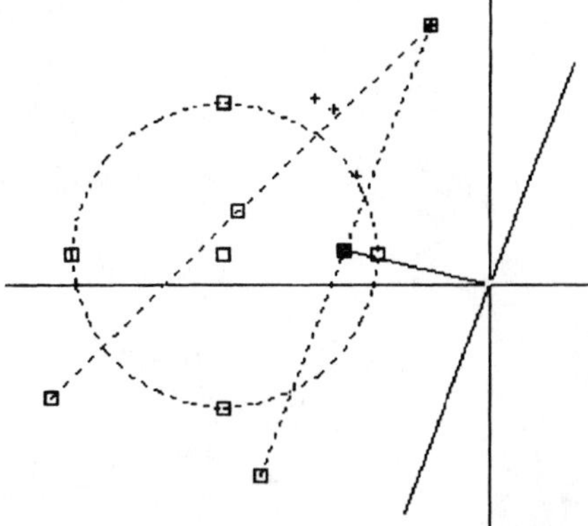

Figure A.2.5 Stretching a line by midpoint grip.

```
Command: **STRETCH**
<Stretch to point>/Base point/Copy/Undo/eXit:
```

The default option is <Stretch to point>. The point can be selected using the cursor or by entering coordinates of the new point from the keyboard. To specify a base point other than the base grip enter **base** or **b.** To copy the entity enter **copy** or **c.**

Undo the last command and make the grip at the top of the lines hot. Then press <**return**>. The option at the command line is now Move. Move the entities as illustrated in Fig. A.2.6. All highlighted entities move as a system.

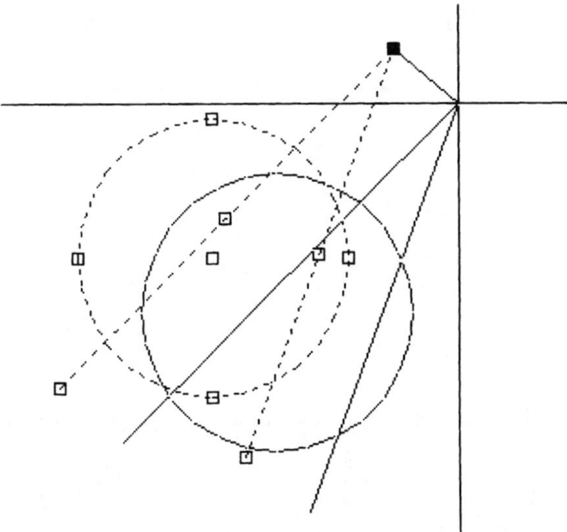

Figure A.2.6 Move option.

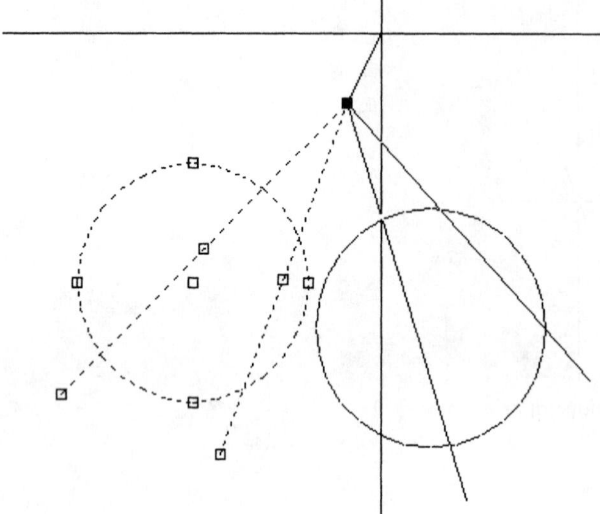

Figure A.2.7 Rotate option.

Undo the command. Make the same grip hot again and press <**return**> <**return**>. The option is now Rotate. Try the Rotate option as illustrated in Fig. A.2.7.

Undo the command. Make the same grip hot and press <**return**> <**return**> <**return**>. The option is now Scale. Scale the entities as illustrated in Fig. A.2.8.

Undo the command. Make the grip hot and press <**return**> <**return**> <**return**> <**return**>. The option is now Mirror. Mirror the entities as illustrated in Fig. A.2.9.

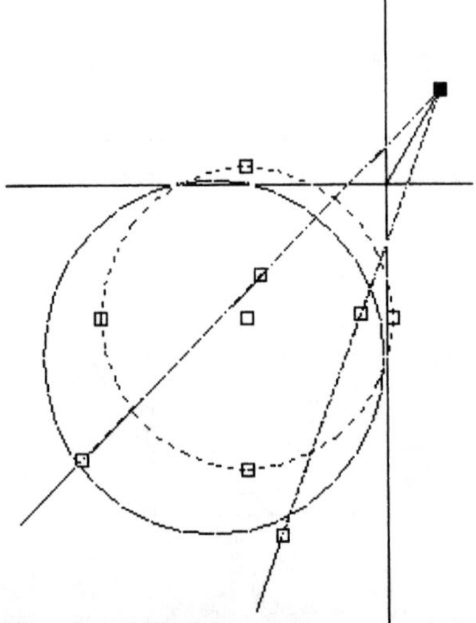

Figure A.2.8 Scale option.

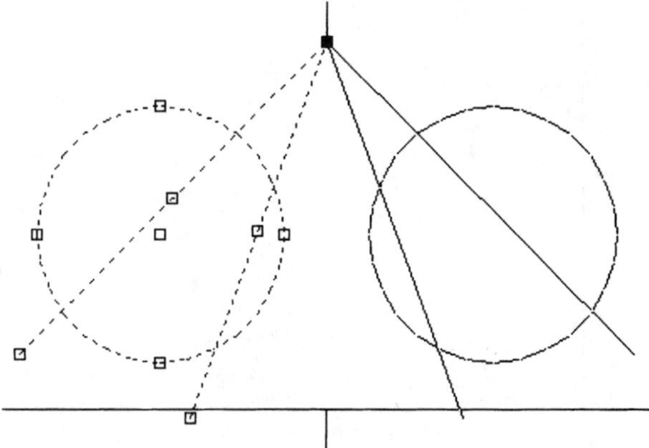

Figure A.2.9 Mirror option.

Undo the command. Make the grip at the peak of the two lines hot. Then enter **b** (base) to select a different base point, and pick the grip at the midpoint of the line on the right side as the base point. Stretch the lines as illustrated in Fig. A.2.10. Compare this Stretch to that illustrated in Fig. A.2.5. The hot grip at the top of the connecting lines linked the two lines together.

Undo the last command. Now try Scaling the entities using the hot grip at the midpoint of the line on the right side as illustrated in Fig. A.2.11. Compare this with scaling using a controlling grip at the top of the two lines illustrated in Fig. A.2.8.

Undo the last command. Anchor the line on the right side by pressing the Shift key as you pick the two grips at the end of the line on the right side as illustrated in Fig. A.2.12. Then use the controlling (hot) grip at the midpoint of

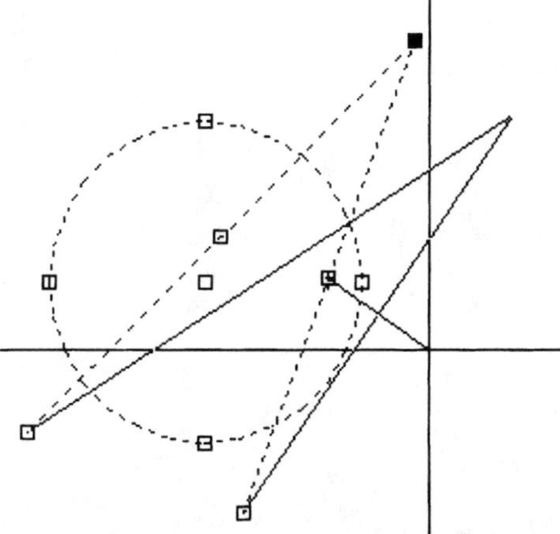

Figure A.2.10 Stretching linked entities.

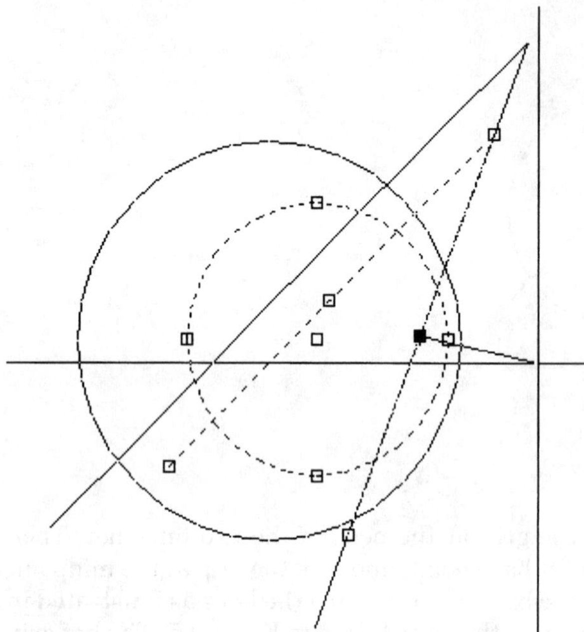

Figure A.2.11 Controlling grip and scale option.

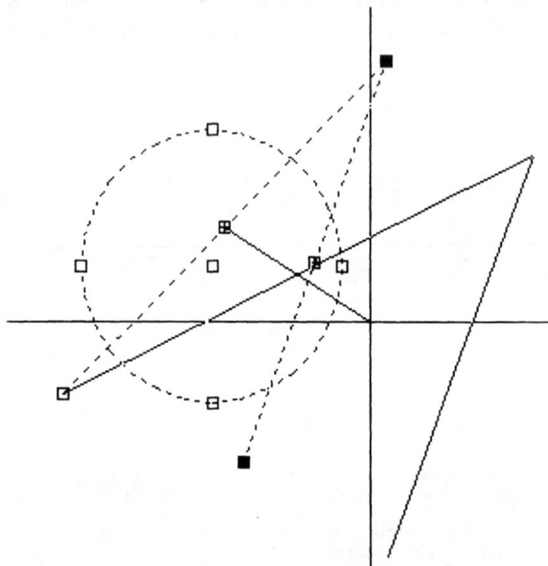

Figure A.2.12 Controlling grips and stretch option.

the line on the left to stretch the entities. The anchored line does not stretch, but the line on the left side does.

The Ddgrip command can be used to modify the color and size of grips. Also, the grip on an inserted block is usually the insertion point. The grips inside the block can be enabled by setting the enabling button in the Ddgrip dialogue box.

A.3 Dimensioning Hints

1. A dimension placed earlier in the drawing can be continued or used as a baseline by invoking the Continue or Baseline commands. If Continue or Baseline is selected and the previous dimension was a linear dimension, AutoCAD LT prompts `Second extension line or Return to select.` If the previous dimension was not linear or you press return, AutoCAD LT prompts you to select a linear dimension to use as the basis for the next dimension.
2. Diameter dimensioning is governed by the settings in Fig. A.3.1.
3. Setting the dimension Text Gap (Fig. 6.24) to 0 keeps text inside more often. If the text does go outside it keeps the text closer to the second extension line.
4. The Modify menu's Edit Dimension submenu (App. E, Fig. E.7.1) provides commands to change the value of dimension text (Change Text, Move Text, Rotate Text, and Update Dimensions).
5. The dimension command options are as follows:

`Draw` <pick> `Linear Dimension` <pick> `Horizontal` <pick> `First extension line origin or RETURN to select:` Pick a point <pick> `Second extension line origin:` <pick> Pick a point. <pick> `Dimension line location (Text/Angle):`

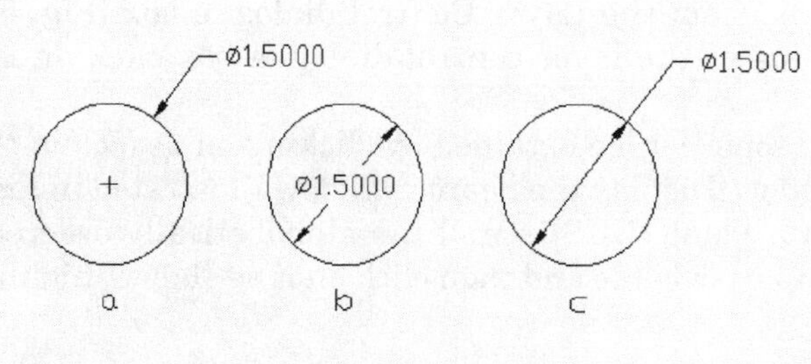

Figure A.3.1 Diameter dimensioning.

Figure A.3.1	Text location (see Fig. 6.20)	Dimension line (see Fig. 6.21)
a	Default	Force Interior Lines—off
b	Force Text Inside	Force Interior Lines—off
c	Default	Force Interior Lines—on

Normally the dimension line location is entered. If **a** (Angle) is entered AutoCAD LT responds with:

```
Enter text angle:
```

Enter an angle. AutoCAD then requests the text and places the text in the dimension line with the text printed on an angle using the preceding angle entered

If **t** (Text) is entered instead of a, AutoCAD LT requests the text and responds with "Dimension line location (Text/Angle)." You enter the text location (or a for Angle) and AutoCAD LT draws the dimension using the text entered.

A.4 Using AutoCAD LT's Help

Help is available in AutoCAD LT (or any other Windows application) by pressing the F1 key, choosing Help in the menu bar, or pressing the Help button in the a dialogue box. The following gives a brief overview of how to use the Help menu (Fig. A.4.1) in the menu bar:

```
Help <pick> How to use Help <pick>
```

The `Contents for How to Use Help` window, illustrated in Fig. A.4.2, is displayed. Items in green and underlined are topics on which you can get information by clicking on the item. To learn what the buttons at the top of the window mean scroll the contents list up until `Help Buttons` is on the screen, and then click on it. (If you don't know how to scroll, click on Scroll Through a Help Topic.) The Help Buttons screen is shown in Fig. A.4.3.

Press the `Contents` button to display the Contents help window shown in Fig. A.4.4. Click on `Full Menus` as show to see the contents for the full pull-down menus, illustrated in Fig. A.4.5.

To find help on layer control choose `Settings` in the full menu help window list. The Settings menu help window shown in Fig. A.4.6 is displayed. Click on `DDLMODES` in the text beside Layer Control . . . in the list, to display the layer control help window (Fig. A.4.7). The same help window is displayed by choosing Help . . . from the Layer Control dialogue box (Fig. 6.5). To get information on items in the layer control dialogue box click on `Layer Control`. Try it.

Information on a topic can be obtained by clicking on `Search` in the buttons bar in the Help window. Display the Search window illustrated in Fig. A.4.8. To get information on 3 Point (UCS), scroll the alphabetically ordered selection window until the topic is visible and then click on it as shown, highlighting the

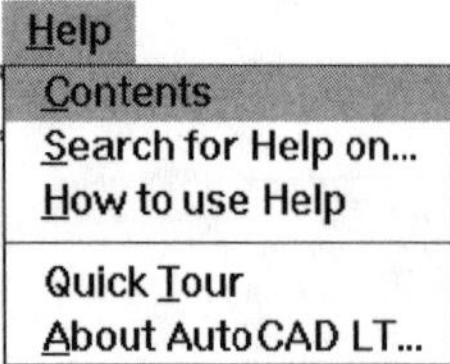

Figure A.4.1 Help menu.

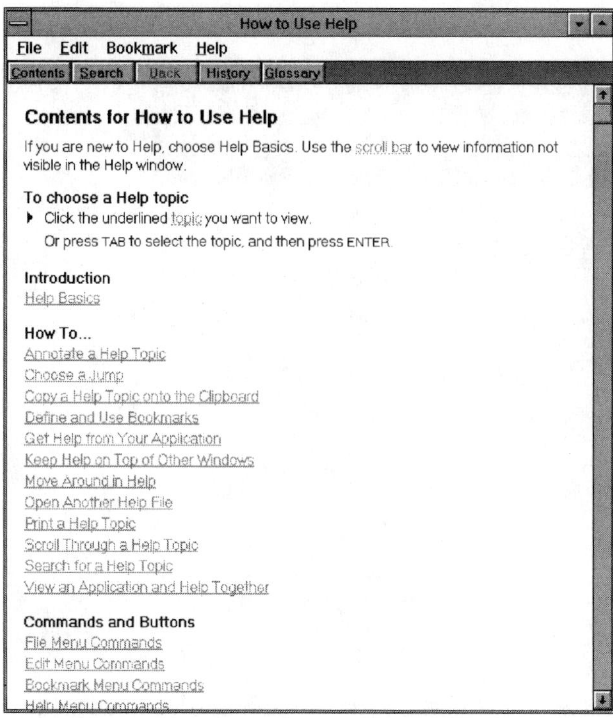

Figure A.4.2 How to use Help.

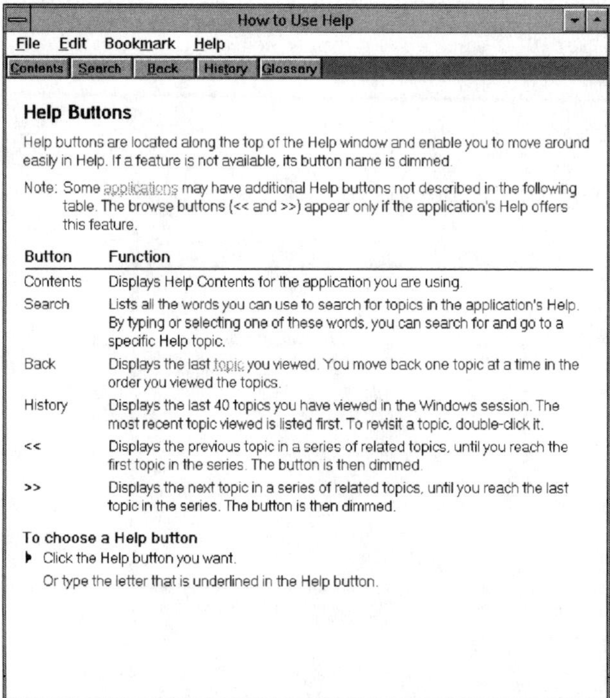

Figure A.4.3 Help buttons.

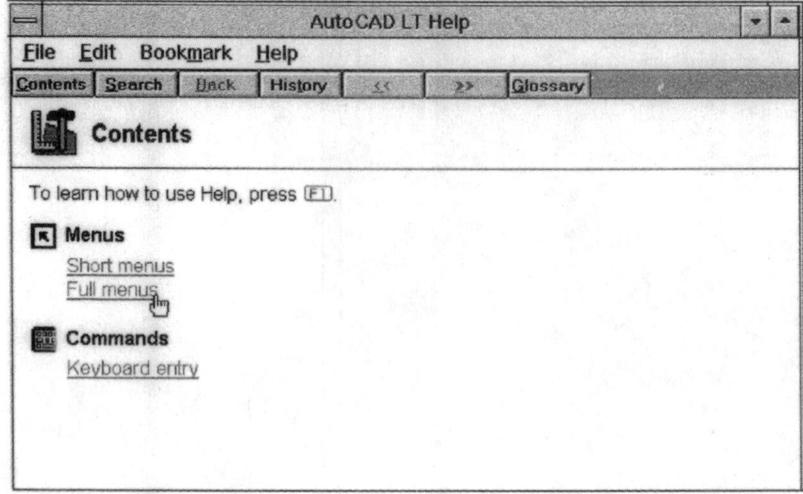

Figure A.4.4 Contents help window.

topic and moving it to the Show Topics window. Click the `Show Topics` button, and related topics (i.e., UCS Command) are listed in the related topics window. Click on Go To to get information on the topic. The same help window is displayed by choosing the following commands in AutoCAD LT's drawing window:

> `Assist` <pick> `Set UCS` <pick> `3 Point:` <pick> `Origin point <0,0,0>:` Press the F1 function key.

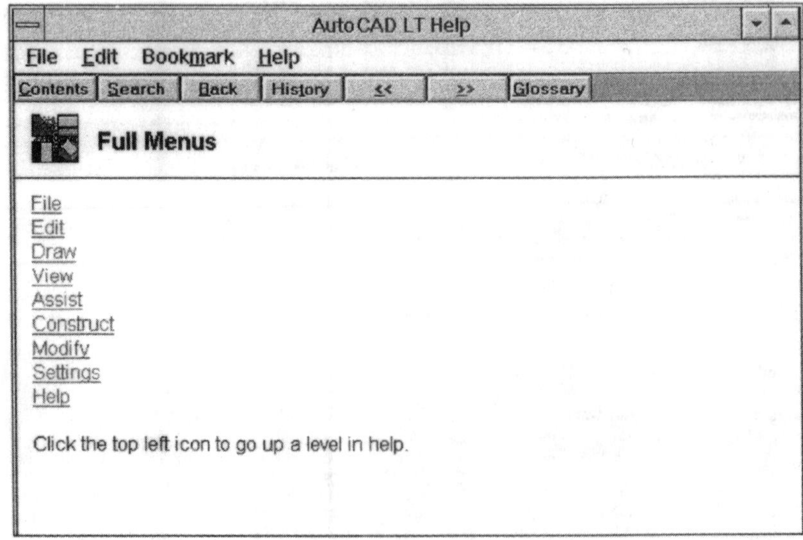

Figure A.4.5 Full menu help window.

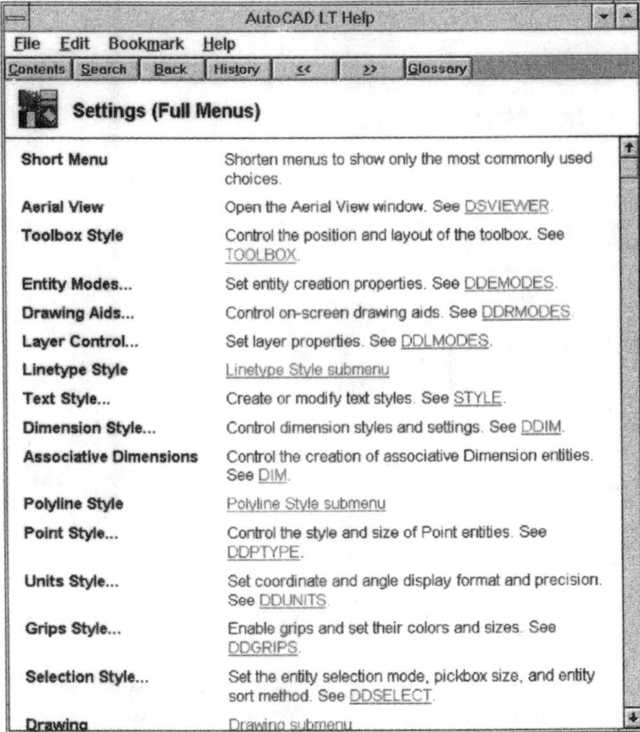

Figure A.4.6 Settings menu help window.

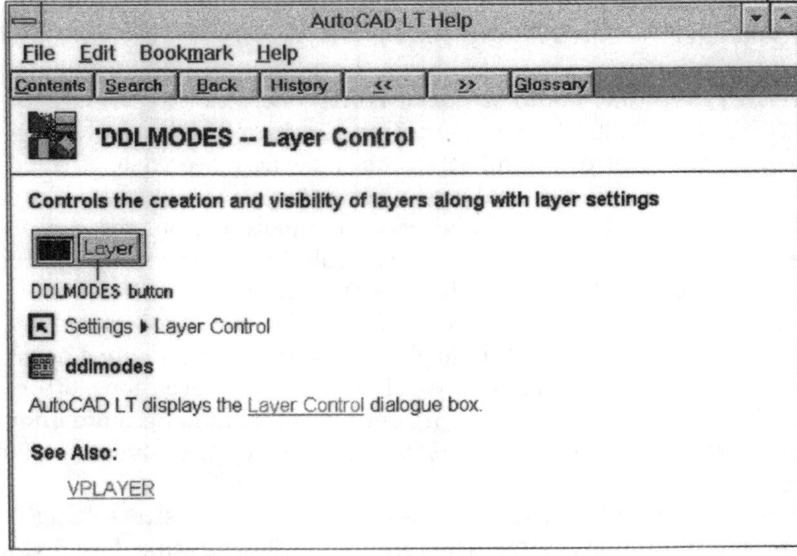

Figure A.4.7 Layer control help window.

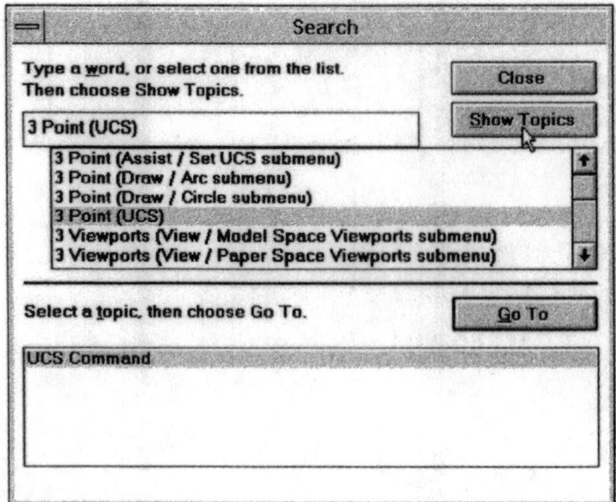

Figure A.4.8 Search help window.

A.5 Printer Problems

1. The procedure for installing system printer/plotter drivers is discussed in Chap. 7, Sec. 7.2. For more information refer to your Windows manual. If your plotting device is not supported by the standard Windows drivers, your printer/plotter manufacturer may be able to provide you with an appropriate driver.

2. The original HPGL printer/plotter driver shipped with Microsoft Windows 3.1 does not properly support AutoCAD LT (and other vector based software). Microsoft and Hewlitt-Packard are in the process of resolving this problem, and the version of AutoCAD LT you have may include an updated printer driver. Devices that may not plot correctly include: HP 7220, 7470, 7475, 7550, 7580, 7585, 7586, Colorpro, Draftpro, Draftpro DXL and EXL, and Draftmaster I. Other plotters emulating these devices are also affected. Autodesk has available software that provides an "interim" solution. If you have one of the mentioned plotters, and you have plotter problems contact Autodesk product support for the HPGL interim solution. Your printer/plotter manufacturer may also be able to provide you with a corrected driver.

3. If your plotter is not responding check that you have set the proper communications port for the printer in Window's Control Panel. Normally a parallel port, LPT, is used for printers and a serial port, COM, is used for plotters. Refer to your Windows manual and your printer/plotter manual for more information. Also check that your plotter/printer cable is correctly seated and that you have the correct cable for your plotter.

4. Truncated plots are often caused by an improper paper size setting in AutoCAD LT for your plotter/printer, or an incorrect plotting scale. Use AutoCAD LT's plot preview option prior to plotting (Chap. 7, Sec. 7.3).

5. If you are plotting from paper space and the plot appears out of scale, the drawing may actually be in model space (Chap. 13, Sec. 13.1.3).

6. If the plot is oriented wrong on the paper, check that you have set the rotation angle correctly, or that the sheet x- and y-sizes are entered correctly for your plotter/printer (Chap. 7, Sec. 7.3).

7. If your pens are skipping slow down the plotter speed.

8. Problems with line weights, missing arrow heads, pens not lifting from the paper between text letters, etc. are usually due to mixing units when specifying pen sizes and dimension units, i.e. MM dimension units and inch pen sizes (Chapt. 7, Sec. 7.3).

9. Proper maintenance of your printer/plotter can resolve many printing/plotting problems.

Appendix B

Plot Drawing Scale Factors

Scale	Scale factor	Scale	Scale factor
	Drawing units = meters (decimal)		
1:1	1000	1:30	33.33334
1:1.5	666.6667	1:40	25
1:2	500	1:50	20
1:2.5	400	1:100	10
1:3	333.3334	1:200	5
1:4	250	1:250	4
1:5	200	1:300	3.333334
1:10	100	1:400	2.5
1:15	66.66667	1:500	2
1:25	40		

Drawing units = millimeters (decimal)			
1:1	1.0	1:30	3.333334E-02
1:1.5	.6666667	1:40	.025
1:2	.5	1:50	.02
1:2.5	.4	1:100	.01
1:3	.3333334	1:200	.005
1:4	.25	1:250	.004
1:5	.2	1:300	3.333334E-03
1:10	.1	1:400	.0025
1:15	6.666667E-02	1:500	.002
1:25	.04		

Drawing units = feet (architecture)			
1⁄16″ = 1′0″	5.208334E-03	½″ = 1′0″	4.166667E-02
3⁄32″ = 1′0″	.0078125	¾″ = 1′0″	.0625
⅛″ = 1′0″	1.041667E-02	1″ = 1′0″	8.333334E-02
¼″ = 1′0″	2.083333E-02	1½″ = 1′0″	.125
⅜″ = 1′0″	.03125	3″ = 1′0″	.25

Drawing units = feet (engineering)

1″ = 1′0″	8.333334E-02	100″ = 1′0″	8.333333E-04
1.5″ = 1′0″	5.555556E-02	150″ = 1′0″	5.555556E-04
2″ = 1′0″	4.166667E-02	200″ = 1′0″	4.166667E-04
2.5″ = 1′0″	3.333334E-02	250″ = 1′0″	3.333334E-04
3″ = 1′0″	2.777778E-02	300″ = 1′0″	2.777778E-04
4″ = 1′0″	2.083333E-02	400″ = 1′0″	2.083333E-04
5″ = 1′0″	1.666667E-02	500″ = 1′0″	1.666667E-04
10″ = 1′0″	8.333334E-03	1000″ = 1′0″	8.333334E-05
15″ = 1′0″	5.555556E-03	1500″ = 1′0″	5.555556E-05
20″ = 1′0″	4.166667E-03	2000″ = 1′0″	4.166667E-05
25″ = 1′0″	3.333333E-03	2500″ = 1′0″	3.333333E-05
30″ = 1′0″	2.777778E-03	3000″ = 1′0″	2.777778E-05
40″ = 1′0″	2.083334E-03	4000″ = 1′0″	2.083334E-05
50″ = 1′0″	1.666667E-03	5000″ = 1′0″	1.666667E-05

Appendix

C

AutoCAD Scale and Text Heights

TABLE C.1 AutoCAD Scale and Text Heights—Imperial Units

A. Drawing units: Feet (AutoCAD decimal units)

			3/32″ Text		1/8″ Text		3/16″ Text	
Drawing scale	Hatch	Ltscale	Txt	Dimscale	Txt	Dimscale	Txt	Dimscale
1/8″ = 1′0″	8.00	6.00	0.75	4.17	1.00	5.56	1.50	8.33
3/16″ = 1′0″	5.33	4.00	0.50	2.78	0.67	3.70	1.00	5.56
1/4″ = 1′0″	4.00	3.00	0.38	2.08	0.50	2.78	0.75	4.17
5/16″ = 1′0″	3.20	2.40	0.30	1.67	0.40	2.22	0.60	3.33
3/8″ = 1′0″	2.67	2.00	0.25	1.39	0.33	1.85	0.50	2.78
1/2″ = 1′0″	2.00	1.50	0.19	1.04	0.25	1.39	0.38	2.08
5/8″ = 1′0″	1.60	1.20	0.15	0.83	0.20	1.11	0.30	1.67
3/4″ = 1′0″	1.33	1.00	0.13	0.69	0.17	0.93	0.25	1.39
7/8″ = 1′0″	1.14	0.86	0.11	0.60	0.14	0.79	0.21	1.19
1″ = 1′0″	1.00	0.75	0.09	0.52	0.13	0.69	0.19	1.04
1.5″ = 1′0″	0.67	0.50	0.06	0.35	0.08	0.46	0.13	0.69
2″ = 1′0″	0.50	0.38	0.05	0.26	0.06	0.35	0.09	0.52
1/4 size	0.33	0.25	0.03	0.17	0.04	0.23	0.06	0.35
1/2 size	0.17	0.13	0.02	0.09	0.02	0.12	0.03	0.17
Full size	0.08	0.06	0.01	0.04	0.01	0.06	0.02	0.09

B. Drawing units: AutoCAD architectural or engineering units

			3/32″ Text		1/8″ Text		3/16″ Text	
Drawing scale	Hatch	Ltscale	Txt	Dimscale	Txt	Dimscale	Txt	Dimscale
1/8″ = 1′0″	96.00	72.00	9.00	50.00	12.00	66.67	18.00	100.00
3/16″ = 1′0″	64.00	48.00	6.00	33.33	8.00	44.44	12.00	66.67
1/4″ = 1′0″	48.00	36.00	4.50	25.00	6.00	33.33	9.00	50.00
5/16″ = 1′0″	38.40	28.80	3.60	20.00	4.80	26.67	7.20	40.00
3/8″ = 1′0″	32.00	24.00	3.00	16.67	4.00	22.22	6.00	33.33
1/2″ = 1′0″	24.00	18.00	2.25	12.50	3.00	16.67	4.50	25.00
5/8″ = 1′0″	19.20	14.40	1.80	10.00	2.40	13.33	3.60	20.00
3/4″ = 1′0″	16.00	12.00	1.50	8.33	2.00	11.11	3.00	16.67
7/8″ = 1′0″	13.71	10.29	1.29	7.14	1.71	9.52	2.57	14.29
1″ = 1′0″	12.00	9.00	1.13	6.25	1.50	8.33	2.25	12.50
1.5″ = 1′0″	8.00	6.00	0.75	4.17	1.00	5.56	1.50	8.33
2″ = 1′0″	6.00	4.50	0.56	3.13	0.75	4.17	1.13	6.25
1/4 size	4.00	3.00	0.38	2.08	0.50	2.78	0.75	4.17
1/2 size	2.00	1.50	0.19	1.04	0.25	1.39	0.38	2.08
Full size	1.00	0.75	0.09	0.52	0.13	0.69	0.19	1.04

TABLE C.1 AutoCAD Scale and Text Heights—Imperial Units (*Continued*)

C. Drawing units: Engineering (feet) (AutoCAD decimal units)

			3/32″ Text		1/8″ Text		3/16″ Text	
Drawing scale	Hatch	Ltscale	Txt	Dimscale	Txt	Dimscale	Txt	Dimscale
1:3000	250.00	187.50	23.44	130.21	31.25	173.61	46.88	260.42
1:2500	208.33	156.25	19.53	108.51	26.04	144.68	39.06	217.01
1:2000	166.67	125.00	15.63	86.81	20.83	115.74	31.25	173.61
1:1500	125.00	93.75	11.72	65.10	15.63	86.81	23.44	130.21
1:1250	104.17	78.13	9.77	54.25	13.02	72.34	19.53	108.51
1:1000	83.33	62.50	7.81	43.40	10.42	57.87	15.63	86.81
1:750	62.50	46.88	5.86	32.55	7.81	43.40	11.72	65.10
1:600	50.00	37.50	4.69	26.04	6.25	34.72	9.38	52.08
1:500	41.67	31.25	3.91	21.70	5.21	28.94	7.81	43.40
1:400	33.33	25.00	3.13	17.36	4.17	23.15	6.25	34.72
1:300	25.00	18.75	2.34	13.02	3.13	17.36	4.69	26.04
1:200	16.67	12.50	1.56	8.68	2.08	11.57	3.13	17.36
1:100	8.33	6.25	0.78	4.34	1.04	5.79	1.56	8.68
1:50	4.17	3.13	0.39	2.17	0.52	2.89	0.78	4.34
1:25	2.08	1.56	0.20	1.09	0.26	1.45	0.39	2.17
1:20	1.67	1.25	0.16	0.87	0.21	1.16	0.31	1.74

TABLE C.2 AutoCAD Scale and Text Heights—SI Units

A. Drawing units: Meters, English measurement system set

			2.5-mm Text		3-mm Text	
Drawing scale	Hatch	Ltscale	Txt	Dimscale	Txt	Dimscale
1:10	0.25	0.19	0.03	0.14	0.03	0.17
1:20	0.51	0.38	0.05	0.28	0.06	0.33
1:30	0.76	0.57	0.08	0.42	0.09	0.50
1:40	1.02	0.76	0.10	0.56	0.12	0.67
1:50	1.27	0.95	0.13	0.69	0.15	0.83
1:100	2.54	1.91	0.25	1.39	0.30	1.67
1:200	5.08	3.81	0.50	2.78	0.60	3.33
1:250	6.35	4.76	0.63	3.47	0.75	4.17
1:300	7.62	5.72	0.75	4.17	0.90	5.00
1:400	10.16	7.62	1.00	5.56	1.20	6.67
1:500	12.70	9.53	1.25	6.94	1.50	8.33
1:750	19.05	14.29	1.88	10.42	2.25	12.50
1:1000	25.40	19.05	2.50	13.89	3.00	16.67
1:2000	50.80	38.10	5.00	27.78	6.00	33.33
1:5000	127.00	95.25	12.50	69.44	15.00	83.33

B. Drawing units: Millimeters, English measurement system set

			2.5-mm Text		3-mm Text	
Drawing scale	Hatch	Ltscale	Txt	Dimscale	Txt	Dimscale
1:1	25	19	2.5	14	3.0	17
1:2	51	38	5.0	28	6.0	33
1:3	76	57	7.5	42	9.0	50
1:4	102	76	10.0	56	12.0	67
1:5	127	95	12.5	69	15.0	83
1:10	254	191	25.0	139	30.0	167
1:20	508	381	50.0	278	60.0	333
1:50	1270	953	125.0	694	150.0	833
1:100	2540	1905	250.0	1389	300.0	1667
1:200	5080	3810	500.0	2778	600.0	3333
1:250	6350	4763	625.0	3472	750.0	4167
1:300	7620	5715	750.0	4167	900.0	5000
1:400	10160	7620	1000.0	5556	1200.0	6667
1:500	12700	9525	1250.0	6944	1500.0	8333
1:750	19050	14288	1875.0	10417	2250.0	12500

Appendix

D

Contour.bas Program

```
10   CLS:KEY OFF
20   PRINT TAB(25);:PRINT"CONTOUR CALCULATION PROGRAM ":COLOR 7,0:PRINT
30   PRINT"The output for this program is printed on a lineprinter, Turn
     the lineprinter on NOW."
40   PRINT:COLOR 0,7:PRINT "Press any key to continue":COLOR 7,0
50   C$=INKEY$:IF C$="" THEN 50
60   LPRINT TAB(10) "ELEVATION";TAB(25) "X-DIST.";TAB(40) "Y-DIST"
100  CLS:INPUT "Distance between rows of grid";DROW
110  PRINT:INPUT "Distance between columns of grid";DCOL
120  PRINT:INPUT "Enter number of rows in grid";NROW
130  PRINT:INPUT "Enter number of columns in grid";NCOL
140  PRINT:INPUT "Enter contour interval";UNIT:PRINT
150  DIM EL(NROW,NCOL)
160  FOR I=1 TO NROW
170    FOR J=1 TO NCOL
180    PRINT"Enter elev. of row";I;"column";J;":";:INPUT EL(I,J)
190    NEXT J
200  NEXT I
210  FOR I=1 TO NROW
220    FOR J=1 TO NCOL-1
230    ELL=EL(I,J):ELR=EL(I,J+1)
240    IF ELL=ELR AND ELL<>INT(ELL) THEN 340
250    IF ELL=ELR THEN XDIST=DCOL*(J-1):YDIST=DROW*(I-1):
       ELEV=ELL:GOSUB 500:IFJ=NCOL-1 THEN XDIST=DCOL*(J):
       YDIST=DROW*(I-1):GOSUB 500
260    IF ELL<ELR THEN LO=ELL:HI=ELR ELSE LO=ELR:HI=ELL
270    ELEV=INT(LO+.99)
280      WHILE ELEV<=INT(HI):IF ELEV=HI AND ELR>ELL AND J<NCOL-1 THEN 320
290      XDIST=(ELEV-LO)/(HI-LO)*DCOL:YDIST=DROW*(I-1)
300      IF ELL<ELR THEN XDIST=XDIST+DCOL*(J-1) ELSE XDIST=DCOL*(J)-XDIST
310      GOSUB 500
320      ELEV=ELEV+UNIT
330      WEND
340    NEXT J
```

```
350  IF I=NROW THEN 480
360   FOR J=1 TO NCOL-1
370   ELB=EL(I,J):ELT=EL(I+1,J)
380   IF INT(ELB)=INT(ELT) THEN 470
390   IF ELB<ELT THEN LO=ELB:HI=ELT ELSE LO=ELT:HI=ELB
400   ELEV=INT(LO+1)
410     WHILE ELEV<=INT(HI):IF ELEV=HI THEN 450
420     YDIST=(ELEV-LO)/(HI-LO)*DROW:XDIST=DCOL*(J-1)
430     IF ELB<ELT THEN YDIST=YDIST+DROW*(I-1) ELSE YDIST=DROW*(I)-YDIST
440     GOSUB 500
450     ELEV=ELEV+UNIT
460     WEND
470   NEXT J
480  NEXT I
490  END
500  LPRINT TAB(10) ELEV;TAB(25) XDIST;TAB(40)YDIST
510  RETURN
```

Appendix

E

AutoCAD LT Menu Bar Tables

File	Edit	Draw	View	Assist	Construct	Modify	Settings	Help
E1	E2	E3	E4	E5	E6	E7	E8	E9

The following tables are based on Long Menu set in The Settings menu (Fig. E.8). (If Short Menu is displayed in the listing, Long Menu is set.)

TABLE E.1 File Menu

Menu command		Description
New . . .		Creates new drawing
Open . . .		Opens existing drawing
Save . . .		Saves current drawing using default file name; does not exit drawing
Save As . . .		Saves current drawing—you specify directory and file name; does not exit drawing
Print/Plot . . .		Plots drawing
Import/Export >	View Slide	Views a single slide
	DXF In . . .	Imports a DXF file
	WMF In . . .	Imports a WMF file
	WMF In Options . . .	Controls display of solid fills and wide lines in WMF files
	Make Slide . . .	Makes a slide of current screen
	DXF Out . . .	Saves current drawing in DXF format
	Block Out . . .	Defines a block and writes it to disk
	Attributes Out . . .	Writes attribute information to a file
	PostScript Out . . .	Create a PostScript file from current drawing
	WMF Out . . .	Saves entities to a WMF file
	BMP Out . . .	Creates a bitmap image of screen
Run Script . . .		Runs a script file
Unlock Files . . .		Unlocks files
Preferences . . .		Customizes AutoCAD window interface and AutoCAD environment
Exit . . .		Exits AutoCAD

TABLE E.2 Edit Menu

Menu command	Description
Undo	Undoes last command
Redo	Redoes an undo
Copy Image	Copies selected area of screen to clipboard in Windows Bitmap format
Copy Vectors	Copies selected drawing entities to Window's clipboard in drawing and Windows metafile format
Copy Embed	Copies entities of drawing to clipboard to embed in another document
Copy Link	Links entities of drawing to another document
Paste	Pastes image from clipboard into AutoCAD LT
Paste Command	Copies text from clipboard to AutoCAD LT command line
Text Window	Turns AutoCAD LT text window on or off

TABLE E.3 Draw Menu

Menu command		Description
Line		Draws multiple line segments
Arc >	(See Fig. E.3.1)	
Circle >	Center,Radius	Draws circle based on center point and radius
	Tan,Tan,Radius	Draws circle based on two entities the circle is tangent too and the circle radius
	3 Point	Draws circle based on three points on the circumference
Text		Draws text dynamically in drawing screen
Polyline		Creates 2-D polylines
Point		Draws a single point
Hatch . . .		Hatches an object
Solid		Draws a filled triangle or quadrilateral
Donut		Draws a filled circle or ring
Ellipse		Draws an ellipse
Polygon		Draws a 2-D polygon
Rectangle		Draws a rectangle
Double Line		Draws double lines
Insert Block . . .		Inserts a block
External Reference >	(See Fig. E.3.2)	
Linear Dimensions >	(See Fig. E.3.3)	
Ordinate Dimensions >	(See Fig. E.3.4)	
Radial Dimensions >	(See Fig. E.3.5)	
Angular Dimensions		Generates a dimension arc with extension lines
Leader		Constructs a complex leader with dimension text

TABLE E.3.1 Draw/Arc Submenu

Menu command	Description
Start,Center,End	Draws arc using start, center, and end points
Start,Center,Angle	Draws arc using start point and center point spanning an angle
Start,End,Angle	Draws arc using start point, end point, and angle
Center,Start,End	Draws arc using center, start and end points
Center,Start,Angle	Draws arc using center point, start point, and angle
3 Point	Draws arc using 3 points
Continue Line/Arc	Draws an arc from the last point on a line or arc

TABLE E.3.2 Draw/External Reference Submenu

Menu command		Description
Attach		Attaches Xref
Bind		Changes an Xref to a permanent entity in the drawing
Detach		Removes and erases an Xref from the drawing
Reload		Updates an Xref
Change Path		Edits an Xref path
List?		Lists Xref information
Retain Settings		Current drawings On/Off, Freeze, Thaw, color, and linetype settings are saved with current drawing (Visretain =1)
Bind Symbols >	Block	Binds a dependent block to drawing
	Dim Style	Binds a dependent dimension style to the drawing
	Layer	Binds a dependent layer to drawing
	Linetype	Binds a dependent linetype to drawing
	Text Style	Binds a dependent text style to drawing

TABLE E.3.3 Draw/Linear Dimension Submenu

Menu command		Description
Linear Dimensions >	Horizontal	Generates a linear dimension with a horizontal dimension line
	Vertical	Generates a linear dimension with a vertical dimension line
	Aligned	Generates a linear dimension with a dimension line aligned with selected extension line origins
	Rotated	Generates a linear dimension with dimension line at specified angle
	Baseline	Continues a linear dimension using the first extension line of a previous dimension
	Continue	Continues a linear dimension from the second extension line of a dimension

TABLE E.3.4 Draw/Ordinate Dimensions Submenu

Menu command		Description
Ordinate >	Automatic	Dimensions an x or y coordinate of a feature
	X-Datum	Dimensions the x coordinate of a feature
	Y-Datum	Dimensions the y coordinate of a feature

TABLE E.3.5 Draw/Radial Dimensions Submenu

Menu command		Description
Radial >	Diameter	Dimensions the diameter of a circle or arc
	Radius	Dimensions the radius of a circle or arc
	Center Mark	Draws center mark or center lines of a circle or arc

TABLE E.4 View Menu

Menu command		Description
Zoom >	(See Fig. E.4.1)	
Pan		Moves display window
View >	Delete	Deletes a saved view
	Restore	Restores a saved view to screen
	Save	Saves current viewport display
	Window	Saves rectangular portion of current display
	List?	Displays list of named views
Redraw		Redraws and cleans up the screen
Regen		Regenerates the entire drawing
Paper Space		Turns Tilemode on/off
Viewports >	(See Fig. E.4.2)	
Viewport Layer Visibility >	(See Fig. E.4.3)	
3-D Viewpoint >	Axes	Set viewpoint using axis tripod
	Rotate	Set viewpoint using X and X,Y angles
	Vector	Set viewpoint by entering 3-D coordinates
3-D Viewpoint Presets >	(See Fig. E.4.4)	
3-D Plan View >	Current UCS	Regenerates a plan view of current UCS
	World UCS	Regenerates a plan view of world UCS
	Named UCS	Regenerates a plan view of a named UCS
3-D Dynamic View		Creates a perspective view of drawing
Hide		Redraws object with hidden lines temporarily removed
Shade >	(See Fig. E.4.5)	

TABLE E.4.1 View/Zoom Submenu

Menu command	Description
All	Zooms to screen or viewport limits
Center	Zooms on area defined by selected center point
Extents	Zooms to extents of drawn entities
Previous	Zooms to previous screen
Window	Zooms on selected window
Scale	Zooms to a specified magnification factor

TABLE E.4.2*a* View/Viewports Submenu (Model Space)

Menu command	Description
Single	Causes graphics to revert to a single viewport
2 Viewports	Creates two viewports
3 Viewports	Creates three viewports
4 Viewports	Creates four viewports
Join	Joins two adjacent viewports into one
Save	Names and saves a viewport configuration
Restore	Restores a named viewport configuration
Delete	Deletes a named viewport configuration
List?	Lists named viewport configurations

TABLE E.4.2*b* View/Viewports Submenu (Paper Space)

Menu command	Description
Make Viewport	Creates a rectangular viewport
Fit Viewport	Creates a viewport sized to fill the graphics area
2 Viewports	Creates two viewports
3 Viewports	Creates three viewports
4 Viewports	Creates four viewports
Restore	Creates viewports in paper space using viewport configurations saved in model space
Viewport ON	Turns a viewport on and regenerates its model space view
Viewport OFF	Turns a viewport off clearing its model space view
Hideplot	Instructs AutoCAD LT to perform hidden line removal when plotting the contents of the viewport

TABLE E.4.3 View/Viewport Layer Visibility Submenu

Menu command	Description
Freeze	Freeze named layers in viewports in paper space
Thaw	Thaw named layers in viewports in paper space
Reset	Reset the default visibility of layers in viewports in paper space
New freeze	Create new layers frozen in all viewports in paper space
VP Default Visibility	Set default visibility of layers for new viewports in paper space
List?	List the names of frozen layers in a viewport in paper space

TABLE E.4.4 View/3D Viewport Presets Submenu

Menu command	Description
Top	Sets current isometric plane to top face
Front	Sets current isometric plane to front face
Left	Sets current isometric plane to left face
Right	Sets current isometric plane to right face
Back	Sets current isometric plane to back face
Iso View SW	Sets viewpoint from lower-left corner (–1,–1,1)
Iso View SE	Sets viewpoint from lower-right corner (1,–1,1)
Iso View NE	Sets viewpoint from upper-right corner (1,1,1)
Iso View NW	Sets viewpoint from upper-left corner (–1,1,1)

TABLE E.4.5 View/Shade Submenu

Menu command	Description
256 Color	Creates shaded face with no edge highlighting
256 Color Edge Highlight	Creates shaded face with edges highlighted in background color
16 Color Hidden Line	Simulates a hidden line rendering
16 Color Filled	Draws faces in original color without shading

TABLE E.5 Assist Menu

Menu command		Description
Object Snap . . .		Sets running object snap
Select >	Last	Selects most recently created visible entities
	All	Selects all entities not on frozen or locked layers
	Fence	Selects entities that touch a selection fence
	WPolygon	Selects entities enclosed by a window selection polygon
	CPolygon	Selects entities within and touching a crossing selection polygon
	Add	Places select object prompt in add mode
	Remove	Places select object prompt in remove mode
	Previous	Selects the most recent selection set in response to select objects
XYZ Filters >	(See Fig. E.5.1)	
Preset UCS . . .		Switches coordinate system to a preset UCS; i.e., top, bottom, left, right, front, and back
Named UCS . . .		Switches coordinate system to a named UCS
Set UCS >	(See Fig. E.5.2)	
UCS icon		Allows setting of UCS icon
ID Point		Returns coordinates of a selected point
Distance		Returns distance between two points
Area		Returns the area and perimeter enclosed by a sequence of points or defined by a circle or polyline
List		Displays data stored for an entity
Time		Displays current status of AutoCAD time variables

TABLE E.5.1 Assist/XYZ Filters Submenu

Menu command	Description
.X	Allows entry of x coordinate isolated from yz coordinates
.Y	Allows entry of y coordinate isolated from yz coordinates
.Z	Allows entry of z coordinate isolated from yz coordinates
.XY	Allows entry of xy coordinates isolated from z coordinate
.XZ	Allows entry of xz coordinates isolated from y coordinate
.YZ	Allows entry of yz coordinates isolated from x coordinate

TABLE E.5.2 Assist/Set UCS Submenu

Menu command	Description
World	Sets current UCS to World Coordinate System
Origin	Shifts origin of current coordinate system
Z Axis Vector	Defines a UCS based on a new origin and *z* axis
3 Point	Defines a UCS based on a new origin and direction of its positive *x* and *y* axis
Entity	Defines a UCS by pointing to an entity
View	Defines a UCS with its *xy* plane parallel to the computer screen
X Axis Rotate	Rotates UCS about *x* axis
Y Axis Rotate	Rotates UCS about *y* axis
Z Axis Rotate	Rotates UCS about *z* axis
Previous	Restores the previous UCS
Restore	Restores a named UCS
Save	Saves and names the current UCS
Delete	Deletes a named UCS
List	Displays a list of named UCSs

TABLE E.6 Construct Menu

Menu command	Description
Array	Creates a rectangular or circular array of selected objects
Copy	Creates a copy of a selected object
Mirror	Mirrors a selected object about a specified axis
Offset	Creates a copy of a line or curve, parallel to it at a specified distance
Chamfer	Trims two intersecting lines a specified distance from the intersection and connects the trimmed ends with a line
Fillet	Constructs an arc of specified radius between two lines, arcs, or circles
Make Block . . .	Defines a block using a dialogue box
Define Attribute . . .	Associates text with a block using a dialogue box

TABLE E.7 Modify Menu

Menu command		Description
Erase		Invokes Erase command
Oops		Cancels last erase command
Move		Moves an object
Rotate		Rotates an object
Scale		Alters size of an object
Stretch		Stretches a portion of an object
Break		Erases part of a line, circle, arc, or polyline
Extend		Extends a line, arc, or polyline to meet another object
Trim		Trims a portion of an entity extending past a specified boundary
Change Point		Modifies location and properties of objects
Change Properties		Modifies properties of objects
Rename . . .		Renames named objects
Edit text		Edits text and attribute definitions
Edit Polyline		Edits 2-D and 3-D polylines
Edit Dimensions >	(See Fig. E.7.1)	
Edit Attribute		Edits attributes
Explode		Breaks a block or polyline into its constituent parts
Purge >	Block	Removes unused Blocks from drawing database
	Dimension Style	Removes unused Dimension Styles from drawing database
	Layer	Removes unused Layers from drawing database
	Text Style	Removes unused text Styles from drawing database
	All	Removes all unused named objects from drawing database

TABLE E.7.1 Modify/Edit Dimensions Submenu

Menu command	Description
Change Text	Changes existing dimension text
Home Position	Returns moved or stretched dimension text to its original location
Move Text	Adjusts dimension text location and orientation
Rotate Text	Changes orientation of dimension text of associative dimensions
Oblique Dimensions	Modifies dimensions at specified oblique angle
Update Dimensions	Updates dimension entities

TABLE E.8 Settings Menu

Menu command		Description
Short Menu		Changes Settings menu to short listing
Aerial View		Displays aerial view window
Toolbox Style		Controls position and layout of toolbox
Entity Modes . . .		Sets entity creation properties
Drawing Aides . . .		Sets on-screen drawing aids
Layer Control . . .		Sets layer properties
Linetype Style >	Create	Creates a new linetype
	Load	Loads linetype files
	Set	Sets a new current linetype
	List?	Lists available linetypes
	Linetype Scale	Sets the global linetype scale
	Pspace LT Scale	Sets a viewport linetype scale in paper space
Text Style . . .		Creates or modifies text styles
Dimension Style . . .		Sets dimension styles and variables
Associative Dimensions		Toggles associative dimensioning on/off
Polyline Style >	(See Fig. E.8.1)	
Point Style . . .		Sets style and size of point entities
Units Style . . .		Sets coordinate and angle display format and precision
Grips Style . . .		Enables grips and their colors and sizes
Selection Style . . .		Sets the entity selection mode, pickbox size, and entity sort method
Drawing >	Base	Specifies the insertion base point for the current drawing
	Limits	Specifies the drawing boundaries

TABLE E.8.1 Settings/Polyline Style Submenu

Menu command	Description
Linetype Generation	Generates the linetype in a continuous pattern through the vertices of a polyline
Spline Frame	Controls the display of the original polyline frame on which the spline curve is based
Spline Segments	Controls the fineness or coarseness of a spline approximation
Quadratic B-Spline	Generates a quadratic B-spline
Cubic B-Spline	Generates a cubic B-spline

TABLE E.9 Help Menu

Menu command	Description
Contents	Starts AutoCAD for Windows Help
Search for Help on . . .	Searches for Help topics by keyword
How to use Help	Explains how to use on-line Help system
Quick Tour	Provides an overview of AutoCAD LT features and capabilities
About AutoCAD LT	Displays information about the loaded version for AutoCAD

TABLE E.10 Keyboard Shortcuts

Function key	Other keys	Description
F1		AutoCAD for Windows Help
F2		Toggles text screen
F4	Ctrl + T	Toggles Tablet on/off
F5	Ctrl + E	Toggles ISO (Isometric) planes
F6	Ctrl + D	Toolbar coordinate display control
F7	Ctrl + G	Toggles Grid mode on/off
F8	Ctrl + O	Toggles Otho mode on/off
F9	Ctrl + B	Toggles Snap mode on/off
F10<return>		Displays File menu
	Ctrl + C	Cancels current command

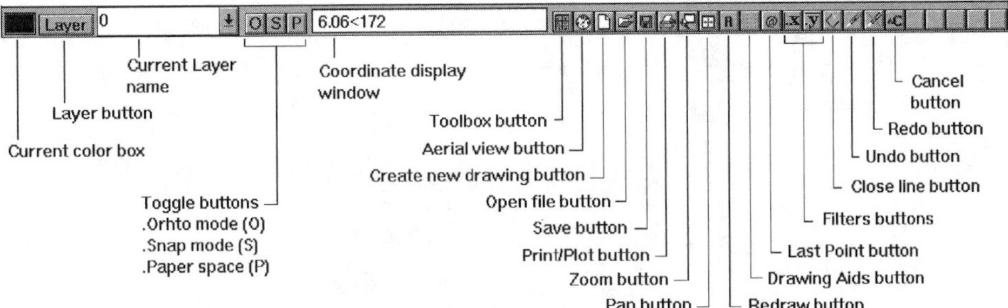

Figure E.11 AutoCAD LT Buttons bar.

Appendix

F

AutoCAD Windows Menu Bar Tables

File	Edit	View	Assist	Draw	Construct	Modify	Settings	Render	Model	Help
F1	F2	F3	F4	F5	F6	F7	F8	F9	F10	F11

TABLE F.1 File Menu

Menu command			Description
New . . .			Creates new drawing
Open . . .			Opens existing drawing
Save . . .			Saves current drawing; does not exit drawing
Save As . . .			Saves current drawing—you specify a directory and file name; does not exit drawing
Save DIB			Saves as device independent bitmap file
Recover			Recovers damaged drawing
Print/Plot . . .			Plots drawing
ASE	>		AutoCAD SQL Extension submenus
Import/Export	>		Import/Export submenus
Xref	>	Attach . . .	Attaches Xref
		Detach	Removes Xref
		Reload	Updates Xref
		List	Lists Xref information
		Change path	Edits Xref path
Preferences . . .			Customizes AutoCAD window interface and AutoCAD environment
Configure			Configures AutoCAD
Compile . . .			Compiles shape and font files
Utilities . . .			Lists, deletes, copies, unlocks, and renames files
Applications . . .			Loads AutoLISP and ADS files
Exit AutoCAD . . .			Exits AutoCAD
Find File . . .			Searches for files by specified data

TABLE F.2 Edit Menu

Menu command	Description
Undo	Undoes last command
Redo	Redoes an undo
Copy Image	Copies selected area of screen to clipboard in Windows Bitmap format
Copy Vectors	Copies selected drawing entities to Window's clipboard in drawing and Windows metafile format
Copy Embed	Copies entities of drawing to clipboard to embed in another document
Copy Link	Links entities of drawing to another document
Paste	Pastes image from clipboard into AutoCAD
Paste Command	Copies text from clipboard to AutoCAD command line
Text Window	Turns AutoCAD text window on or off
DDE >	Dynamic Data Exchange menus used to link drawing data with other Window applications such as a spreadsheet
Select >	See Fig. F.2.1

TABLE F.2.1 Edit/Select Submenu

Menu command	Description
Point	Adds a single selected object to selection set
Window	Adds all entities that lie entirely within selection window to selection set
Last	Adds last created entity to selection set
Crossing	Adds all entities within or crossed by selection window to selection set
All	Adds all entities not on frozen or locked layers to selection set
Fence	Adds all entities crossed by or touching selection fence to selection set
WPolygon	Adds all entities completely within a selection polygon to selection set
CPolygon	Adds all entities within or crossed by a selection polygon to selection set
Add	Toggles Add mode on to allow adding entities to selection set
Remove	Toggles Remove on to allow removal of entities from selection set
Multiple	Selects multiple objects in single search
Previous	Uses entities stored in selection set for current operation

TABLE F.3 View Menu

Menu command			Description
Redraw			Redraws current viewport
Redraw All			Redraws all viewports
Zoom	>	Zoom submenu (See Fig. F.3.1)	
Pan			Moves display window
Tilemode			Toggles Tilemode on/off
Toggle Viewport			Turn a viewport on by cycling through active viewports
Model Space			Turns model space mode on
Paper space			Turns paper space mode on
Mview	>	MView submenu (See Fig. F.3.2)	
Set View	>	Set View submenus (See Fig. F.3.3)	
Layout	>	MV Setup	Set up drawing title block, viewports, scale factor
		Tiled Viewports . . .	Displays Tiled Viewport Layout dialogue box if Tilemode is on

TABLE F.3.1 View/Zoom Submenu

Menu command	Description
Window	Zooms on selected window
Dynamic	Zooms on area defined dynamically by view box
Previous	Zooms to previous view
All	Zooms to screen or viewport limits
Extents	Zooms to extents of drawn entities
Vmax	Zooms to maximum of viewport's virtual screen without forcing a regeneration

TABLE F.3.2 View/Mview Submenu

Menu command	Description
Create Viewport	Issues MVIEW command
Viewport ON	Turns selected viewport on, causing regen
Viewport OFF	Turns selected viewport off, removing display from viewport
Hideplot	Removes hidden lines for objects in current viewport during paper space plot
Fit Viewport	Creates single viewport to fit current paper space view
2Viewports	Creates two viewports in specified area
3Viewports	Creates three viewports in specified area
4Viewports	Creates four viewports in specified area
Vplayer	Sets viewport visibility for existing and new layers

TABLE F.3.3 View/Set View Submenu

Menu command			Description
Dview			Defines perspective views dynamically
Plan View	>	Current UCS	Sets coordinate system to current UCS
		World	Sets coordinate system to World UCS
		Named UCS	Sets coordinate system to predefined UCS
Viewpoint	>	Axes	Sets viewpoint using axes tripod
		Presets . . .	Displays Viewpoint Presets dialogue box
		Set Vpoint	Invokes Vpoint command
Named View . . .			Displays View Control dialogue box

TABLE F.4 Assist Menu

Menu command			Description
Cancel			Cancels current command
Object Filters . . .			Displays Entity Selection Filters dialogue box
Object Snap	>	Center	Snaps to center of arc or circle
		Endpoint	Snaps to closest endpoint
		Insert	Snaps to insertion point of block/text/shape/attribute
		Intersection	Snaps to intersection of line, arc, or circle
		Midpoint	Snaps to midpoint of arc or line
		Nearest	Snaps to nearest point of line, arc, circle, or point
		Node	Snaps to node point
		Perpendicular	Snaps perpendicular to arc, line, or circle
		Quadrant	Snaps to quadrant point
		Tangent	Snaps to tangent point
		None	Turns off OSNAP mode
Close			Closes line and polyline command
Inquiry	>	List	Lists entity data
		Status	Lists drawing statistics and modes
		Area	Computes area of polygon, polyline, or circle
		Distance	Lists distance/angle between two points
		ID Point	Lists coordinates of point
Calculator			Loads a geometric calculator

TABLE F.5 Draw Menu

Menu command			Description
Line	>	Segments 1 Segment Double Line Sketch	Draws multiple-line segments Draws a single-line segment Draws continuous double-line segments and arcs Draws freehand
Arc	>	(See Fig. F.5.1)	
Circle	>	(See Fig. F.5.2)	
Point		Draws single point	
Polyline	>	2D 3D	Draws a polyline Draws a 3-D polyline
Donut			Draws rings with specified ID and OD
Elipse	>	Axis,Eccentricity Center,Axis,Axis	Draws elipse using two endpoints + eccentricity Draws elipse using center point + endpoint of one axis + length of second axis
Polygon	>	Edge Circumscribed Inscribed	Draws equal-sided polygon using endpoints of one edge Draws equal-sided polygon circumscribing a circle Draws equal-sided polygon Inscribed in circle
Rectangle			Draws rectangle based on two points
Insert . . .			Inserts a drawing into current drawing
3D Surfaces	>	(See Fig. F.5.3)	
Hatch . . .			Hatches an object
Text	>	(See Fig. F.5.4)	
Dimensions	>	(See Fig. F.5.5)	

TABLE F.5.1 Draw/Arc Submenu

Menu command	Description
3 Point	Draws arc using 3 points
Start,Center,End	Draws arc using start, center, and endpoints
Start,Center,Angle	Draws arc using start point and center point spanning an angle
Start, Center, Length	Draws arc using start point, center point, and length of chord
Start,End,Angle	Draws arc using start point, end point, and angle
Start,End,Radius	Draws arc using start point, end point, and radius
Start,End,Direction	Draws arc using start point, end point, and direction from start point
Center,Start,End	Draws arc using center, start, and end points
Center,Start,Angle	Draws arc using center point, start point, and angle
Center,Start,Length	Draws arc using center point, start point, and length of chord

TABLE F.5.2 Draw/Circle Submenu

Menu command	Description
Center,Radius	Draws circle based on center point and radius
Center,Diameter	Draws circle based on center point and diameter
2 Point	Draws circle based on 2 endpoints of diameter
3 Point	Draws circle based on 3 points on circumference
Tangent,Tangent,Radius	Draws circle based on 2 entities circle is tangent tog and circle radius

TABLE F.5.3 Draw/3-D Surfaces Submenu

Menu command	Description
Edge defined Patch	Edgesurf draws a polygon mesh defined by 4 adjoining path curves
Ruled Surface	Rulesurf draws polygon mesh as ruled surface between two curves
Surface of Revolution	Revsurf draws polygon mesh revolving a surface of revolution about a defined axis
Tabulated Surface	Tabsurf draws a polygon mesh defined by a path curve and a direction vector
3D Face	3dface Draws a face, or plate, in space using 3 or 4 specified corners
3D Objects . . .	Displays a dialogue box of defined 3-D objects

TABLE F.5.4 Draw/Text Submenu

Menu command		Description
Dynamic		Dtext draws text dynamically in drawing screen
Import Text		Imports ASCII text file into drawing
Set Style . . .		Displays Select Text Font dialogue box
Attributes >	Define . . .	Ddatdef displays Attribute Definition dialogue box to associate text with a block
	Edit . . .	Ddate displays Edit Attributes dialogue box to edit an attributes definition
	Extract . . .	Ddattext displays Attribute Extraction dialogue box to extract attribute data from a drawing and write to a file

TABLE F.5.5 Draw/Dimension Submenu

Menu command			Description
Linear	>	Horizontal	Generates a linear dimension with a horizontal dimension line
		Vertical	Generates a linear dimension with a vertical dimension line
		Aligned	Generates a linear dimension with a dimension line aligned with selected extension line origins
		Rotated	Generates a linear dimension with dimension line at specified angle
		Baseline	Continues a linear dimension using the first extension line of a previous dimension
		Continue	Continues a linear dimension from the second extension line of a dimension
Radial	>	Diameter	Dimensions the diameter of a circle or arc
		Radius	Dimensions the radius of a circle or arc
		Center Mark	Draws center mark or center lines of a circle or arc
Ordinate	>	Automatic	Dimensions an x or y coordinate of a feature
		X-Datum	Dimensions the x coordinate of a feature
		Y-Datum	Dimensions the y coordinate of a feature
Angular			Generates a dimension arc with extension lines
Leader			Constructs a complex leader with dimension text

TABLE F.6 Construct Menu

Menu command	Description
Array	Creates a rectangular of circular array of a selected object
Array 3D	Creates an array in 3-dimensional space
Copy	Creates a copy of a selected object
Mirror	Mirrors a selected object about a specified axis
Mirror 3D	Mirrors an object about an arbitrary plane in 3-dimensional space
Chamfer	Trims two intersecting lines a specified distance from the intersection and connects the trimmed ends with a line
Fillet	Constructs an arc of specified radius between two lines, arcs, or circles
Divide	Divides a selected object into equal parts using markers
Measure	Places markers at specified intervals along an object
Offset	Creates a copy of a line or curve, parallel to it at a specified distance
Block	Forms a single entity from a compound object, for insertion into drawings

TABLE F.7 Modify Menu

Menu command			Description
Entity . . .			Modify properties of selected objects
Erase	>	Select	Erases multiple selected objects
		Single	Erases a single object
		Last	Erases last object created
		OOPS	Cancels last erase command
Break	>	Select Object, 2nd point	Breaks object at selection point and a second point
		Select Object, two points	Breaks object at two specified points
		At Selected points	Splits object into two objects at selected point
Extend			Extends a line, arc, or polyline to meet another object
Trim			Trims a portion of an entity extending past a specified boundary
Align			Translates an object in 3-D space
Move			Moves an object
Rotate			Rotates an object
Rotate 3D			Rotates an object about a 3-D axis
Scale			Alters size of an object
Stretch			Stretches a portion of an object
Change	>	Points	Modifies location and properties of objects
		Properties . . .	Modifies properties of objects
Explode			Breaks a block or polyline into constituent parts
Polyline Edit			Edits polylines
Edit Dimensions	>	Dimension text>	(See Fig. F.7.1)
		Oblique Dimensions	Modifies dimensions at specified oblique angle
		Update Dimensions	Updates dimension entities

TABLE F.7.1 Modify/Edit Dimensions/Dimension Text Submenu

Menu command	Description
Change Text	Changes existing dimension text
Home Position	Returns moved or stretched dimension text to its original location
Move Text	Adjusts dimension text location and orientation
Rotate Text	Changes orientation of dimension text of associative dimensions

TABLE F.8 Settings Menu

Menu command				Description
Drawing Aids . . .				Displays Drawing Aids dialogue box
Layer Control . . .				Displays Layer Control dialogue box
Object Snap . . .				Displays Running Object Snap dialogue box
Entity Modes . . .				Displays Entity Creation Modes dialogue box
Point Style . . .				Lets you control size and type of point entities
Dimension Style . . .				Displays Dimension Style and Variable dialogue box
Units Control . . .				Displays Units Control dialogue box
UCS	>	Named UCS . . .		Displays UCS Control dialogue box
		Presets . . .		Displays dialogue box of preset UCS orientations
		Origin		Shifts origin of current coordinate system
		Axis >	X	Rotates UCS about x axis
			Y	Rotates UCS about y axis
			Z	Rotates UCS about z axis
		Icon	On	Toggles coordinate system icon on/off
			Origin	Displays icon at origin of current UCS
Selection Settings . . .				Displays Entity Selection Settings dialogue box to set entity selection modes
Grips . . .				Displays Grips dialogue box
Drawing Limits				Sets drawing limits (boundaries)
Menu Bitmaps				Toggles display of icons/text in Draw, Construct and Modify pull-down menus

TABLE F.9 Render Menu

Menu command			Description
Render			Creates shaded image of 3-D object using geometry, view, and light information
Shade			Creates a shaded picture with no lighting effect
Hide			Redraws object with hidden lines temporarily removed
Views . . .			Displays View Control dialogue box
Lights . . .			Controls lighting in a rendered drawing
Scenes . . .			Saves lights and a view to a scene
Finishes . . .			Controls surface finish of an object
Preferences . . .			Displays Rendering Preferences dialogue box
Statistics . . .			Displays statistics of last rendering
Files	>	Replay Image . . .	Displays Replay dialogue box
		Save Image . . .	Displays Save Image dialogue box to save a rendered image
Unload Render			Unloads Render
RenderMan . . .			Runs Autodesk RenderMan AutoLISP routines

TABLE F.10 Model Menu

Menu command			Description
Extrude			Extrudes circles, polylines, or regions
Revolve			Revolves circles, polylines, or regions
Solidify			Converts AutoCAD entities into regions
Primitives . . .			Creates solid primitives
Union			Combines solids/regions
Subtract			Subtracts solids/regions
Intersect			Generates an entity from the intersection of two solids/regions
Modify	>	Move Object	Moves solids/regions
		Change Primitive	Edits solids/regions
		Separate	Separates solids/regions
		Cut Solids	Cuts a solid
		Chamfer solids	Chamfers a solid
		Fillet solids	Fillets a solid
Setup	>	(See Fig. F.10.1)	
Inquiry	>	List Objects	List properties of regions/solids
		Mass Property . . .	Displays mass properties of regions/solids
		Area Calculation	Calculates areas of regions/solids
		Interference	Calculates interference of solids
		Set Decomposition	Sets variable controlling mass decomposition direction
		Set Subdivision	Sets variable controlling mass subdivision
Display	>	(See Fig. F.10.2)	
Utility	>	(See Fig. F.10.3)	

TABLE F.10.1 Model/Setup Submenu

Menu command	Description
Variables . . .	Displays System Variables dialogue box
Engineering Units	Sets variables and parameters for Engineering units
British Units	Sets variables and parameters for British units
CGS Units	Sets variables and parameters for CGS units
SI Units	Sets variables and parameters for SI units
Upgrade Variables	Upgrades variables and parameters from AME1 to AME2 values
Double Precision	Sets solids conversion variables to double precision
Script Compatability	Sets AME compatability with AME1 or AME2

TABLE F.10.2 Model/Display Submenu

Menu command	Description
Mesh	Displays meshed solids/regions
Wireframe	Displays wireframe solids/regions
Set Wire density	Sets variable controlling wire density of solids/regions
Copy Feature	Extracts edges or faces from solids/regions
Selection Solids	Cross-sections a solid
Profile Solids	Creates a profile image of a solid

TABLE F.10.3 Model/Utility Submenu

Menu command	Description
Material . . .	Defines/edits/changes properties of materials for solids/regions
SolUCS	Aligns UCS with a face/edge of a solid/region
ASM In . . .	Imports an AutoSolid file
ASM Out . . .	Stores solid objects in an AutoSolid file
Purge Objects	Purges AME solids/regions
Unload Modeler	Unloads AME or Region Modeler from AutoCAD

TABLE F.11 Help Menu

Menu command	Description
Contents	Starts AutoCAD for Windows Help
Search for Help on . . .	Searches for Help topics by keyword
How to use Help	Explains how to use on-line Help system
About AutoCAD	Displays information about loaded version for AutoCAD

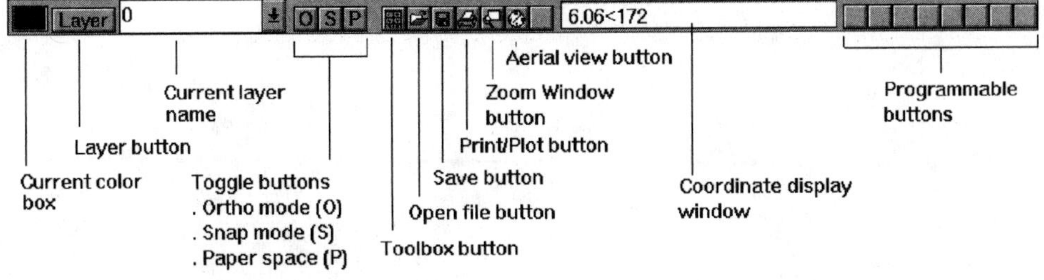

Figure F.12 AutoCAD Windows buttons bar.

Appendix

G

Aclt2.mnu Menu

```
***POP0
[Osnap]
Center
Endpoint
Insert
Intersection
Midpoint
Perpendicular
None

***POP1
[Easy1]
Line
Circle
[Border]pline \w 0.2 0.2
Erase W
[Erase L]erase 1;;
Oops
[--]
Plot
Save
Quit

***POP2
[Title Blk]
[->Metric]
[A Size]limits -5,-5 280,215 zoom a +
insert c:/drawings/am-hbdr;0,0 1 1 0
[<-B Size]limits -5,-5 430,280 zoom a +
insert c:/drawings/bm-hbdr;0,0 1 1 0
[->Imperial]
[A Size]limits -0.2,-0.2 11,8.5 zoom a +
insert c:/drawings/ai-hbdr
[<-B Size]limits -0.2,-0.2 17,11 zoom a +
insert c:/drawings/bi-hbdr;0,0 1 1 0
```

```
***POP3
[Attach]
[->Xref]
[Attach]xref attach
[Detach]xref detach
[Reload]xref reload
[Bind]xref bind
[<-Change path]
[->Block]
Insert
[<-Explode]explode
[->Edit]
Move
Erase
Ltscale
[<-Undo]undo

***POP4
[Full Size]
[->Metric]
[A Size]layer make border1;;limits 0,0 255,185 zoom a +
line 0,0 255,0 255,185 0,185 c insert c:/drawings/title;255,0 +
1 1 0 \\\\\\\\\\\\block b2;0,0 c 0,0 255,185;;$p4=ma $p4=*
[<-B size]layer make border1;;limits 0,0 380,240 zoom a +
line 0,0 380,0 380,240 0,240 c insert c:/drawings/title;380,0 +
1 1 0 \\\\\\\\\\\\block b2;0,0 c 0,0 380,240;;$p4=mb $p4=*
[->Imperial]
[A-Size]layer make border1;;limits 0,0 10,7.25 zoom a +
line 0,0 10,0 10,7.25 0,7.25 c insert c:/drawings/title;10,0 +
0.039 0.039 0 \\\\\\\\\\\\block b2;0,0 c 0,0 10,7.25;;$p4=ia $p4=*
[<-B-Size]layer make border1;;limits 0,0 15,9.5 zoom a +
line 0,0 15,0 15,9.5 0,9.5 c insert c:/drawings/title;15,0 +
0.039 0.039 0 \\\\\\\\\\\\block b2;0,0 c 0,0 15,9.5;;$p4=ib $p4=*

**ia
[Scale]
[->Archit.]
[1/8"=1'-0"]limits 0,0 960,696 insert b2;0,0 96 96 0 zoom a +
layer set 0;;$p4=POP4
[1/4"=1'-0"]limits 0,0 480,348 insert b2;0,0 48 48 0 zoom a +
layer set 0;;$p4=POP4
[1/2"=1'-0"]limits 0,0 240,174 insert b2;0,0 24 24 0 zoom a +
layer set 0;;$p4=POP4
[3/4"=1'-0"]limits 0,0 160,116 insert b2;0,0 16 16 0 zoom a +
layer set 0;;$p4=POP4
[1"=1'-0" ]limits 0,0 120,87 insert b2;0,0 12 12 0 zoom a +
layer set 0;;$p4=POP4
[<-1:N ]limits 0,0 \insert b2;0,0 \\0 zoom a +
layer set 0;;$p4=POP4
```

```
**ib
[Scale]
[->Archit.]
[1/8”=1’–0”]limits 0,0 1440,912 insert b2;0,0 96 96 0 zoom a +
layer set 0;;$p4=POP4
[1/4”=1’–0”]limits 0,0 720,456 insert b2;0,0 48 48 0 zoom a +
layer set 0;;$p4=POP4
[1/2”=1’–0”]limits 0,0 360,228 insert b2;0,0 24 24 0 zoom a +
layer set 0;;$p4=POP4
[3/4”=1’–0”]limits 0,0 240,152 insert b2;0,0 16 16 0 zoom a +
layer set 0;;$p4=POP4
[1”=1’–0” ]limits 0,0 180,114 insert b2;0,0 12 12 0 zoom a +
layer set 0;;$p4=POP4
[<-1:N ]limits 0,0 \insert b2;0,0 \\0 zoom a +
layer set 0;;$p4=POP4

**ma
[Scale]
[->Metric m]
[1:10]limits 0,0 2.55,1.85 insert b2;0,0 0.01 0.01 0 zoom a +
layer set 0;;$p4=POP4
[1:20]limits 0,0 5.1,3.7 insert b2;0,0 0.02 0.02 0 zoom a +
layer set 0;;$p4=POP4
[1:50]limits 0,0 12.75,9.25 insert b2;0,0 0.05 0.05 0 zoom a +
layer set 0;;$p4=POP4
[1:100]limits 0,0 25.5,18.5 insert b2;0,0 0.1 0.1 0 zoom a +
layer set 0;;$p4=POP4
[1:250]limits 0,0 63.75,46.25 insert b2;0,0 0.25 0.25 0 zoom a +
layer set 0;;$p4=POP4
[1:300]limits 0,0 76.5,55.5 insert b2;0,0 0.3 0.3 0 zoom a +
layer set 0;;$p4=POP4
[1:400]limits 0,0 102,74 insert b2;0,0 0.4 0.4 0 zoom a +
layer set 0;;$p4=POP4
[1:500]limits 0,0 127.5,92.5 insert b2;0,0 0.5 0.5 0 zoom a +
layer set 0;;$p4=POP4
[1:1000]limits 0,0 255,185 insert b2;0,0 1 1 0 zoom a +
layer set 0;;$p4=POP4
[<-1:N ]limits 0,0 \insert b2;0,0 \\0 zoom a +
layer set 0;;$p4=POP4

**mb
[Scale]
[->Metric m]
[1:10]limits 0,0 3.8,2.4 insert b2;0,0 0.01 0.01 0 zoom a +
layer set 0;;$p4=POP4
[1:20]limits 0,0 7.6,4.8 insert b2;0,0 0.02 0.02 0 zoom a +
layer set 0;;$p4=POP4
[1:50]limits 0,0 19,12 insert b2;0,0 0.05 0.05 0 zoom a +
layer set 0;;$p4=POP4
```

```
[1:100]limits 0,0 38,24 insert b2;0,0 0.1 0.1 0 zoom a +
layer set 0;;$p4=POP4
[1:250]limits 0,0 95,60 insert b2;0,0 0.25 0.25 0 zoom a +
layer set 0;;$p4=POP4
[1:300]limits 0,0 114,72 insert b2;0,0 0.3 0.3 0 zoom a +
layer set 0;;$p4=POP4
[1:400]limits 0,0 152,96 insert b2;0,0 0.4 0.4 0 zoom a +
layer set 0;;$p4=POP4
[1:500]limits 0,0 190,120 insert b2;0,0 0.5 0.5 0 zoom a +
layer set 0;;$p4=POP4
[1:1000]limits 0,0 380,240 insert b2;0,0 1 1 0 zoom a +
layer set 0;;$p4=POP4
[<-1:N ]limits 0,0 \insert b2;0,0 \\0 zoom a +
layer set 0;;$p4=POP4

***AUX1
^C^C

***AUX2
$PO=*
```

Index

ABOUT THE AUTHOR

John D. Hood is the author of *Using AutoCAD with AutoLISP* and three editions of *Easy AutoCAD,* a beginner's guide to the DOS-based product. He is chairman of the School of Science and Technology at Cambrian College in Sudbury, Ontario and has taught AutoCAD to students and practitioners for more than twelve years.